NEBRASKA SCHOOL
OF AGRICULTURE
CURTIS

Flour Milling in America

Flour Milling in America

by

HERMAN STEEN

Publishers

T. S. DENISON & COMPANY, INC.

Minneapolis

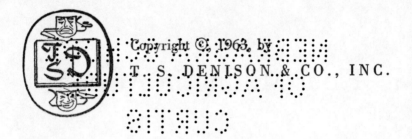

Contents

Company Histories

Preface and Acknowledgments

Flour milling literature has concentrated heavily upon the perfection of the processes by which cereal grains are converted into the flour from which is baked the world's bread. For the most part, it deals sparingly with the business of milling. Only in the trade journals and a few company histories has adequate consideration been given to the many and varied elements that have largely determined whether a milling venture would meet with success or otherwise.

This volume is concerned primarily with the economic development of flour milling in the United States. It seeks to bring into perspective the main events in the history of American milling as a business. It begins with the grist mills of the early colonial period, and leads through the transformation of these pioneer community enterprises into the complex industrial structure that characterizes present-day flour milling. It highlights the changes that have occurred in the oldest industry in the world—changes initiated and spurred on by such diverse forces as revolutionary advances in transportation, development of new wheats, discoveries in nutrition, operation of central grain markets, growth of commercial baking, perfection of new merchandising techniques and methods of distribution, and enlargement of governmental activities, to name only a few out of the many.

The subject matter of milling industry history is divided here into two parts. The first, which ends with Chapter XII, relates the chief events that have had an important bearing upon the course of the industry as a whole. Narration of these events follows a chronological pattern, as far as seemed feasible. It has been felt necessary, however, to depart from this plan to some degree, and certain phases of milling are thus presented separately in Chapter XII.

About two-thirds of the text is devoted to histories of individual companies—408 in all. This group includes all companies that have operated plants of 1000 cwt. capacity at any time since the end of the first World War. The accounts are reasonably complete in all except a few cases where it was apparently impossible to develop the desired information.

Preparation of this milling history would have been all but out of the question without the assistance of many persons and many sources of information. Living companies provided data freely, in some instances going to great trouble to establish long-forgotten facts. Many persons once connected with former companies were equally helpful. In some cases, information was obtained from grain companies, banks, chambers of commerce and many individuals. In seeking mill data, I had correspondence or conversations with more than 600 individuals, ranging from former President Truman to a retired flour packer, and from the great-granddaughter of a once-famous miller to a man who sold flour briefly more than half a century ago. In all but a few instances, there was a gratifying response to inquiries.

Among the libraries that provided most help were those of Missouri Historical Society, St. Louis; American Institute of Baking, Chicago; Minneapolis Public Library; Buffalo Historical Society; Rochester Historical Library; Seattle Public Library; Wisconsin Historical Library, Madison; LaCrosse (Wis.) Public Library; and United States Census Bureau, Washington.

Special mention should be made of the milling periodicals. Files of *American Miller & Processor*, *Northwestern Miller* and *Southwestern Miller* were scanned for upwards of a half-century, and they were sources not only of a vast amount of routine information but their occasional historical articles were also exceedingly valuable.

The chapter on ancient and medieval milling has been adapted to some extent from the excellent book, *Flour for Man's Bread,* by Storck and Teague.

The text of practically every page in this book has been read by one or more members of the milling industry—in many cases, by half a dozen. The number of persons who have thus rendered great assistance in assuring maximum accuracy runs to several score.

The milling industry, through Millers' National Federation, has underwritten the entire expense incurred in collecting material and preparing the text for publication. Characteristically, the industry has not made any editorial suggestions.

For all these forms of assistance I am duly grateful.

Herman Steen

Wheaton, Illinois, March 16, 1963

Foreword

By Senator Thruston B. Morton

Along with all others who have had any association with "Flour Milling in America," I am grateful to Herman Steen for writing this interesting book. Because of his intimate knowledge of the milling industry and the men who built it, he certainly is eminently qualified to write its history.

One of the most exciting and dynamic developments of this century in America has been the evolution and, indeed, the revolution in the processing and marketing of food products. The flour millers of our country have made their contribution to this exciting development.

I don't consider myself an old man in spite of the fact that some of my newer colleagues in the Senate insist on calling me "sir." Yet I can remember the old 196-pound wooden barrel of flour in the pantry of my grandparents' house. This is a far cry from the package I noticed the other day in the kitchen cabinet of our small Washington apartment. This package contained flour but it looked like an oversized saltshaker. On the label were just two recipes, both for gravy. This was certainly a dramatic departure from "a barrel of wood" as in days gone by we wrote up the orders in the "Deep South."

I am glad that Herman Steen has seen fit to sketch the history of more than 400 companies and include the roles of so many fine men who fought hard for business but fought cleanly and as gentlemen. Competition in the milling business has always been aggressive and, in all candor, we must admit at times cutthroat. In spite of this, there has developed over the years a fraternity and camaraderie among flour mill executives which has not been the case in many other American industries.

I well remember the disastrous Ohio Valley Flood of 1937. The old Ballard Mills with which I was associated was out of commission for ten weeks. We actually had muddy water over our entire roll floor. Since our business was almost entirely family flour, it was imperative that we keep our brands on the grocery shelf. Our shutdown gave our competitors a golden opportunity but, because they were decent people, they didn't take it.

I remember that J. Allen Smith & Co. offered to pack our brands for us at cost. General Mills was not operating its old Washburn-Crosby plant in Louisville to capacity, and they had one unit which was shut down. They turned this over to us, let us use our own men, and charged us a toll which I felt was fair and reasonable. After all this was over, I got a letter saying that they had made more money in their Louisville operation during the ten weeks we used their facilities than they had expected. They therefore enclosed a check which was upwards of five thousand dollars. Quaker Oats, knowing that we had a sizable business in carton products, offered their facilities at cost to relieve some of our packaging problems.

In the competitive system of today there is generally a tendency to kick the fellow who is down. This is certainly not true in the milling business. I will always treasure my years with the mill and the friendships and associations which I made during those years. Politics is something else, but this is not the time or place to discuss that sphere of activity.

Again let me say that along with all who may read this book I am grateful to Herman Steen for a job well done.

CHAPTER ONE

The American Milling Industry

Flour milling in the United States, viewed in thumbnail perspective, is carried on by a hundred companies. These companies operate 230 mills of commercial importance, using that term in a broad sense and including any mill that ships flour out of its immediate community.

Sixty large mills produce approximately half of the nation's flour. These are mills with more than 5000 cwt. daily capacity each. The largest, with 30,900 cwt., is also the world's largest. The other commercial mills, 170 in number and running down to 400 cwt. in size, have a total output that is about equal to that of the larger mills.

In addition to the commercial mills, there are perhaps four hundred small mills that serve local communities; in total, they produce less than one per cent of the nation's flour.

Commercial flour mills are located in 36 states. Their total capacity is close to 1,000,000 cwt. daily. Their facilities represent a replacement value of $1,000,000,000. Value of the product ranges around $2,100,000,000 annually. Of this amount, almost $1,700,000,000 is paid out for materials.

American flour production was 262,000,000 cwt. in 1962. More than one fifth of this amount went to foreign countries, to the farthest corners of the world. Domestic consumers use more than 200,000,000 cwt. each year. About three fourths go to bakers and other secondary processors. The remainder is used in home kitchens.

Flour millers provide a market for more than 600,000,000 bushels of wheat each year.

Flour mills employ about 28,000 persons. This is a small number for a large industry, a fact that reflects the high degree of mechanization. Forty years ago, there were almost 64,000 workers in flour mills, with total production about the same as at present. Total annual payroll is about $140,000,000.

Buffalo is the nation's largest milling center. It is, in fact, the world's largest. Volume of flour milled in the city on Lake Erie is equal to that of its next two competitors—Kansas City and Minneapolis—combined. Next are Toledo and Wichita. Others follow in this order: Springfield, Ill., Los Angeles, Dallas, Chicago, Seattle, the Kansas towns of Arkansas City and Salina, Chattanooga, Spokane, Ogden and St. Louis.

Flour milling has been transformed during the past three or four generations from a semi-agricultural occupation, often somewhat seasonal in character, into a complex industry. Number of flour mills has declined more than 97 per cent in a century, but the industry's productivity has more than tripled in that time. Milling processes have undergone a revolution, as have also the transportation and distribution and usage of product. These are the fundamental factors in the changes that have occurred.

At mid-point in the nineteenth century, the typical American flour mill was a small structure on stream or pond. It housed stone buhrs that were turned by the power of running water. The mill ground wheat grown in the community, and its product was used in approximately the same area; in those cases in which shipments were made, they usually went to a city to be sold by a commission merchant. There were thousands of these mills, usually with capacities from 20 to 100 cwt. per day. Anything above that size was regarded as a large mill. In such cities as Richmond, Baltimore, Rochester and St. Louis, there were considerably larger mills, but they were few in number, and the plants of greatest size did not exceed 2500 cwt. daily capacity.

The little grist mill of story and song, of legend and nostalgic memory has all but disappeared. Stone buhrs have become collectors' items. Waterwheels still exist, but chiefly as attractions in public parks. The small mills of the present era bear little resemblance to their pioneer counterparts.

Modern flour mills are fabricated of steel and concrete, and are flanked by great batteries of wheat storehouses. They are equipped with corrugated steel rolls of almost infinite variety and purpose. A vast majority are operated by electric power. They draw wheat from wide regions, often from a quarter of the nation, and the destination of product is even wider in scope. As always, milling is still an art that requires great skill, but it has also become a science in which leading roles are played by the engineer and the chemist.

Equally great is the transformation in the merchandising sphere. Packaging has run the gamut from wooden barrels to large textile bags to large and small paper sacks to shipment in plastic-lined rail cars. Transportation has ranged across water carriers to railroads to motor trucks and now back to barges. Brands have become established and then have declined in importance. Flour merchants and salesmen and advertising plans have come into the picture. The commercial baker has supplanted the homemaker in making yeast bread. Specialty products have become popular in later years. The miller of a century ago was primarily an artisan—the miller of the present era is still an artisan, but he also is a businessman.

The conversion of flour milling from pioneer establishments that served small communities into great commercial enterprises is one of the romances of industrial history. It is a story that began with inventions by a mechanical genius not long away from a Delaware farm, Oliver Evans, who believed that the power that turned the mill could also be utilized to do most of the hard manual labor in milling. His automatic mill doubled the efficiency of man-hours in producing flour. It was one of the most startling events in the industrial revolution early in the nineteenth century.

Milling had a revolution that was uniquely its own some sixty years after Evans. It was then that the middlings purifier and steel rollers came to America from France and Hungary, and they supplanted the stones that had been the means of milling for more than two thousand years. A new and more efficient and more exact milling system came into being almost overnight.

The story continues through the slow perfection of a myriad of improvements in the techniques of milling, that most ancient of industries. These changes relate to every facet of the business, and include (to name only a few things) such diverse advances as baking tests, bulk trucks, plant sanitation, concrete grain elevators, flour enrichment, wheat quality improvement, milling-in-transit, malted wheat flour, new wheat cleaning machinery, educational efforts for wheat products, maturing flour, export promotion—and a thousand more that combine to spell out the progress of the industry. It all adds up to the fact that the past century has witnessed more changes in flour milling than took place in the previous two thousand years taken together—and the end is not yet.

CHAPTER TWO

The World's Oldest Industry

Far back in antiquity it was discovered that the seeds of a wild grass would appease hunger and sustain human life. This simple event proved to be momentous, for it started man on the road that led to civilization, and the cardinal fact about the rise of civilization is that every forward step went hand in hand with the production and use of wheat.

Primitive man was a hunter and wanderer, who led a homeless and precarious existence. His only skills were in catching game and fashioning crude tools to aid that objective. The discovery of cereal grains transformed him slowly, almost imperceptibly, into a farmer, a process that apparently covered countless generations of time. In the course of this process, there evolved fixed places of habitation, possession and ownership of land, domestication of animals, establishment of villages and then of tribes and nations. Then followed the formation of governments, building of cities, the rise of commerce, development of the arts and sciences and the beginnings of industry.

Of utmost significance is that the ancient world recognized clearly that its civilization had come into existence by virtue of the beneficence of wheat. This was not only true of the Assyrians, the Egyptians and the Jews, and later the Greeks and Romans, those about whom we know the most, but also of numerous other peoples who are less familiar. Almost all of the early religious beliefs characterized wheat as the symbol of life, and they glorified the harvest and venerated bread as the gift of the gods. The Egyptians worshipped Isis, the goddess of fertility and agriculture, and her counterparts were Demeter of the Greeks and Ceres of the Romans; and one of the greatest ceremonies of the Jewish year was in honor of the wheat harvest.

We do not know within a range of many thousands of years how much time has elapsed since some famished and desperate hunter first chewed the wild grass which was a prehistoric ancestor of wheat. Nor do we know how long was required for man to learn to sow this forerunner of wheat on cultivated ground and to store the harvested crop, nor when he found that cooking improved its taste and palatability, nor when some inventive soul reasoned that stones would be better than the jaws of man as the means of grinding. Likewise, we do not know when bread, the basic food of mankind, was first conjured up from the addition of leavening to ground wheat mixed with water. Important as these things are, we do not know when any of them took place; but, taken together, they may have spanned a period of close to a thousand centuries.

Southwestern Asia, the cradle of the human race, was also the area in which all the principal cereals originated, save only corn. Far back in prehistoric times, man learned to make use of einkorn and emmer, primitive cereals from which wheat was later developed. Einkorn and emmer were widely known in the ancient world and they grow wild here and there to this day all the way from the shores of the Mediterranean to Afghanistan.

Wheat emerged as a distinct cereal species perhaps ten thousand years ago. That was almost simultaneous with the first practice of agriculture. Emmer was more widely known in the ancient world than was wheat; more than four thousand years ago it had found the way from its Asiatic homeland to Palestine and thence to Egypt; to China and India via Turkestan; and from Egypt to other Mediterranean lands and finally to Western Europe. Emmer was the source of a large proportion of the breadstuffs of the Roman period. Wheat, on the other hand, moved from Iran to South Russia and thence to the Danubian countries before it spread to the West; despite its superiority, wheat was secondary to emmer through the Roman era, largely because it was more costly.

Grain was ground for human use at least sixty thousand years ago, perhaps much longer. The oldest milling artifacts that have been found consist of stones, on one of which grain was placed and another that was used for pounding. In the course of time the lower stone was hollowed so as to form a receptacle and the pounder became smaller and somewhat convex, thus approaching the mortar-and-pestle. As the stones became more rounded, pounding gradually gave way to a form of rubbing that had a shearing effect on the grain rather than smashing it. It seems certain that all through this long period of time, covering untold thousands of years, the grinding of grain was a household chore done chiefly by women.

Between four and five thousand years ago the earlier means of milling were supplanted in the main by the saddlestone, larger and longer and with a rolling surface, and over this surface was pushed or rolled a rounded or elongated stone. This device was the first major change in grinding grain. The saddlestone required considerable strength to operate, and milling moved out of the household, at least in the cities, and was done largely by slave labor. As the saddlestone was improved and enlarged, it was found that a man could make a great deal more flour in a day than could be used in a household. That opened the way for the production of flour for sale, the first industrial enterprise in the world.

The saddlestone era covered considerably more than two thousand years, including virtually all of the Old Testament period. This was during the time when the ancient cities first reached great size, and as the urban areas grew the milling of flour shifted from the homes to large establishments that both milled flour and baked bread for city dwellers. However, in the villages and on the farms, milling continued to be done in the home, and the equipment for making flour was rated as one of man's most precious possessions. This is illustrated strikingly in the command in the laws of Moses: "No man shall take the nether or the upper millstone to pledge, for he taketh a man's life to pledge." Mortgaging of millstones was prohibited as they were regarded as too vital to man's existence.

As the cities grew, and as milling and baking establishments increased in size, men sought means of milling with greater productive capacity than the saddlestone. This led to such devices as the quern, the hourglass mill and several others, all of which were based upon the principle of rotary grinding as opposed to rubbing back and forth in the case of the saddlestone and to pounding in more primitive milling. These newer methods came into use several centuries before the Christian era, and while their origin is obscure the Greeks probably had something to do with their development.

Outside of urban districts, in the villages and on the farms, milling flour continued to be largely a household task well into the Middle Ages. This was the case over most of the known world. Hand milling necessarily was done by ancient methods such as the familiar mortar-and-pestle.

Millstones first came into use more than two thousand years ago. They consisted of a bed stone in a fixed position and a revolving upper stone, both having corrugations on the opposing surfaces. This method was far superior to all others then known, as for the first time man had an instrument of milling with a reasonably constant distance between the two grinding surfaces. It enabled a greater volume to be produced, it made more efficient use of labor and it turned out much better flour. Such were the times, however, that for several hundred years the millstone, the quern and the saddlestone were all in common use, but in the end the millstone survived and the others were discarded by all except the most backward societies.

The perfection of millstones—and it is not certain whether credit belongs to the Greeks or to the Volsinians of the Italian peninsula—was the first great milling revolution. They remained as the most common system of milling wheat and other grains until less than a century ago.

Rome's greatest contribution to milling progress was that of harnessing the power of falling water to operate the machinery of flour mills. The waterwheel was developed just before the Christian era. It was almost as important as the revolving millstone, for it made possible the use of much larger milling units than had previously existed. Mechanical power ended the use of slaves in turning the mills and it also greatly reduced the use of animal power. The waterwheel came into general use rather rapidly, considering the times, and it continued to be the chief source of power for flour mills until toward the end of the nineteenth century. However, in the low-lands of Western Europe and to some extent elsewhere, the windmill was utilized after the eleventh century.

Pliny's description of Roman milling establishes beyond question that the millers of his time (first century) made sep-arations into grades not dissimilar to those of modern times. How long this practice had prevailed we do not know, but that it had been carried on for centuries is indicated by repeated references in the Old Testament to meal and to fine flour. Both the Jews and the Egyptians, as well as the Romans, were fa-miliar with the use of sieves, and it is certain that the separa-tion of coarse and fine portions of flour was practiced thou-sands of years ago. The theory advanced by many food fad-dists that white flour was not known until modern times is therefore untenable.

The extent to which the Romans used wheat as food can perhaps best be illustrated by the fact that it was customary for their legions to carry wheat as an emergency ration in time of war. The armies had portable mills. On one notable occasion Roman soldiers mutinied when they were fed meat instead of bread.

Although milling became a business following the develop-ment of the saddlestone and the rise of ancient cities, it was a business that was carried on chiefly by the state or under strin-gent state control. In Egypt and in the empires of the Near East, many of the mills were the property of the priesthood. This may well have been due to the belief that because wheat was the gift of the gods, the milling of flour should be carried on only by their agents. Many of the principal Roman mills were owned and operated by the government. There all sons and sons-in-law of millers were compelled to follow the mill-ing profession. Their status was that of slaves, or at best of bond-servants. It is true that some of the Roman mills were independently owned, but they were government-controlled because of the grain monopoly.

In the feudal system that prevailed for centuries after the fall of Rome, millers were servants of the king or of the nobility or clergy. In many countries the ownership of millstones was reserved to these privileged classes, although as a practical matter great numbers of people continued to mill flour in their homes by ancient methods that had been handed down from generation to generation. Only in a few cities of Western Europe did milling rise above this submerged condition and there but to a limited degree.

During the long ages when the economic status of the miller remained low and stagnant, no significant change took place in milling techniques. No forward progress can be found for considerably more than fifteen hundred years after the inception of the revolving millstone and the waterwheel. Flour was milled for century after century just as it had been, with no perceptible improvement in the milling art. Wheat was likewise grown and harvested and stored the same as it was many generations before. There was precious little progress in anything mechanical during medieval times, and milling flour was in harmony with that condition. There was little incentive for improvement, but even when some change was logical it was usually stifled by the heavy hand of medieval bureaucracy.

When advances in milling did come about, in the early modern era, it was in France that they were most evident. The French developed buhr stones that were much superior to anything previously used. They also found that certain silks made much better sieves than the cloths of the past. French millers also learned how to make much better flour through a process of gradual reduction instead of the instant crushing that had been the universal practice, but the government sternly prohibited the innovation—a prime example of progress being blocked by bureaucratic devotion to the status quo. At about the same time or a little later, German engineers began to study the relation of millstone speed to milling efficiency and were wondering if something better than a millstone could not be found for grinding wheat.

Meanwhile free enterprise had entered the milling picture throughout Western Europe, but especially in England. There the ownership and control of mills passed slowly, ever so slowly, from the lords and earls and squires and bishops to individuals whose ancestors a few generations earlier had been serfs. And in England, too, there grew up a romantic body of legends and ballads and songs about millers and milling—the jolly miller, the singing miller, the honest miller—that in the course of time crossed the Atlantic and became a part of American folklore.

CHAPTER THREE

Early American Milling

Corn was the great native cereal of the Western Hemisphere. It was developed far back in prehistoric times, probably from teosinte and probably in Central America, and by the time of Columbus' voyages it was being grown quite widely in what is now the United States. It was a staple article of diet for a large majority of the Indian tribes that roamed over the continent. Corn was parched or ground, or both, and when ground the usual means in the northern and eastern parts of this country was a mortar-and-pestle with a hollowed log constituting the mortar. In the southwest a modified saddlestone was the customary milling tool.

The Mayans of Yucatan may have been the first American millers. They had milling equipment close to fifteen thousand years ago that was superior to the stones in use at that time in the Old World. However, little improvement took place subsequently, probably because corn milling is a simple operation and there was no very urgent reason to better the system that the Mayans found satisfactory.

26

Wheat was first brought to the New World in 1494 by Christopher Columbus, but several attempts to produce it in the West Indies and elsewhere in Spanish America all resulted in failure. It thus remained for the early English colonists to be the first wheat growers in North America and likewise the first flour millers.

Corn was growing in relative abundance in the vicinity of the first two English permanent settlements—at Jamestown, Virginia, in 1607, and at Plymouth, Massachusetts, in 1620—and the colonists soon learned to eat this strange cereal. The alternative in many cases was starvation, but it was not long before corn had been adopted as a food by both Captain John Smith's colony and the Pilgrims. They nevertheless undertook to grow wheat, but farming tools and know-how were so scarce that the crop attained little importance for a time.

A grist mill built at Jamestown in 1621 may well have been the first of its kind on the continent. It is certain that both corn and wheat had been ground in the homes before that year, but there is no record of a mill at an earlier date. The first known mill in Massachusetts was the one built in 1631 at Watertown, but another was established at Dorchester two years later and about that time one was erected in Boston. The Dutch who first settled Manhattan Island had a windmill in use˙ as early as 1627, and in Maryland there was a water-powered mill at St. Mary's in 1634.

The dates given above point clearly to the fact that grist mills were established very early in the life of each of the colonial settlements. After the pioneers built crude habitations for themselves, they usually hastened to put up a church; and a grist mill was such a vital necessity that it was generally built as soon as a sufficient grain crop was harvested to justify such a step. The mother country did not encourage manufacturing of any kind—it discouraged and even prohibited any such thing —but grist milling was regarded as an adjunct to farming and it never fell under the ban.

There were grist mills in almost every village or settled community in New England. This was also the case in New York, New Jersey, Pennsylvania and Delaware, and it was true in considerable parts of Maryland and Virginia. Aside from the pioneers' homes and their church, the grist mill was the most important establishment in each settlement. It was a place where of necessity everyone had to go from time to time, and many of the early mills became community centers. The American grist mills were patterned after those of Western Europe, particularly England, but they departed considerably from the pattern.

All through the colonial period there was a contest for supremacy between corn and wheat. Some students of that era believe that far more corn than wheat was used for human food. That was very likely the case, as corn was being grown successfully in all the colonies whereas wheat growing was limited largely to the area from New York to Virginia inclusive, and transportation facilities were so primitive that it was difficult to move wheat far from areas of production, especially to inland points. New England largely abandoned wheat production after the early years except in the Connecticut Valley, and even that fertile region turned to other crops in a relatively short time. Except for a small part of North Carolina, the southern colonies never grew much wheat. Their coastal towns were supplied with flour from the wheat areas, but several generations of colonial Americans who lived far inland had johnnycake as their dietary mainstay.

In addition to the grist mills in the villages and at crossroads, a good many flour mills were built later at points that were strategically located with reference to wheat supplies. The chief wheat growing areas in colonial times were around New York City and up the Hudson Valley, a broad strip of Central New Jersey between New York and Philadelphia, the south-eastern arc of Pennsylvania, Delaware, the eastern half of Maryland and a good part of tidewater Virginia. After the settlements became well established, farmers in these areas produced considerably more wheat than was needed for flour to supply the colonies, and in the course of time a substantial export trade developed both in wheat and in flour.

New York City was recognized as early as 1664 as the foremost merchant milling center in the colonies; it became, in fact, the largest such center in the world. Its mills were supplied by farms both in New York and New Jersey and by boats that plied the Hudson. Philadelphia, which finally surpassed New York in 1750 as a milling center, drew on its nearby fine farming district as well as shipments by boat on the Schuykill and the Delaware. Baltimore, Wilmington and Richmond all became milling points of importance in the colonial period, as did the Pennsylvania town of Easton, which boasted eleven flour mills. All of them had access by water to areas of substantial wheat production. There was also a considerable number of small mills scattered over the wheat belt, and when they had a surplus of flour over local needs it was marketed in the larger centers.

Three chief markets were supplied by the colonial mills. First, there were such cities as Boston and Charleston, and other towns along the American seacoast that had a deficit of flour. Next were the West Indies, the most important points being Barbados and Jamaica. Third was Portugal, the Madeira Islands and a few scattered European outlets. Largest of these markets was Barbados, which evidently was a port of transshipment to many parts of Spanish America. The export flour trade began long before the end of the seventeenth century, at least from New York, and in later years it reached an impressive volume. Early figures on the extent of this business are missing, but in later colonial years they show, for example, that Philadelphia exported 522,000 cwt. of flour in 1774—not by any means all was milled there—and 725,000 cwt. in 1789, amounts that would have been regarded with respect even in the recent past. Year after year agricultural commodities constituted the predominant part of colonial exports, and wheat flour was invariably first. Indeed, it often exceeded the value of all other export items combined. Flour milling was by far the most important industry in the six central colonies for more than 50 years before independence.

Although the colonies were founded by men who sought to be free from political or religious or industrial conditions that prevailed in Europe, the colonial governments indulged in a surprising amount of regulation of their flour mills. As early as 1645 Virginia fixed a legal rate for toll milling, and ultimately all the others followed the same course. Most of the colonies had statutes that custom mills must operate on certain days and merchant mills were under compulsion to set aside certain stones for custom work. New York law for a time stipulated that all flour exported must be bolted in a city mill, a step that was opposed violently by the country millers. Pennsylvania, Maryland and Virginia inspectors certified the quality and grade of export shipments, probably doing so under pressures from Barbados importers who complained about being imposed upon. Adulteration (a not uncommon practice) and weights were checked by most of the colonies. Some cities had ordinances that made inspection necessary for flour milled elsewhere, their own mills being exempt.

Most of the colonial milling regulations were probably welcomed by the millers, at least by a majority of them. There is some evidence that the leading millers supported compulsory inspection and grading of export shipments. Arbitrary actions such as the New York City bolting monopoly were of course resisted, but there was even some justification for that step as many country mills made an inferior product that was adulterated in too many cases with ground corn.

Not all the colonial milling regulations were punitive. Some of them were protective and clearly designed to encourage and foster local industry. Several colonies prohibited the importation of flour, and they also refused to sanction wheat exports if their own millers needed wheat to grind, or thought they did.

There was one colonial miller whose flour had such a great reputation that it was exempt from inspection for export, and it likewise was exempt from inspection at West Indies ports. That was George Washington. A small flour mill was on the Mount Vernon estate when he inherited the property in 1752. Discouraged by unsatisfactory returns on his tobacco crops, Washington took up wheat growing in a large way and rebuilt and enlarged the mill in 1770. He became one of the most prominent millers of his time, building up a substantial trade in the West Indies, and even when he was engaged in military or executive duty he never seemed to forget his mill and he sent frequent directions to his overseer for its operation. Washington was a deep student of the milling art, as well as having excellent business sense about flour milling. The Mount Vernon mill remained in use until 1860 and was later torn down, but was restored in 1930 by the state of Virginia.

The young nation that succeeded the colonies grew rapidly, population rising from 3,000,000 at the end of the Revolution to more than 7,000,000 in 1810. It was in this period that there began the tremendous westward surge of settlement, moving first into the hinterlands of the old colonies and then flowing over the Alleghenies into Ohio and Kentucky and beyond. More people and more settlements meant more flour mills in those days. As was the case nearly two centuries earlier when their forebears landed on the seacoast, the settlers in a new community seldom waited after their first crop was harvested to set about the construction of a mill. How many mills were established was not recorded, but if there were a thousand when the Constitution was ratified (as some have guessed) there must have been two or three times that number before a quarter century had passed.

A vast majority of the flour mills of the period around 1800 operated on the custom basis—i.e., farmers brought in wheat to be milled into flour, usually paying a toll of from one-twelfth to one-eighth of the wheat. Many of the custom or grist mills also bought wheat, or ground their toll wheat, and thus had flour for sale. Only the relatively few mills in the cities did no custom business and were purely merchant mills. The merchant mills were larger than the grist mills, but none were large by later standards. When Gallego Mills of 1800 cwt. daily capacity was built in Richmond in 1798, it was nearly twice the size of the next largest in the nation. Most of the grist mills probably ranged between 20 and 100 cwt. capacity, and few of the merchant mills exceeded 200 cwt.

Philadelphia retained first place among American milling centers for more than half a century. However, by 1805 Baltimore had forged ahead. At that time there were 50 merchant mills within 18 miles of the Maryland city, with total capacity of about 7000 cwt., and in 1825 there were 60 mills in the area. Baltimore's pre-eminence as a milling point was due to several factors: Larger wheat supplies available to its mills than to rival centers; an aggressive group of merchant millers, more than a third of their business being export, mostly to Brazil, West Indies and Great Britain; and to the adoption of Oliver Evans' automatic mill ahead of other milling districts.

Oliver Evans (b. 1755 Del., d. 1819), a famous engineer and inventor of numerous mechanical contrivances, was also the author of the first American milling revolution. Astounded by the tremendous amount of hard physical labor used in flour mills—in those days all movement of wheat and product in, around and out of a mill was done of the backs of men—Evans developed an automatic system powered by the waterwheel that turned the millstone. This system consisted of bucket elevators, screw conveyors, hopper boy and a few other devices. It took wheat to the top of the mill by mechanical power, carried it down by gravity through the grinding process, elevated the product and carried it down through the bolting sieves and spread it out to cool. The Evans system reduced the amount of manpower needed in a mill by more than half and it eliminated nearly all of the back-breaking labor. It also increased the extraction of flour from wheat.

It required 20 years and much persuasion for millers to adopt Evans' system. The mills in his home country on the Brandywine refused even to consider it. The first mill of standing to install the system was that of Ellicott Brothers, near Baltimore, and the results were so sensational that many others in Maryland followed. Evans' patents were widely infringed and were declared invalid, and in 1808 he appealed to Congress for relief. Jonathan Ellicott, who had been Evans' patron, became his bitter opponent, aided by President Thomas Jefferson. Said Jefferson, in a letter to Congress, "Mr. Evans has not really invented anything, . . . but in any case his devices are too valuable for anyone to be permitted to control them." Evans nevertheless won his case, and he collected $80.60 from Jefferson for a license to use the automatic system in the mill on his Monticello estate. To this day Evans' critics assert that he did not devise anything new, that all he did was utilize long-known ideas; perhaps so, but he put the ideas to work—nobody before him had done so.

The flour milling trend had been somewhat away from localized semi-agricultural undertakings before Evans' time, but his inventions hastened the growing movement toward making mills into large industrial enterprises. This was basically due to the fact that Evans' mills required considerable capital for machinery, buildings, equipment, etc. The grist mill was dealt a hard blow, but it had so many inherent advantages that it remained on the milling scene to some degree for more than another century.

After their initial skepticism, American millers generally adopted the Evans system without much more delay, with the result that their plants were recognized as being the most advanced in the world. It is a strange fact, however, that although the automatic mill was well known in European milling circles soon after it came into use here, millers there continued in almost all cases to operate their plants with hand labor until the last quarter of the nineteenth century.

The growth of flour milling kept pace with the growth of the new nation, and it continued for many years to be America's foremost industry.

CHAPTER FOUR

Baltimore, Rochester and St. Louis

Population of the United States was nearing 10,000,000 in 1820. It reached 17,000,000 in 1840. It stood above 31,000,-000 on the eve of the Civil War. It surged up past 50,000,000 in 1880. Vast increases in cereal crops accompanied these gains in population.

Grain production moved westward with the pioneers. Seed wheat and corn were among the most precious items in the saddlebags of the settlers who left the Atlantic seaboard, trudged over muddy trails into the wilderness, fought Indians and established homes in the clearings or on the prairies. Ohio became the premier wheat state in 1839, displacing the Pennsylvania area that had been in first place from early colonial days. Illinois took over the lead in 1858 and remained there a majority of the time for a quarter of a century.

Wheat—but not corn—also became established on the Pacific Coast. It was there to welcome the gold seekers, and wheat fields spread out over the valleys to such an extent, after the population zoomed, that for a time California rivalled the eastern wheat states in total production. It was from this area that the great China trade in flour was built up and continued for more than three quarters of a century.

Grain production was greatly stimulated by two almost simultaneous inventions—the reaper, first built in 1831 at Abingdon, Virginia, by Cyrus H. McCormick (b. 1809 Va., d. 1884), and the chilled steel plow, perfected at Grand Detour, Illinois, in 1837 by John Deere (b. 1804 Vt., d. 1886). The tough sod of the prairies resisted other plows but it yielded to Blacksmith Deere's device. The reaper (and later the self-binder) speeded up harvesting immeasurably.

Flour mills followed close behind the westward march of wheat from the Atlantic over the valleys and prairies. The first harvest was followed by the construction of the inevitable grist mill, and one of the greatest attractions for land seekers was a community that already had such a mill.

Statistics are lacking for the earlier years, but in 1850 the census enumeration covered 11,891 mills in the United States. This figure included corn mills and feed mills as well as flour mills. If the proportion of flour mills to the total that prevailed when the first separation was made (1900) also applied to the earlier years, then there were some six thousand mills in 1850 that ground wheat. In 1860 there were 13,868 mills of all kinds, and this rose to 22,573 in 1870 and 24,338 in 1880.

Broken down by states, these figures are more vivid. In 1870, for example, Pennsylvania had 2985 mills of all kinds, the most of any state. New York followed with 1610, then Virginia 1556, North Carolina 1415, Ohio 1396, Georgia 1097 and Tennessee 1058. Among others, Indiana had 962, Illinois 941, Missouri 894, Wisconsin 581 and Iowa 501. Far to the rear were Minnesota with 216 and Kansas 106. How many were flour mills and how many corn and feed mills can only be conjectured, but it is certain that in the northern states flour mills constituted considerably more than half of the state totals and in the South much less than half.

Lancaster county, Pennsylvania, reported 172 mills in 1870. It seems certain that two-thirds or more of them milled flour. A commentary on the size of these mills is afforded by the fact that they employed 275 persons in all. The 22,573 milling establishments in the United States that year had 58,448 workers, only a bit more than two-and-a-half persons per mill.

Almost all cities had flour mills and some of them had a surprising number. Nine mills were destroyed in the Chicago fire of 1871. Dayton boasted of twelve mills at about that time. Detroit had even more and San Francisco was only a little behind. Some of the smaller towns had a number of mills each. Mascoutah, Illinois, had seven; and as late as 1900 there were also seven in Fergus Falls, Minnesota.

In the period under consideration, practically every community that grew wheat had its own mill. In many areas there was a mill every four or five miles in all directions. These mills were essentially grist mills and sold but little flour unless they were near towns or cities. Few of them ran regularly. Many were combination flour mills and sawmills, and they might grind wheat only two or three days per week at most. If the water in stream or pond was low, they were forced to close. Many of them were operated by men who doubled as farmers, and when the pressure of farm work became heavy the mill was often idled for days or even weeks.

The great number of community mills that were established in the wake of the westward tide of settlement tends to obscure the fact that merchant mills were growing rapidly, both in size and in numbers. Here again statistics are lacking, but we know that flour mills of 500 cwt. capacity were becoming quite common, that mills of 1000 cwt. were in operation in a good many places and that several mills of larger size were in existence. Most conspicuous of the latter group were the mills in Richmond, where Haxall Mills, dating from 1809, and Gallego Mills, more than a decade older, were the nation's largest until the 1870's. These mills had capacities of about 2500 cwt. each in their later years.

The tendency toward larger mills grew out of several factors. Growth of population and especially the increased size of the cities provided outlets for flour beyond the ability of small mills to supply, and when a mill established a reputation for good flour its owner was often under pressure to expand its capacity. There was also the fact that production costs per unit of product declined to some extent as capacity increased, although this was not as well understood then as it was later. Still another factor was that the mechanized mill required more capital than did its predecessor, and more capital implied a degree of business management that may not have been regarded as necessary in earlier and smaller concerns.

Perhaps of most importance in increasing mill size was the dramatic growth of the railroads. Total trackage of 10,982 miles in 1851 grew to 31,286 in 1861, and then rose to 60,301 miles in 1871 and to more than 100,000 miles in another ten years. The coming of the railroads opened great new vistas in market outlets, and it did more to influence the course of business as a whole than did any other event. In the case of milling, a concern that had been limited to its own community suddenly found itself able to reach markets that had previously been as unavailable as if they had been in the middle of Asia. Not by any means did all mills take advantage of these opportunities, but some did.

The clearest index to an industry's growth is the total volume of product. Earlier figures are lacking, but in 1860 the flour output of United States mills was 78,000,000 cwt. By 1870 this had reached almost 94,000,000 cwt., and in 1880 it stood at 126,000,000 cwt. Corn products were still strong competitors, particularly in the South and Midwest, but wheat flour was forging ahead.

As has been noted, flour was the largest foreign trade item in the colonial period and in the early decades of the republic. It ceased to hold this exalted position only after trading in cotton, pork and wheat, and later in manufactured goods, grew to large volume. However, flour shipments abroad grew steadily and they constituted an important factor in export trade. In the 1820 decade, the annual exports of wheat flour averaged 1,784,000 cwt., and they remained at about that point during the 1830's before going to 3,638,000 cwt. in 1841-50 and 5,670,000 cwt. in 1851-60. An increase to 6,118,000 cwt. took place in the 1860 decade despite the Civil War, and in 1871-80 the average rose to 7,759,000 cwt. per year. The last-named period was on the threshold of a sensational increase that got underway just before 1880.

Water power continued to be the chief means of running flour mills, although the steam engine was beginning to make inroads. In 1870, of the 22,573 mills, 21,213 had water wheels and 5383 used steam power—some had both—and there were a few windmills and horse mills. In many cases more than one kind of power was employed in a mill. Two-fifths of all the water wheels in the United States were in flour mills. One of the amusing things about water power was the widespread belief on the part of old millers that water wheels turned faster at night than during the day. Even as late as 1890 this issue continued to be debated in millers' meetings.

Baltimore was the No. 1 milling center for almost a third

of a century, ending in 1836, but a close second for most of that time was Richmond. These cities had tidewater locations, access to large supplies of wheat, and their mills had built up handsome outlets abroad for their flour in addition to sizable markets in their own areas and along the Atlantic seaboard. The Baltimore millers were aggressive and alert and they did a large business long after their city lost first place. Richmond's mills were destroyed at the end of the Civil War and were rebuilt only in part.

Rochester had been rising in importance and it became the industry leader for more than 20 years. Several strong factors aided the Rochester millers: Location on the Erie Canal, thus giving easy access to New York and other markets of importance; extensive wheat production in nearby areas; development of a large outlet in European markets; and, perhaps greatest of all, harnessing the immense power of the Genesee River. Rochester's milling district was spectacular. Its mills, which at one time numbered 31, stood side by side or facing each other along a millrace that carried a heavy flow of water around the falls of the Genesee. The Rochester mills were larger than those of Baltimore, but most of them ranged only between 300 and 500 cwt. until later years. Rochester's greatest output was more than 3,000,000 cwt. in 1878 and again in 1901, long after the city had given up the mantle of industry leadership.

St. Louis forged ahead of the eastern cities late in the 1850's, signalizing the rising importance and future domination of flour milling by the Middle West. This city had 22 mills in 1850, their total capacity being 5600 cwt., but by 1862 it had 35 mills and total capacity of 24,000 cwt. and production of almost 1,300,000 cwt. that year. Notwithstanding the trade disturbances of the Civil War, St. Louis grew in importance all through its period of industry leadership and its peak production was 4,200,000 cwt. in 1879, of which 1,238,-000 cwt. were sent to Europe and South America.

St. Louis was centrally located in the heart of what was then the nation's most important wheat growing territory and a network of railroads and rivers gave it unexcelled transportation facilities. It might well have continued to lead the industry had it not been for two great unforeseen developments that occurred almost simultaneously: Introduction of hard wheat in both the Kansas and Minnesota districts, and the adoption of what was called the "new process" milling. The latter consisted of the middlings purifier and the corrugated steel roller mill. These events precipitated a milling upheaval of unprecedented proportions, and although St. Louis continued to be a milling point of considerable importance it lost its top place to Minneapolis in 1880.

The period of St. Louis milling leadership also represented the high-water mark of soft wheat in the United States. Until the 1870's the hard wheats had been of small consequence in this country, and nearly all the production consisted of the soft varieties. The combination of the new hard wheats and the new milling techniques not only created another milling revolution—it had almost as much effect upon wheat growing.

CHAPTER FIVE

The American Milling Revolution

Perfection of the middlings purifier and development of the roller mill, innovations in milling techniques that came into use in the United States during the 1870's, had a profound effect upon all facets of milling. The ancient millstone became obsolete and was relegated to oblivion, flour production units of giant size became practical, flour character was vastly improved, wheat emphasis was shifted from soft varieties to hard and commercial baking was enabled to develop. The sum of these events constitutes the most far-reaching revolution in all the annals of flour milling.

To put milling affairs of the 1870's into perspective, let it be remembered that the settlement of Minnesota proceeded rapidly after the Treaty of Traverse des Sioux in 1851; that the first settlers had scant success with winter wheat brought from Illinois and elsewhere; that the hard spring wheat, Scotch Fife, imported from Ontario, was found to be ideally suited to northern conditions; that Fife was difficult to mill with the equipment of that day; and that spring wheat flour was discriminated against rather severely in the markets and was disliked by the trade and by consumers because it contained so many bran specks that it had a grayish or mottled apppearance.

There were resourceful individuals among the pioneer millers of Minnesota, especially those in the valleys of the Cannon and Vermillion Rivers—streams of relatively small size that flow in a generally eastward direction 40 miles or more south of the Twin Cities. Several of these millers began to experiment about 1865 with high grinding—i.e., setting the millstones slightly farther apart than normal. The effect was first to crack and break the wheat berries rather than pulverize them instantly, and the grinding process was continued gradually until all the flour was extracted. Millstones were turned at much less than conventional speeds, so as not to overheat or injure the product.

Gradual reduction of wheat through a succession of grindings was no new thing, although it had apparently not been used in America up to that time. It was widely practiced by the Egyptians in ancient times and probably also by others. The art was then lost for centuries and was rediscovered by a miller named Piegault more than three hundred years ago in France, but for some reason that historians have failed to record the practice was prohibited a century later. However, the idea did not die and was revived after a generation or two by the French and it spread also to Hungary. Millers in these countries produced limited amounts of very fancy flour for which they charged tremendous prices, and it was milled by high grinding and gradual reduction.

Sensational results came from high grinding and gradual reduction in Southern Minnesota. Millers who mastered the art were rewarded with a great demand for their product and it commanded generous premiums over other flours, especially in the East. The flour came to be known as New Process, and it was produced principally by Stephen Gardner of Hastings, John S. and E. T. Archibald of Dundas, John W. North and Alexander Faribault of Northfield, and later A. G. Mowbray of Winona. Several of these men had learned their milling in Canada on hard wheat, and they doubtless were trained in high grinding there. There is no certainty who first employed the practice in this country, although there is some belief that the honor belongs to Gardner.

In milling spring wheat, one of the chief problems in those days was the difficulty of obtaining a complete separation of bran from the middlings stock. It was a two-edged sword, because if the bran were not separated the flour was mottled, and if the middlings were taken away from the bran the loss of flour was often prohibitive. Edmund LeCroix (d. 1874), a French milling engineer, built a mill for Faribault in 1865, and when posed with this problem his mind ran back to a device that he had known in his native land. This employed a blast of air upon the mixture of middlings and bran as they were being sieved and it caused them to separate. LeCroix built the first such machine to be used in an American mill.

LeCroix was employed by George H. Christian in 1871 to install purifiers in Gen. C. C. Washburn's mill in Minneapolis, the first large mill to be so equipped, and the development of the purifier is due in considerable part to Christian's sponsorship and encouragement. A millwright named George T. Smith (b. 1841 N. Y., d. 1920) made some improvements in LeCroix's machine, principally a travelling brush to keep the cloth clean, thus permitting better control of the air currents. Smith then installed purifiers in other mills and he patented the entire device, LeCroix having failed to do so because of his limited knowledge of English and his unfamiliarity with

American law. Smith and his associates obtained control of numerous other patents that had a bearing on the process, notably the Cochrane patent, and a company that Smith headed manufactured purifiers in large numbers for years but it eventually became insolvent.

Neither LeCroix nor Smith invented the purifier, and Le-Croix never claimed to have done so. What he did was adapt or copy from memory a machine that was developed in 1860 by Perrigault in France. Purifiers had been commonly used in mills in Central Europe, most of them following a crude device built in 1814 by Ignatz Paur, an Austrian miller. A French writer on milling, P. Benoit, published in 1847 a treatise on means of separating middlings from bran, and it is reasonably certain that LeCroix was familiar with all these developments and that they were the basis of his work.

LeCroix's services were of inestimable value to the milling industry but he obtained little recognition or reward. In fact, he received shabby treatment. During the purifier litigation he refused a substantial fee to testify for the patent owners who were suing his former employers for infringement. He died shortly after in poverty and want.

New Process flour soon became thoroughly established, and it enjoyed a tremendous demand for some years. This was the chief basis for the rapid development of the milling industry in Minneapolis, beginning in the early 1870's. Practically all the Minnesota mills were soon equipped to produce New Process flour, as were many other mills that were able to obtain hard wheat supplies. Long before the American market was saturated, foreign outlets were established and for several decades approximately one-third of the Minnesota flour production was shipped abroad. There it came in competition with Hungarian and French fancy flours, the former being regarded as the best in the world, but the American product more than held its own.

New Process flour clearly excelled the old process product in its baking characteristics, uniformity and color. Most consumers who became acquainted with its performance would have no other. It cost more to make, as for a time the reduced speed of the millstones and the system of regrinding cut mill capacities from a quarter to a half. For some years it commanded premiums that more than covered the extra expense, and it was the basis for more than a few milling fortunes.

Installation of middlings purifiers in American mills was hardly well under way before the industry began to consider seriously an even more radical step—abandoning the stone buhrs that had been the all-but-universal method of grinding wheat through most of the Christian era. A committee of Minneapolis millers travelled to Europe late in 1873 to investigate the roller process then in use in Hungary, and upon their return several of them began to experiment with rolls in grinding wheat. At that time rolls were used only in the first stages of the milling process, but in 1876 the first all-roller mill in America went into operation in Philadelphia, John Sellers being the owner of the concern.

Roller mills were by no means novel in the 1870's. European inventors had been trying for no less than two hundred years to develop the idea, and several roller mills had been built in Germany and Switzerland during the 1830's. Jacob Sulzberger, a Swiss engineer, built one in Budapest, Hungary, in 1839 that had continued to operate, although not without plenty of difficulties, and in the late 1860's the millers in several European countries were beginning to install roller systems. The rolls were made of several materials—iron, marble and porcelain, among other things—before it was learned that chilled steel was best. The early roller systems did not employ rolls throughout, millstones being retained to grind the middlings stream in the tail of the mill. In reminiscences written many years later, William D. Gray, the celebrated Scotch-American milling engineer, insisted that there were no all-roller mills in Europe when he inspected its mills in 1879. After the Sellers mill, which remained in operation only a few months before the site was taken for municipal purposes, the next all-roller mill in the United States was the Washburn "C" mill in Minneapolis, built in 1878 after the "B" mill was demolished in an explosion. Before that time, however, several other mills had been partially equipped with rolls.

Once the feasibility of roller milling was demonstrated, adoption of the process was rapid. No all-millstone mill of any importance was built after 1880, and rolls were substituted for buhrs on at least the first and second breaks in practically all of the milling plants of more than grist classification throughout the nation. In the tail of the mill buhrs continued in rather general use for about another decade, but by 1900 they had almost disappeared from mills in the United States.

Rolls had several points of superiority over stones. They were far better adapted to the gradual reduction milling techniques; they eliminated the high cost of stone dressing; they turned out a product that was more uniform and of nicer appearance and much more appealing to the consumer; and they made more flour from a given amount of wheat. These important economic advantages were not offset to any extent by shortcomings. The older generation of millers was reluctant to dispense with millstones, but their sentimental attachment to this historic method of grinding bowed to the economic gains that were brought in by its successor.

The roller system had another inherent advantage — it

opened the way for much larger plants than had ever before been known. The Washburn mill of 5000 cwt. was quickly followed by the celebrated Pillsbury "A" that had 10,000 cwt. by 1880. The Pillsbury mill was able to produce almost four times as much flour as any mill that was in existence in the United States before 1878, and it was by far the largest mill in the world at that time. In fact, it was freely asserted before the two mills were built that they would find it impossible to bring together enough wheat to enable them to operate. The common size of milling plants, that had ranged from 300 to 500 cwt. and only occasionally above 1000 cwt. in the millstone era, soon moved up to 1000 to 3000 cwt., but with no ceiling on capacity.

The higher yield of flour that was obtained from the roller process as compared with millstones deserves more emphasis than it has had in milling literature. Results obtained varied greatly from one mill to another, and data from careful comparisons are fragmentary, but it seems certain that no less than three per cent more flour was extracted from the same quantity of wheat and in some cases the gain was as high as five to seven per cent. Buhrs were not celebrated for their efficiency in milling, and neither were the early roller mills for that matter, but in the course of time millers learned how to improve their performance in this respect—a process that has continued, very slowly, to the present day.

A good many sentimental tears have been shed over the passing of the millstone. Most old millers gave up this method of milling with genuine regret, and it was often said that "a mill doesn't seem like a mill without the noise of millstones." One school of emotion has never ceased to mourn for millstones, maintaining that flour made in that way is better than any other. Perhaps these people do not realize that the stone method of grinding would be a bit deficient in the light of modern sanitation requirements, nor do they know that a German scientist calculated before 1800 that for each 4385 bushels of wheat ground on millstones, one ton of sand was cast off into the flour.

There is a common opinion, even in the industry, that once the milling revolution was complete no more changes took place in the process of making flour. This view is far from the fact. Throughout the more than eight decades that have elapsed since the purifier and corrugated steel rolls became conventional pieces of mill equipment, other changes have been introduced and become generally employed in flour mills—improvements in bolting, installation of dust collectors, development and refinement of tempering, a complete overturn in packing flour, adoption of roller bearings, perfection of pneumatic handling of stock, to name only a few out of the many —but these steps in milling progress have lacked the sensational quality that marked the great events of the milling revolution. Milling techniques have continued to advance a little at a time, and in fact this forward tempo has accelerated considerably in late years.

Minneapolis went into first place as a milling center in 1880, a position that the city at the Falls of St. Anthony continued to enjoy for an even half century. St. Louis, the former leader, made about as much flour as before, but the Minneapolis volume doubled and trebled and then continued to rise. Minneapolis production of 4,000,000 cwt. in 1880 jumped to 8,000,000 cwt. four years later, then leaped to 15,000,000 cwt. before 1890, to 30,000,000 cwt. in 1900 and reached its crest of 40,000,000 in 1916. Thereafter it declined considerably, but through all this long period Minneapolis was recognized as the foremost milling center in the world as well as in the United States.

Illinois remained as the first state in wheat production into the 1870's, then surrendered its place to Iowa for four years before recovering the lead for three. After top rank see-sawed briefly between Indiana and Ohio, Minnesota went into first place in 1883 and retained this position every year but one before 1900; the exception was 1888, when California was the wheat king. Total spring wheat production rose rapidly through the 1870's, partly due to rapid settlement of the northwest states, partly to extension of railroad mileage and partly to mill demand.

Meanwhile a wheat miracle was taking shape in Kansas, to result in the creation of another major segment of America's milling industry. It was set in motion in faraway Russia, where a great colony of Mennonites took refuge in 1783 under an agreement with Catherine the Great that freed them of military service for a century. A ten-year notice that this agreement would not be renewed sent them by the thousands to Central Kansas in 1873 and 1874. The Mennonites were wheat growers in Crimea, and many of them brought seed wheat to America. This was a hard winter wheat, called Turkey Red, unlike anything previously grown in this country. It proved to be much better suited to Kansas conditions than the soft and semihard wheats that the settlers had been growing, and it became the ancestor of practically all the hard winter wheat now grown in America. Turkey Red spread rather slowly outside of the Mennonite communities, however, and Kansas did not become very important as a wheat state until after 1890. Early in the twentieth century Kansas became the first wheat state and along with the crops of its neighboring southwestern states hard winter wheat volume was greater than the total of any other class of wheat.

Hard winter wheat usually ran somewhat lower in protein than spring wheat, but in the course of time both the export market and this country's commercial bakers learned to use southwestern flour in large amounts. The flour mills that had somewhat hesitantly sprung up in the wake of mounting wheat production there became an important group in the industry by 1900, and subsequently they grew in total until their capacity was approximately equal to that in the spring wheat area.

The nation's population, which had exceeded 50,000,000 in 1880, rose almost to 63,000,000 in 1890 and close to 76,000,000 in 1900. Wheat production increased even more rapidly, going from about 200,000,000 bushels annually in the 1860's to an average of 340,000,000 bushels in the 1870's, and then jumping to 480,000,000 bushels in the 1880's and 588,000,000 bushels in the 1890's.

Total number of mills, including corn and feed plants, moved upward a little from 1870 to 1880—22,573 to 24,338; and then under the impact of the roller mill dropped to 18,470 in 1890. However, this went to the all-time high of 25,338 in 1900, but only 13,188 reported the production of wheat flour. The amount of flour milled went up from 126,000,000 cwt. in 1880 to 163,000,000 cwt. in 1890 and 207,000,000 cwt. in 1900. Flour exports, which had averaged 7,759,000 cwt. annually during the 1870's, more than doubled—to 17,266,000 —in the next decade and then leaped to a sensational 30,775,000 cwt. during the 1890's.

The last quarter of the nineteenth century in flour milling was marked by the introduction of new milling equipment and then by its standardization and general adoption; the predominance of Minneapolis as the milling center; a considerable increase in the average size of merchant mills; and the shaping up of economic factors that continued to play a large role in the subsequent history of the industry.

CHAPTER SIX

Growing Pains of an Industry

Nineteenth century milling history was so dominated by the introduction of middlings purifiers and steel rolls that it is not always remembered that other changes in considerable number and of an astonishing nature also transpired in that period.

Merchant mills were producing more than 90 per cent of the nation's flour by 1900, whereas a century earlier they had accounted for little more than half, and had exports been excluded they made less than half. The balance was the product of grist milling. The decisive trend toward merchant milling had been set in motion by the growth of towns and cities; and it had been carried along by increased overseas trade in flour, by the transportation system that had come into being, by Oliver Evans' automatic mill and the great milling revolution of the 1870's, by the establishment of commercial baking and by consumer preference for a more uniform product than could be made consistently by a crossroads mill.

To be sure, some eight thousand or more small mills were operating at the end of the century, but a large majority were not primarily grist mills. Here and there was a mill that ground out grist as farmers brought in wheat, but for one of that kind there were a dozen or a score that milled flour for sale and when a grower took wheat in for flour the deal was handled on an exchange basis. Some of the little mills of that period still used millstones, but they were a small minority. Custom milling had largely supplanted grist milling. Strictly speaking, nearly all the small mills were merchant mills; some confined their business to their home communities but many shipped their surplus above local needs to a city flour market.

Roller milling had a strong tendency to increase the size of merchant mills. That was due in part to the fact that the mill building that formerly housed millstones could accommodate enough rolls to produce more flour than had been ground before. Many of the mills that ranged from 200 to 500 cwt. capacity in millstone days were rebuilt with 500 to 1000 cwt. when equipped with rolls. Then, too, new mills were being erected every year, the 2000 or 3000 cwt. plant soon ceased to be a novelty and there were a few giants that, as already noted, could mill the unbelievable amount of 6000 to 10,000 cwt. in a 24-hour period.

Enlargement of mills or the construction of new mills of large size meant that a great deal of new capital was flowing into the industry. In many cases this was provided by the owner out of accumulated profits or borrowings, but elsewhere it signalized the entry into the business of a man or group that did not necessarily have milling experience. This last was contrary to historical precedent, for milling had been a trade rather than a business. It must be noted, however, that a large share of the mills in Rochester in the great days of milling on the Genesee were owned by men who had not previously been millers. This was likewise true of most of the mills built in Minneapolis in the 1870's; almost without exception they were owned by Yankees who had a little capital or could command capital, and only a few of them had ever milled flour. In the course of time, more than a few of these newcomers became so well established in milling that their sons and then their grandsons succeeded to the concerns that they founded.

Flour mill locations went through a great deal of reshuffling during the nineteenth century. At its beginning, Philadelphia, Baltimore and Richmond were the chief milling centers; a generation later, Rochester was ascendant, then St. Louis became the leader; toward the end, Minneapolis was milling almost one-sixth of the nation's flour and far behind were Superior, Milwaukee and St. Louis, the next most important milling points.

The shift in milling centers was primarily a response to vast improvements in transportation facilities. These improvements not only had a great bearing upon the areas where wheat was produced but they also greatly influenced the location of flour mills. In the early days, a majority of the merchant mills were clustered in or near port cities that were markets of some consequence in themselves and also were points of shipment coastwise and overseas; but along the rivers other mills produced flour for the same markets. It gradually became a point of argument whether mills should be near their markets or near their sources of wheat supply. This continued after the coming of the railroads, although it was then transferred to a much wider area.

As time went on, the trend was finally established rather firmly in favor of wheat-related locations. This first became evident in the rise of Rochester and the decline of New York as a milling point; in the early days the wheat for Rochester mills originated along the Erie Canal in western New York. The principle was confirmed a little later in the pre-eminence of St. Louis, located virtually in the center of a great wheat district that extended in all directions. It was further confirmed in striking fashion in Minneapolis, which was an outstanding gathering point as well as having some nearby wheat production. The great growth in flour milling that got under way around 1850 was chiefly in the states from Ohio to Missouri and Minnesota, and later it extended southwest through Kansas to Texas. On the other hand, there was no overall milling gain in this period in or near metropolitan areas in the East (except, later on, Buffalo, which was a special case). In the Pacific states, the distances between the wheat fields and the cities are relatively small but the bulk of the capacity was located in the country until a much later date.

Chief reasons for the inland trek of flour milling seem to have been three in number. First was the fact that a miller in or near a wheat growing area was much more secure in his wheat supply than was a distant miller. Storage space was limited, transportation facilities not wholly dependable, market information not very available at that time—the miller far from the wheat country had quite a handicap. Another factor was the lower cost of shipping 100 pounds of flour than the 140 or 145 pounds of wheat from which it was milled. Until the late years of the nineteenth century milling offal was not regarded as having much value and so the shipment of wheat involved paying freight for a great deal of dead weight. The third factor that bore heavily in favor of interior locations was that many flour mills of consequence were the successors to small community mills that had been operated a generation or two earlier by family members. As these mills increased in size, they usually remained in the spot occupied by the early mill, sometimes through inertia but also for the practical reason that a mill is not easily moved. The first two factors that favored country locations lost most of their validity two full generations ago, and the third is much less important than it was. Meanwhile in later years new factors have tended to reverse the location trend, at least to some degree.

From colonial days there existed city flour markets of importance, to which flour was shipped from country points for sale, usually through commission merchants. The principal markets of this kind were originally New York, Philadelphia, Baltimore, Charleston and Boston. The first three were also milling centers, but Charleston and Boston had no mills. Boston was largely supplied by English mills until this trade was cut off during the War of 1812; and one Boston flour distributor of the present day, Sands, Taylor & Wood Co., has been in continuous existence since 1790, when it was established as a flour commission firm.

St. Louis and Cincinnati became the most important flour marketing centers in the Middle West, as they were strategically located with reference to the South, which has always been a flour deficit area. St. Louis was the largest point of flour distribution through the third quarter of the nineteenth century. Chicago, Nashville, Pittsburgh and Buffalo were also distribution centers of some importance.

City flour markets handled a large volume for several generations, but beginning about 1875 they began to decline in importance and by the time of the first World War the practice of consigning flour shipments had about ceased. This was due to the decadence of small mills that had no other avenue to market, to the establishment by most other mills of their own sales departments and of brands under which they merchandised flour, to the development of flour brokerage firms in all cities of importance and to the considerable degree of disrepute into which commission selling of flour had fallen. This last was caused by a minority of more or less unscrupulous commission men who preyed on millers, and they hastened the end of the business even though many upright firms were engaged in the trade.

Before the railroad era, waterways and wagon roads were the only means of transportation. The network of navigable rivers in the Atlantic states enabled wheat to be moved to market or mill and flour to go from mill to distribution point. This was extended early in the nineteenth century by the Erie Canal and several other now almost-forgotten canal systems, notably in Maryland, Pennsylvania and Ohio. As the pioneers settled the Middle West, some of them hauled their crops almost incredible distances by wagon roads that were not worth the name; journeys of a week each way were commonplace. It was under these conditions that the Baltimore & Ohio began operating in 1831, the first unit of the railroad industry that grew with amazing speed. Building the railroads was of course the most important peacetime event in nineteenth century American history, and its revolutionizing effect brought basic changes into every aspect of human activity.

Upon no line of endeavor did the creation of railroads have a more pervading effect than upon flour milling. The railroads extended the wheat areas inland two thousand miles from the Atlantic and a thousand miles from the Pacific. They made possible the rapid and complete development of at least half the nation's land area. It would be impossible to visualize how much use could have been made of Kansas, for example, with a minimum of navigable rivers and lacking the water to operate canals. As wheat moved inland, flour mills followed and thus was established what was for many years the most important industry of interior America. Moreover, many a small mill that had been able to do only a local business, before the iron horse grew into an enterprise of respectable size, was then able to reach markets that previously had been beyond its horizon. Grain and grain products provided the largest tonnage of many of the chief railroad lines, a condition that has continued right down to the present day.

Vital as the railroads were, their establishment created new and perplexing problems. Foremost among them were rates that favored some areas or concerns and discriminated against others. This condition became a business nightmare and it prevailed many years, not being cleared up until early in the twentieth century.

A direct by-product of transportation sytems that spread out over the nation's surface was the establishment of grain marketing machinery that was the prototype of today's facilities. To be sure, grain markets of a sort had existed from the earliest colonial days, but they were local in character. Even after New York had become a flour milling and wheat shipping center of considerable importance, the price of grain in other markets was not necessarily related to that in New York. In fact, what existed was a series of markets that reflected supply and demand in their respective areas, and they were little affected by each other even though relatively not far apart. No less a man than George Washington was puzzled by the fact that the Philadelphia wheat market might fall while that in Baltimore was rising, or vice versa. The railroads brought this confused and somewhat chaotic condition to an end by furnishing the means whereby grain might be hauled quickly for hundreds of miles, and the result was the formation of marketing facilities that extended throughout the nation.

The Board of Trade of the City of Chicago was organized in 1847, and within a few years it attained such prestige and importance in grain trading that the day of wide price differences within short distances was over. This came about for the most part because of the huge volume of future trading in Chicago. It is probable that in the first years of the Chicago market its principal value to the miller was the fact that prices on all other markets, except those on the Pacific Coast, were related to Chicago prices, and for the first time in history there was in existence a national wheat market.

As the size of mills increased, and it was necessary for millers to own substantial stocks of wheat in advance of the time when it would be ground, there arose the practice of hedging which was the transfer to the speculative market of part of the risk of ownership. This was of great value in any period of fluctuating prices. Unfortunately, there were occasions in which millers did not confine themselves to hedging, and more than a few fine milling businesses were wrecked through speculation; but others were just as badly injured by taking positions on cash wheat inventories. It should also be noted here that millers were among the most severe critics of the futures market manipulations that occurred periodically for many years, as these deals often had a severe adverse effect upon the worth of the market for hedging purposes. It may surprise millers of the present era to know that throughout the half century that ended with the passage of the Federal Grain Futures Act of 1922, few subjects had as much attention at millers' meetings as the bull and bear raids that made hedging hazardous.

Another subject of frequent complaint in the period just referred to was the wide variation in wheat grades in different markets. This became important only after mills became so large that part of their supplies had to be drawn from a distance. For a long time, a wheat grade meant only what a shipper wanted it to mean, then some of the markets established grades but other markets used different criteria for their own grades. This condition continued to be a source of annoyance and loss until after the federal standards for wheat went into effect in 1917. Uniformity in grades throughout the nation had been an objective desired by millers for many years before that, and the milling industry was the only trade group that gave active and wholehearted support to legislation that authorized the Department of Agriculture to establish federal grades.

So little were mill offals esteemed that it was common practice for mills until at least 1850 to give them gratis to anyone who would haul them away. In the East millfeeds reached a level of three or four dollars per ton after that, but in the Middle West with its surplus of feedstuffs the usual disposition of bran and middlings was to spout them into the stream that turned the millwheel. William Kelly, a pioneer Kansas miller, once related to the author his experiences in using bran for fuel. A new era opened in 1882, when Fred C. Pillsbury, brother of the miller who founded the family company in Minneapolis, demonstrated the feeding value of millfeeds in a well-publicized experiment and thereafter a market developed that utilized all mill offals. It did not, however, add to the millers' incomes as the realization from millfeed was usually treated as a reduction in material costs in figuring flour prices.

That insurance rates on flour mills were prohibitively high is not surprising in view of the frequent and disastrous fires that destroyed many frame mills. Agitation on this subject finally led to the organization in 1875 of the Mill Owners' Mutual Fire Insurance Co., Des Moines, and it was followed in due course by six other similar concerns in areas ranging from Pennsylvania to Texas. Despite the hazards of insuring mill property, these companies managed to operate successfully, but in later years they took risks on varied kinds of property as well as mills.

Adulteration of flour was a condition that existed from the earliest days, and several of the colonies were obliged to employ inspectors to examine exports and in some cases domestic shipments. Little more was heard about it until after the Civil War, when there were growing complaints that wheat flour was mixed with rice or corn flour in southern markets. The condition grew worse rather than better, and in 1898 it had become so critical that the milling industry appealed to Congress for relief. The result was the enactment of the mixed flour law, under which a license was required for mixing flours, and a tax and special labeling were imposed on mixed flours containing more than 50 per cent of wheat flour. After a few years adulteration practically disappeared, and in 1940 the law was repealed at the instance of the industry because the practice was covered amply by other laws that meanwhile had reached the statute books.

There were numerous other changes in flour milling during the period of its greatest growth. Among them were the partial replacement of the wooden barrel by large cotton bags and then the use of small cotton and paper bags as flour containers; the growing chorus of criticism of the worth of white bread as a food, tracing largely to the faddist doctrine originated by Rev. Sylvester Graham; the development of commercial baking, which around 1900 made 10 to 15 per cent of the nation's bread, a figure that rose to twice that amount by the first World War; the beginning of a reduction in per capita consumption of flour; and the introduction of durum wheat in 1898 and the beginning of durum milling about 1909. During the last years of the nineteenth century and continuing through the first part of the twentieth there was a period in which the first mill consolidations took place, events that to some degree were related to all the other changes that are chronicled here and that are related especially to the industry's earnings.

No authentic data of consequence exist as to flour mill earnings when mills were small or comparatively small. It may be surmised that in many cases their operations were profitable, this belief being based upon the fact that certain owners managed their properties so that over a period of time their small mills grew to considerable size and continued to thrive. By the same reasoning, one may properly conclude that in many other cases profits were small at best, as the mills became moribund or ceased to exist.

Possibly the first significant data that are available relate to the period of great milling prosperity and are covered in a statement made many years later by George H. Christian. Said he: "In our first year of New Process milling, our mills made a net profit of fifty cents per barrel; in the second year, a dollar; the third year, two dollars; and in the fourth year, we made four dollars and a half per barrel." This statement is discounted in some quarters as being the too-enthusiastic reminiscence of an old man, but more than a little evidence exists to sustain its essential conclusion that New Process milling was highly profitable for several years. It may well have been the most lucrative period in the industry's history, although by no means the only one. Earnings through most of the 1880's were perhaps drab in comparison with the opulent years, but they could hardly have been really unsatisfactory. However, as the decade neared the end several Minneapolis mills were experiencing losses, and the same condition prevailed elsewhere. For the first time millers were faced with a condition that continued nearly all the time for the next sixty-five years—an excess of flour milling capacity.

At this juncture there took place the first milling merger of importance—the formation in 1889 of Pillsbury-Washburn Flour Mills, Ltd., representing a consolidation of C. A. Pillsbury & Co. and Washburn Mill Co. (The latter had been the property of Senator W. D. Washburn, and should not be confused with Washburn Crosby Co.) The new company was the largest in the industry by quite a margin, and it was created by English investors who had heard from afar of American milling profits. However, it failed to pay dividends during a substantial part of the nineteen years in which it was an operating entity.

The size of the Pillsbury-Washburn company so disturbed its smaller competitors in Minneapolis that six of them joined in a merger of their own in 1891, thus launching Northwestern Consolidated Milling Co. The following year three others were amalgamated as Minneapolis Flour Manufacturing Co. In a sort of chain reaction, the five principal mills in New York City merged in 1892 as Hecker-Jones-Jewell Milling Co. The purpose in these cases was to obtain the supposed advantages of large scale operation, although a secondary consideration was the desire by several estates and elderly owners to retire from the business. These factors inspired the organization during the same year of Sperry Flour Co., which brought into one concern the six principal milling companies in California.

Although the operating results secured by these early milling mergers were something less than sensational, there next appeared a much more ambitious proposal; in fact, an attempt to create a milling trust, modeled after the combines that flourished in other lines at that period in American business history. Thomas A. McIntyre, a New York flour man who doubled as a promoter, launched the United States Flour Milling Co. in flamboyant fashion in 1898, with the declared purpose of acquiring most of the principal spring wheat mills and controlling the production and prices of spring wheat flour. His goal was the control of thirty-one mills, in Minneapolis, Superior, Milwaukee, Buffalo and Syracuse, with total daily capacity of almost 200,000 cwt. He succeeded in bringing in companies with about 77,000 cwt., the largest and best-known of which were Northwestern Consolidated and Hecker-Jones-Jewell. However, McIntyre failed by a narrow margin to obtain control of the two largest, Pillsbury-Washburn and Washburn Crosby, due to determined resistance by members of the Pillsbury family and the Washburn Crosby management. This was fatal, and the would-be trust went into receivership early in 1900. It was reorganized as Standard Milling Co., a holding company for several of the chief milling properties. For a time the mills of Standard Milling Co.'s subsidiaries operated more capacity than did any other company in the industry, but they were under separate managements and were not classed as a single entity.

Somewhat before the end of the nineteenth century, flour millers and flour milling had developed a broad pattern that would prevail for several generations: Milling was no longer primarily a trade but had become a business; the main body of the industry, the mills of commercial importance, consisted of four or five hundred companies, virtually all of them family-owned and managed by their owners; none of the largest companies was doing as much as five per cent of the total volume and none even approached a national status; a preponderant majority of the mills was located in or very near areas of wheat production; and millers as a class were rugged individualists in the best sense of that term—independent, self-reliant and proud of their craft and industry.

CHAPTER SEVEN

Early Twentieth Century Milling

During the last decade or so before Kaiser Wilhelm's submarines propelled a reluctant America into the European War, flour milling seemed to many to be an industry that was approaching maturity—its manufacturing processes were well perfected, with little demand for change; its supply of raw materials was abundant and moderate in price; its markets at home were apparently assured for an indefinite period; its outlets abroad seemed reasonably satisfactory; and, despite earnings being modest and sometimes skimpy, most companies were on a more solid economic level than had ever before been known. It is not surprising that a great deal of complacency existed.

Although this assessment seemed to be realistic enough at the time, the future played havoc with most of its features. The comfortable conclusion that flour milling would proceed in largely unchangeable fashion proved to be almost wholly erroneous. In actuality several far-reaching changes were even then under way in the industry and many others were in the making and would soon become evident. These things largely had their origins in the great wave of economic progress that characterized the early years of this century.

The first two decades of the twentieth century witnessed a reduction in per capita consumption of wheat flour of 20 per cent from 224 pounds in 1900 to 179 pounds in 1920. This came about because of changing food habits, the bread-meat-potatoes fare of our grandfathers giving way to a widely diversified dietary, reduced manual labor from industrial mechanization and shorter hours, improved housing, and other related factors that all grew out of changes then taking place in American life. Reduced usage of flour per person took away a market for 85,000,000 bushels of wheat annually, or more than 33,000,000 cwt. of flour equivalent. This was about offset, however, by the population gain of more than 29,000,000 that was taking place in the United States in the same period of time. Flour production leveled off in the general range of 200,000,000 cwt. per year prior to the world demand that was generated during and after the first great war.

The excess capacity condition that first became apparent in Minnesota before 1885 continued until the outbreak of war. It was most evident in the spring wheat area, where there were more mills than were needed to grind the crop and more than were needed to supply the combined domestic and export trade. Competition became severe, its weight falling hardest upon mills in unfavorable locations or with less resources. The result was that a considerable number of mills went out of business in Wisconsin, Minnesota and the Dakotas over a period of 25 years or more.

Excess capacity was also a major problem in the Pacific Coast states, where an overbuilt condition had followed the abnormally large wheat crops of the late 1880's. Population was small there, and although an extensive Oriental trade in flour continued year after year there was not enough business for all and a considerable amount of capacity was closed because of unprofitable conditions.

This was the most glamorous period in soft wheat milling. For the first time there emerged from the great host of small soft wheat mills from Missouri to Pennsylvania several score of larger mills—not really very large, few exceeding 2000 cwt. capacity and most being around 1000 cwt.—that specialized in very short patent flour which set the pattern for southern biscuits. Self-rising flour first became important about 1905, and phosphated flour was introduced about ten years later. Within a short time these products became so popular that they largely displaced other flours in the South and they proved to be large factors in maintaining the family trade in that area. Another soft wheat specialty, household cake flour, began to come into general use at about this time. Despite these developments the total number of soft wheat mills declined considerably.

Hard winter wheat production reached a significant volume in the states from Nebraska to Texas, and a milling industry of corresponding importance was developing in that area. It was an early participant in the Latin American trade, and it was beginning to supply commercial bakers who in turn doubled their volume in twenty years. In metropolitan areas in the North bakers were making more than half the bread.

A portent of things to come was the location of a Washburn Crosby mill in Buffalo in 1903 and its later enlargement to 20,000 cwt. (Subsequently it was almost doubled and then became the world's largest mill.) Until that time Buffalo was relatively unimportant as a milling point, but the advantage inherent in lake transportation brought it out of its long obscurity.

The rise of Buffalo as a milling center was related to some degree, but not exclusively, to the establishment of milling-in-bond, under which foreign wheat is imported and the duty remitted when flour is exported. Canadian wheat was milled in bond in Minneapolis in 1902, and to some extent elsewhere in later years, but it was mainly carried on in Buffalo. When a duty was levied on wheat in 1921, after it had been on the free list for eight years, others mills were built in Buffalo to take advantage of the bonding plan. The practice was strongly assailed by many millers, who asserted that it took away foreign business that they might enjoy; and as stoutly defended by Buffalo and other millers, who insisted that milling-in-bond enabled them to secure business that would otherwise go to foreign mills. The controversy raged for almost twenty years, but has largely disappeared since 1938.

When war came in 1917, the largest mill was Pillsbury "A," which then had 28,000 cwt. Washburn Crosby "A" and "C" mills totaled 44,000 cwt., and both companies also had other mills of smaller size in Minneapolis. Northwestern Consolidated had several connected plants that totaled about 25,000 cwt. The Buffalo mill was next in size, and the Hecker-Jones-Jewell plant in New York City was almost as large. Largest of the Minnesota mills outside of Minneapolis were Duluth-Superior and the Eagle mill in New Ulm, each having about 10,000 cwt. capacity. On the Pacific Coast the largest were Portland Flour Milling Co.'s plant of 10,000 cwt. in the Oregon city and Centennial's Tacoma mill, 9000 cwt. Largest in the Southwest was Southwestern Milling Co., Kansas City, and its 6000-cwt. mill, next being Red Star in Wichita with 4000 cwt. None in Texas and Oklahoma were even half that size.

Among soft wheat mills the lead was jointly held by National Milling Co., Toledo, and Liberty Mills, Nashville, each having plants of 8000 cwt.

Federal legislation first became an important factor in flour milling in this period. The first Food and Drugs Act, adopted in 1906, aroused some fears among millers that it might become a means of harassment, but in most respects it proved to be a decided benefit. An exception was the long drawnout controversy over flour bleaching, not settled until 1917, the story of which is related elsewhere. Amendments to the Interstate Commerce Act ended the era of different rates to different shippers, an action welcomed by most shippers. The Grain Inspection Act opened the way to uniform wheat grades, another legislative development that won the industry's approbation. Much less enthusiasm was probably displayed over the inauguration of the federal income tax in 1914, but it received surprisingly little attention in the milling publications of that year.

Formation of Millers' National Federation in 1902 gave the industry for the first time an agency that could speak for all millers. Only in much later retrospect can it be realized that the Federation first gave many millers a national point of view. Proceedings of earlier meetings of millers related largely to local problems, but from the start the Federation was primarily active in issues of broader scope. In its earliest years the new organization seemed to do little about national legislative matters, but beginning with the long effort to obtain federal grain grades the Federation became increasingly active in Congressional matters.

When automobile ownership became comparatively common, say about 1910, it was inevitable that a universal system of good roads would follow. Until that time rural roads were solely a local concern, but it was not long before improved surfaces were introduced and state and national routes were established. These things completed the destruction of rural isolation, and in doing so they also contributed heavily to the demise of small flour mills. The number of such mills was more than halved in the first three decades of the century, declining from more than 8000 in 1900 to less than 4000, and those that survived usually added other lines and in a great majority of cases flour became a minor part of their activities.

Brands and trademarks rose to their greatest importance during the period under consideration. These insignia had been used from the early colonial era, beginning with millers writing their names on flour barrels. In the second stage the mills themselves were given distinctive names by their owners— Phoenix, Eagle, Atlas, Star and a host of others—and these names were placed on barrel-ends. It is probable, however, that brands were employed first by flour merchants who bought flour in the city markets, and they used different names to designate different qualities. In this period the consumer did not usually know who milled the flour, as it bore only the name and brand of the merchant. However, as mills increased in size and prestige they insisted upon their own names and brands being used; this practice became common from the 1870's and it ultimately was adopted by most mills except those that were chiefly dependent upon flour merchants for their outlets. In those days nearly all flour was used in the household, and brand recognition and acceptance created trade franchises of great value. In time, this led to advertising and other merchandising methods which added to the worth of brands. Many millers owed a large part of their success to the development and maintenance of their flour brands. The number in use reached close to ten thousand, some companies having

scores in regular use. The importance of brands declined somewhat as the bakery trade continued to increase in volume, many
bakers gradually adopting the practice of purchasing on specifications and depending less upon brands. However, in the
period being discussed flour brands were extremely important.

During the prewar years competition remained sharp in
flour milling. This condition probably had a bearing upon the
mergers of most importance that took place—the formation of
Kansas Flour Mills Corp. and Larabee Flour Mills Co., the
first large companies in the Southwest, and the absorption by
Portland Flouring Mills Co. of a considerable share of the
interior mills of the Pacific Northwest. Three other companies
that had been growing continued their expansion by acquiring
additional properties, these being Colorado Milling & Elevator
Co., Russell-Miller Milling Co. and International Milling Co.,
but none of them had yet approached the size and importance
of the others.

Foreign outlets for flour had some ups and downs but they
accounted for about 15 per cent of the total production. During
the ten years that began in 1901, the overseas trade averaged
28,409,000 cwt. This rose in the next decade to 30,520,000
cwt., but these years included the war and postwar periods when
exports were high. The annual average declined only slightly
in the 1920's, being 27,374,000 cwt. despite increased competition from Canada, Australia and other countries.

Wheat production in the United States continued to increase, going up from the 588,000,000-bushel average of the
1890's to 667,000,000 bushels during the succeeding decade
and 774,000,000 bushels in the 1910's. During the latter
period there was the phenomenal 1915 harvest of 1,009,000,-
000 bushels, by far the largest crop up to that time, and production was stimulated in 1918 and 1919 by the war effort.

American entry into the war in April 1917 thrust wheat into the national and international limelight to an almost unprecedented extent. The demands of France and Great Britain for food supplies had absorbed the great wheat crop of 1915 and the subnormal production of the following year. The 1917 harvest was disappointingly small and the market, already at the highest point in years, was soaring. At that juncture, for the first time in American history, the government felt obliged to fix wheat prices. The level established was $2.26 per bushel, basis Chicago. In order to administer the fixed wheat price, all handlers and processors of wheat were licensed. The flour milling industry was thus confronted with its first experience in operating under government controls that regulated all aspects of the business. These controls were administered by the United States Food Administration, the head of which was Herbert C. Hoover. Mr. Hoover turned for advice about milling to his friend, William C. Edgar, longtime editor of *Northwestern Miller,* and was told that the industry would rise to the emergency and its leaders would serve the government in any manner desired.

That was how the famous millers' committee came into being, charged with administering the food control law as it related to flour milling. Its chairman was young James Ford Bell of Minneapolis, and its membership consisted of Bernard A. Eckhart of Chicago, Andrew J. Hunt of Arkansas City, Kan., Edmund M. Kelly of Nashville, Fred J. Lingham of Lockport, N. Y., Albert C. Loring of Minneapolis, Mark N. Mennel of Toledo, Samuel Plant of St. Louis and Theodore B. Wilcox of Portland. The members of this blue ribbon committee each had the responsibility for a specific territory, and they controlled wheat supplies and made allocations of government and foreign flour orders. Mill profits were limited and in the second year of the war the flour extraction rate was also regulated. After a year Bell was moved to the management of the sugar board, and Lingham became head of the millers' committee. It is to the everlasting credit of the milling industry that all but a limited few of its members cooperated with the war program to the best of their understanding and ability, and their performance drew accolades from high officials of the American government and from the allied powers as well.

The demand for flour that was greatly expanded under wartime pressures continued well into 1921. This condition had a potent influence upon milling capacity. Many existing mills were expanded in the years that began in 1917 and an almost astonishing number of new mills was built. The expansion in milling facilities within three years approached 20 per cent. This created no problem as long as the abnormal demand for flour abroad continued, but when it slackened and flour production fell back toward the 200,000,000-cwt. level that had prevailed before the war, there was more excess capacity than the industry had ever known. It was alleviated to some degree, although very painfully, by older plants that had become obsolete going out of production, and by a shocking number of companies going bankrupt in the wheat price debacle that began in the last half of 1920. Despite these adjustments, there was still more milling capacity than could be used to supply the American people with flour and to take care of all available foreign demand. This condition prevailed, although with ups and downs, into the second war period. Except for a few short periods, the excess in capacity was usually no more than 10 to 15 per cent of the total, although millers habitually thought and talked about it as ranging from 35 to 50 per cent. Their error was due to the common inflation of mill sizes above their actual productivity and to the inclusion of a great deal of small mill capacity that was no longer in commercial use and was therefore not effective capacity.

Flour milling in the 1920's was highlighted by the continued growth of commercial bakeries, which were then using almost 40 per cent of the flour produced; by the first of the great bakery mergers; by the rise to importance of grocery chains, and the beginning of a long decline in wholesale groceries; by a reduction in flour exports, especially in the last years of the decade; by an extended reduction in American per capita consumption of flour, although this had little effect on total production because of population increases; by wheat becoming an explosive political issue via the great McNary-Haugen fight in 1925-28 and the adoption of the Hoover program that put the government into the grain business; by a government investigation of pricing practices in the milling industry; and by a significant concentration in the ownership of flour mills.

Mill earnings throughout the 1920's were regarded at the time as being quite unsatisfactory. Except for the fiscal year that ended in 1921, when probably a majority of companies suffered losses, it is not easy to understand why complaints were so numerous. To be sure, the earnings level that prevailed from 1917 to 1920 fell back considerably in subsequent years, but it could not have been maintained in the face of the highly competitive conditions that were nurtured by too much capacity and by rapidly growing concentration among bakers and the growth of grocery chains. Profits were quite pale and anaemic in comparison with what many industries were able to earn in the years of great corporate prosperity, and perhaps it was this contrast that caused many millers to be unhappy with their lot. Although there was a certain amount of mortality among milling companies during the 1920's, it was due (after 1921) more to plants becoming obsolete and to management's failing to keep abreast of changing conditions than to anything inherent in the business. Earnings of the industry may not have been as good as they should have been, but when viewed in the light of earnings for many other periods they were not low.

The Federal Trade Commission investigation into milling practices, which was an offshoot of a study of wheat marketing, sought to show that collusion existed with flour prices. It not only failed in that objective, but it did establish that a wide degree of price variation was the common condition and that millers were often unhappy about their competitors' prices and scolded each other without much restraint but also without much appreciable effect.

The great milling mergers of the 1920's were triggered by rapidly changing conditions, among which bakery consolidations ranked high. Washburn Crosby Co., Inc., acquired mills in Chicago and Kansas City in 1922, and in 1928-29 this company, already the industry's largest, was the keystone in General Mills, Inc., which also included Red Star, Sperry, ElReno and the Kell properties in Texas and Oklahoma. It thus became the first milling company to be national in scope. Its nearest rival, Pillsbury, bought mills in Atchison and Astoria in 1922 and 1929, and built mills in Enid and Springfield. Commander Larabee Corp. was formed in 1926, becoming third largest, being a merger of Larabee Flour Mills Co. and the Sheffield-controlled mills in Minnesota. Not far behind in size was Flour Mills of America, Inc., a 1927 consolidation of Kansas Flour Mills Corp. and Valier & Spies Milling Co. Another step of importance was the organization in 1929 of Tex-O-Kan Flour Mills Co., which brought the seven Burrus-controlled companies into one concern.

The industry that seemed to many casual observers around

1900 to be monotonously stable and having in prospect nothing new of significance proved to be obliged to master a long series of changes. In fact, it went through as many changes and as vital a transformation in three decades as ever occurred before, and at the end of 1929 it was standing on the threshold of even more ahead.

CHAPTER EIGHT

From Depression to War's End

Flour milling history since 1929 has been heavily flavored by actions of the United States government—participation by federal agencies in the wheat market, regulatory measures that delve deeply into corporate practice, establishment of prices in war and postwar periods, overseas trade being determined by government programs and decisions, loan and price support plans that have changed the entire concept of wheat production and marketing, along with many lesser moves of unprecedented nature in this nation.

Government entry into the grain business was initiated in 1929 by Herbert Hoover, of all people. Early in his presidential administration Congress created the Federal Farm Board and appropriated half a billion dollars as a revolving fund to stabilize the markets for farm products. It was confidently believed that this action would halt the downward price trend that had been prevailing and that the worst that might happen would be a stagnant market. However, in less than two years a considerable part of the money was gone and farm prices were lower than they had been in more than a generation.

It would have been decidedly difficult to find a less propitious time for wheat price maintenance than 1929-30. Surpluses that had been accumulating for several years caused a carryover of 245,000,000 bushels in 1929, and the following year this reached the highest level known up to that time— 308,000,000 bushels. Other wheat-exporting nations were confronted with somewhat similar situations. Moreover, in the wave of nationalism that swept over Europe in the 1920's, more and more obstacles and barriers to international trade in wheat were being erected, and their effect was accentuated by the shaky financial structure of the entire world. All these things were in plain sight, but they were seen virtually by nobody because of the boundless optimism that pervaded almost everything in 1929.

The farm board program had two principal effects upon flour milling. First, the stabilization program was somewhat awkwardly administered, not by design but because of its vast extent and the speed with which it was put together. Market relationships were often disrupted, and moves and countermoves followed each other in almost breathless succession. Men who could not possibly know about every local situation were making decisions that had a dollars-and-cents effect upon commercial operations. Except for wartime controls in 1917-18, it was the industry's first experience in being obliged, as it carried on its day-to-day business, to keep one eye upon what an arm of the government might do. The fact that for the most part the officials of Grain Stabilization Corp. were discharging their duties in a conscientious manner alleviated the problem, but the entry of the organization into the market place nevertheless had a distinctly disturbing influence upon normal trade.

The second major respect in which the farm board program adversely affected flour milling was its contribution to loss of overseas flour business. Many millers have bitterly accused the program of destroying their exports, because it held wheat prices above world levels and thus priced their flour out of markets where it had been established for long periods of time. It should be noted, however, that a distinct decline in flour exports began in 1927, two years before the farm board was established, and that this was due to increased tariffs, embargoes, quotas and exchange restrictions, and that these actions were increasing year after year. It is probable that this trend was stimulated by American wheat policies, but any realistic appraisal can only reach the conclusion that a large share of the flour export business that was lost would have gone overboard even if the farm board had never existed. In fact, as early as the spring of 1930 Grain Stabilization Corp. began selling wheat below the market to mills to cover export flour orders, and this step helped to retain much of what foreign business was available.

Wheat prices fell to heartbreak levels in 1932 and 1933, as they did all over the world. One of the first acts of the Roosevelt administration was to establish the Agricultural Adjustment Administration, the essential features of which (as far as wheat was concerned) were the payment of benefits for acreage reduction and the financing of these benefits through the imposition of a tax upon the processing of wheat. Millers became liable for a 30-cent tax upon each bushel of wheat ground on and after July 9, 1933. This created tremendous problems in such areas as the determination of the exact amount of wheat processed and in record keeping, and later in customer relationships. These problems were magnified many fold when the processing tax was declared unconstitutional early in 1936. After the initial suit to test the legality was filed in May 1935 by a cotton manufacturer, most millers had enjoined the collection of the tax; but now they were confronted with a tax on unjust enrichment (often called the windfall tax) plus vigorous demands from customers for reimbursement to the extent that flour prices had been increased by the tax. Bakers' suits to recover from millers resulted uniformly in decisions that denied these claims. In the end, most millers refunded to customers a part of the impounded taxes, and both millers and customers paid large amounts of unjust enrichment tax. Clearing up all phases of processing tax complications required five or six years. Several attempts to reimpose a tax upon processing wheat, with the constitutional infirmity mended, were made between 1936 and 1942 but all failed.

It was widely feared that the heavy tax which caused flour prices to go up radically would result in reducing consumption of wheat products. There is no evidence, however, that it had any appreciable effect. It was also believed to some extent that when the tax became effective the market would go down by the equivalent of the tax, but that not only did not happen but the market advanced considerably during the next few months after enactment.

Another government program of novel nature was initiated in 1933 through the establishment of industrial codes to govern wages, hours and business practices. They were the keystone of the New Deal program for recovery from the great depression. The millers' code went into effect in June, 1934. It established minimum wages and maximum hours in flour mills and it regulated a number of practices that had prevailed in the industry. The code prohibited the payment of commissions to buyers or buyers' agents; severely restricted the use of premiums; required the collection of carrying charges on contracts not delivered within 90 days of sale; prohibited guarantees against decline and fictitious and discriminatory prices;

required the use of signed contracts and of package differentials; and prohibited destructive prices. To administer this code, the industry created the Code Authority of the Wheat Flour Milling Industry, which had its main office in Chicago, with branches in Buffalo, Richmond, Louisville, St. Louis, Minneapolis, Kansas City, Dallas, Los Angeles and Tacoma. Carl F. Dietz (b. 1880 N. Y., d. 1957), an engineer who had briefly been associated with Commander Larabee Corp., was the code administrator.

None of the milling code provisions was particularly revolutionary. The wage minimums resulted in some upward revisions, mostly in small towns, but this process was going on in any case at that time. Maximum hours stimulated a general trend away from ten- and twelve-hour days, which had been usual in many mills, and during the next few years the eight hour day became almost universal in the industry. The prohibitions against certain business practices were generally applauded, as were also the requirements for signed contracts and package differentials; these regulations were in line with what nearly all millers believed ought to be done, and when they were given the force and effect of law they established the fact that previous variation from sound business practice had been greater than was generally thought.

During the year that the millers' code was in effect (the law was declared unconstitutional in May 1935), its net effect was distinctly on the constructive side, as it speeded up and made more general the adoption of practices that ought to have been followed by the industry in any event. Although the wage and hour restrictions caused some friction and resentment, they were in accord with a widespread trend in all business. It is interesting and perhaps significant that although many millers had welcomed this code, and although they conceded that its operation had been beneficial, few of them mourned its demise. The consensus was that business reforms could not be forced via laws and regulations.

Flour milling entered the great depression in 1929 in relatively good shape. Although profits had not been large through the 1920's, they had been sufficient to enable most of the medium-sized and large companies to improve their plants. Old plants in considerable numbers were brought up to date and a number of new mills were built during this period. More than a few old mills that had become obsolete or were in locations impaired in value were dismantled. This was especially the case in the soft wheat states, the spring wheat area and the Pacific Coast. Net change in capacity was almost nil, although every district had more mills than were needed. Some companies were extended at the onset of the depression, but probably a majority had built up reserves of consequence. Everything considered, the industry was in the strongest financial position that it had ever been.

Depression effect upon flour milling was most acute in these ways: First, a two-thirds decline in exports, largely related to foreign conditions, as related above. Second, a widespread mania for cheap flours for the family trade, resulting in many old brands losing their following. Third, slow payments by jobbers and bakers and a considerable increase in insolvencies in these lines. Fourth, confusion in the wheat markets as a result of government stabilization operations. Mill earnings remained on the limited side all through this period, but they were not non-existent as they were in many other businesses, and there were few losses except in cases where they were caused by taking market positions. Most millers were rather thankful that their enterprises had suffered few scars during the panic years, even if their earnings had been small.

After business as a whole moved up from the bottom of the depression, and continuing until a year after the Japanese attack upon Pearl Harbor, flour milling went through a period of decidedly keen competition. The earnings level nevertheless rose well above that of the depression years, except in the fiscal period that ended in 1938. In that year a great millfeed decline occurred after most of the previous summer's bookings had been made, and these sales had precarious margins. Losses were severe, especially in the Southwest, but the effect was felt in all areas.

Buffalo displaced Minneapolis as first milling city in 1930 and retained this position throughout the ensuing third of a century to the present day. At the beginning of its supremacy, the seven plants in Buffalo had aggregate capacity of about 60,000 cwt. per day, but this has increased by steps until in late years it has approximated 100,000 cwt. A noteworthy reduction of Minneapolis' capacity took place in the middle 1930's and again in the 1950's, and the former milling leader fell to third place in the industry in 1937 behind Kansas City.

Wheat production in the 1930's was marked by a four-year period (1933-36) in which the harvest was dismally small, due to excessive drouths in the Great Plains states on top of reduced acreages. In fact, crops were so short that a considerable amount of wheat was imported from Canada, the great carryover of a few years earlier having been dissipated. The 822,000,000-bushel average in the preceding decade dropped to 745,000,000 bushels in the 1930's, but by the end of that period the harvests were again becoming burdensome in size.

The middle and late 1930's witnessed a series of federal legislative enactments that proved to be important to flour milling as well as to practically the entire business spectrum.

These were the Wagner Act, protecting the right of workers to organize and engage in collective bargaining, adopted in 1935; the Fair Labor Standards Act, commonly known as the wage and hour law, passed in 1938; and the revised Federal Food, Drug and Cosmetic Act, which also bore a 1938 date. The Wagner Act was drafted in a vindictive spirit and was administered in a biased and arbitrary manner. Its impact was most violent in the case of industries that employ more labor than do millers, but it was nevertheless detrimental to milling. Some of the most objectionable features of the Wagner Act were modified or eliminated by the Labor Management Relations Act, known as the Taft-Hartley law, passed in 1947. The Fair Labor Standards Act that regulated wages and hours created many problems for small millers in country towns, especially in their elevator operations, but most others were able to adjust to its requirements without major disturbance.

The Federal Food, Drug and Cosmetic Act redefined and considerably extended the powers of the government in this field. Along with most but not all segments of the food industries, millers favored this forward step. As far as millers were concerned, the new law affected them chiefly through its powers of plant inspection, its labeling requirements and its authority for creating definitions and standards of identity for foods. The inspection provisions were used to promote more sanitary conditions in the production and handling of foods, and many loose practices in labeling packages were tightened up.

Millers were among the first to propose federal definitions for their products, and after lengthy hearings in 1940 the official flour definitions and standards went into effect in 1942. At the time of the hearings, much discussion was taking place about the advisability of adding vitamins to flour, and the industry collaborated with scientists in proposing a definition and standard for enriched flour and it was promulgated with the other definitions. However, millers began to put enriched flour on the market early in 1941, almost a year before the definitions became effective. Enrichment was heartily endorsed by all except a few nutritional scientists and it made good headway in a short time. However, credit for the fact that enrichment became universal belongs largely to the persistence with which the program was supported by the milling and baking industries.

Two other events served to highlight 1938. One was the extension of the crop loan program to wheat, but as its important influence upon milling did not occur for more than a decade discussion will be deferred to Chapter IX. The other was an overhaul of the flour sales contract under the joint auspices of the milling and baking industries.

Just when sales contracts forms were first employed by millers has not been determined but their use became fairly common after buyers began to book flour for forward shipment. This was the case in the 1880's and perhaps earlier. First effort to develop a uniform sales contract seems to have been made in 1902 and it met with considerable success. The United States Food Administration required signed contracts on all flour sales in 1917-18, and the milling code of 1934 did likewise. The Federation contract form was most widely used, but there were several others. All of them required the payment of carrying charges on shipments delayed beyond the specified period, but under the stress of competition this provision was breached more often than it was observed.

Various sections of the contract were revised in 1938 by millers and bakers working together, and thereafter it became the general practice of millers to assess and collect carrying charges on shipments made after 120 days from contract date. This was a forward step of the greatest importance, as the effect was to keep contract files much more current than had been the case and to discourage overbooking. Losses that had been incurred in previous years by millers because of abnormally delayed shipments were minimized and a substantial part of the cost of carrying unfilled orders was offset by carrying charge collections. It was one of the most conspicuous victories for sound selling practice on flour.

In 1935 the industry launched an information program in behalf of the merits of foods made from wheat flour. The mechanism employed for this purpose was Wheat Flour Institute, a division of Millers' National Federation, and its main efforts were directed to home economists, physicians and educators.

During the years from the onset of the depression to the outbreak of the great war the merger fever of the 1920's subsided considerably, but was by no means eliminated. The most important deals of this period were the acquisitions by Pillsbury of Globe Grain & Milling Co. and by Russell-Miller of Stanard Tilton Milling Co., and the merger of four independent divisions into Standard Milling Co. John J. Vanier expanded from two mills to four during these years, the Rodney and Ross interests made their first steps in expansion, General Mills and International each acquired an additional mill as did also Colorado Milling & Elevator Co., while Igleheart Bros., Inc., bought two mills. A considerable amount of milling capacity that was largely obsolete was closed during the 1930's, and although some mills were enlarged the net reduction in capacity among the mills of commercial importance was more than 150,000 cwt. New mill construction during the decade was at a minimum.

Flour production during the decade remained almost constant at slightly above 200,000,000 cwt. per year, ranging up to 213,000,000 cwt. in 1940. Contrary to millers' experience in previous periods of hard times, no increase in flour usage took place in the great depression years. Per capita consumption continued its downward trend, going from 169 pounds in 1930 to 154 pounds in 1940. Flour exports averaged but 8,990,000 cwt. in the decade, a decline of almost 70 per cent, but they were on the upgrade again in the late 1930's. The number of small mills, which had been about 4000 after the first World War, was no more than 1500 at the end of the second war.

Just before the outbreak of war, the Justice Department began an extensive investigation of the milling industry, with the result that price-fixing charges were brought against Millers' National Federation, its package differential committee and a number of companies for using the package differential schedule. However, after a trial in mid-1944 Federal Judge Philip L. Sullivan decided that the anti-trust laws had not been violated. This episode is related in detail in Chapter X.

For some months after Pearl Harbor, flour milling continued about as nearly business-as-usual as is possible during a conflict of world-wide nature. There were, of course, such departures from normal as a great number of young men entering the armed services, a large increase in quartermaster purchases of flour, a growing scarcity of many supply items, a sharp reduction in commercial exports because shipping space was not available and upward pressures against all cost factors. However, the volume of flour business increased only slightly from the previous year and prices were almost constant. Wheat supplies were abundant and in many respects the flour trade varied but little from what it had been. The contrast with the first World War was rather striking.

This condition changed radically before the end of 1942. In late September flour prices were frozen at levels then prevailing but wheat prices were left without restraint and they continued to rise. The paralysis that resulted was cleared up with the new year through the issuance of a price ceiling order that had meanwhile been devised under the leadership of Atherton Bean, who had left his company at the request of government officials to undertake this task. Wheat rose again in the fall of 1943 and another price squeeze on flour was resolved by a government subsidy. The subsidy program was continued for more than two-and-a-half years, and the rates were varied from month to month to compensate for the advance in wheat prices after flour ceilings were imposed. Thus for the first time American taxpayers had to foot part of the consumer's grocery bill, this being due to the unwillingness of the authorities for a long time to put ceilings on wheat prices. When they did they refused to allow flour ceilings to move up to an equivalent degree but devised the clumsy subsidy program instead.

Contrary to the situation in most great world wars, wheat stocks were plentiful all through the war period—so plentiful, in fact, that almost a billion bushels were used as livestock feed when corn was scarce and more than a quarter-of-a-billion bushels were ground into grits to make alcohol for wartime use. In both these programs, flour mills played the leading part, as they ground the wheat for livestock feed and made the grits for the alcohol producers. These programs each covered about three years.

Flour production increased from 221,000,000 cwt. in 1942 to about 240,000,000 cwt. in each of the next two years and then jumped up to 274,000,000 cwt. in 1945 under the de-

mands for food in allied lands as they were recovered from
enemy hands, and in occupied areas of enemy countries. The
1945 output of American mills was the largest in history up
to that time. Milling capacity increased approximately 100,000
cwt. during the war years, the increase being distributed over
a large number of mills. However, only a few idle mills were
reopened at this time. The industry's earnings were substantial in this period, especially in 1943-45, although they advanced less than did the profits of many other lines of business
and less than the profits of agriculture and the earnings of
labor.

CHAPTER NINE

To the Present Day

American flour mills operated at close to their maximum rate of production for more than four-and-one-half years—from late in 1943 until after mid-1948. In that time they established new all-time records for output of flour, climaxed by the sensational total of 305,000,000 cwt. in 1947. In addition, during three years of this period they converted immense quantities of wheat into alcohol grits and livestock feed, both being emergency assignments engendered by war conditions. Practically every mill of consequence in the nation ran under forced draft throughout that critical time.

The tremendous demand for flour materialized from the havoc of war, upon which was compounded two of the most unfavorable wheat-growing seasons in modern times in Western Europe along with a near-failure in the rice harvest in Southeastern Asia. The United States was literally feeding a considerable part of the world, and in the course of this undertaking flour exports rose from the general range of 20,000,000 cwt. to about 80,000,000 cwt. in the year of greatest volume. Foreign reliance upon American wheat products did not slacken until after the good harvest of 1948.

The strong and insistent demand for flour of course caused prices to stiffen, but milling profits were tempered perceptibly by price controls, by a large share of the exports being government-to-government deals and by wheat prices advancing faster than flour prices were permitted to do. Even when the intermittent squeezes were relieved by subsidy adjustments, there was invariably a lag before action took place. Earnings were nevertheless handsome as compared to profits in any other part of the past 40 years. They were less flattering, however, when measured by the net of other businesses at that time. The excess capacity situation simply disappeared for four years or more, although its ghost rose occasionally here and there when wheat supplies gave out temporarily. Sales were the least of millers' worries, and for a good share of the time flour orders were literally looking for mills that would give them a home.

There was, however, another side to the coin. For seven years beginning in 1941, mill maintenance and upkeep were at an absolute minimum because supplies and repairs were scarce or not to be had and were often inferior in quality when available. The result was that equipment and facilities in a high proportion of the nation's flour mills were in deplorable condition long before the end of the high operating period. Breakdowns were frequent, the quality of product suffered and there was tremendous deterioration in plants and machinery. A sizeable portion of the earnings in the seeming bonanza years was required to return most mills to efficient operating conditions and standards. In fact, in a significant number of cases the toll taken by the long-continued heavy operation was so great that it was impractical to attempt to counter the relentless move towards obsolescence.

Meanwhile the industry was beset with an assortment of other major problems. Foremost were wheat supplies, which had been abundant, even excessive, during the war years. Harvests during the first half of the 1940's averaged 926,000,000 bushels, up one-fifth from those of a few previous years. The 1940 carryover of 280,000,000 bushels was one of the largest up to that time, but under wartime production incentives the carryover went up above 600,000,000 bushels in both 1942 and 1943, a level of astonishing size. Moreover, there were several corn crops of insufficient size to feed the livestock numbers that had boomed in response to wartime needs, and nearly a billion bushels of wheat were sent to feedlots to fill the gap (about one-sixth of this consisted of Canadian imports). Another huge quantity was used in making industrial alcohol for powder factories. After V-E Day, the desperate calls from Western Europe for food grew to crescendo proportions, and by the end of 1945 American wheat stocks that had seemed so huge a short time before had dwindled to an alarming extent.

Early in 1946 the government, which still possessed wartime powers, instituted a series of wheat conservation steps, one of them requiring that 80 per cent of the weight of wheat be extracted as flour. The long extraction order came at the behest of the State Department, to which the British had addressed bitter complaint that their people had lived on dark bread for more than six years while Americans were still enjoying unlimited amounts of white bread. State Secretary Byrnes promised that we would also adopt 85 per cent extraction, which President Truman reduced to 80 per cent in response to objections by the Department of Agriculture.

The 80 per cent program was resented deeply by millers because no information nor advice was solicited from the industry, because it resulted in degrading their product and because it unleashed a deluge of faddist propaganda against white bread. They felt that the small reduction in wheat usage through lengthening the extraction rate would be offset by increased waste and spoilage. Their objections were apparently vindicated by experience, for Secretary of Agriculture Anderson quietly rescinded the order after six months, effective September 1, 1946.

The wheat shortage continued half way into 1948, and in the preceding year the government created a presidential commission under the auspices of which a nation-wide wheat conservation campaign was conducted, along with other activities. Re-establishment of long extraction flour was narrowly averted, but the effort was dropped when the 1948 harvest caused European needs to diminish greatly. The net effect of the conservation campaign, coming on top of the previous year's poor quality flour, was probably to accelerate the decline in flour use. Per capita consumption dropped from 155 pounds in 1940 to 135 pounds in 1950, most of the reduction coming in the last half of the decade.

No price control program ever works very smoothly, but in a comparative sense OPA flour ceilings served their purpose quite well during the war period. This was the case because the structure was based upon trade experience and because it was developed by men who understood the business. The chief shortcoming of the control program was due to an administration policy that did not permit flour ceilings to be related to wheat ceilings when the latter were established. This led to the costly subsidy expedient, the only merit of which was that it was administered about as well as any such thing could be. After V-J Day a tremendous battle was fought over the continuation of price controls, and a large and vocal element demanded that they be retained more or less indefinitely. The suspicion grew that the real objective of this group was to keep business permanently under the thumb of the government, and Congress refused to extend the price control law after June 30, 1946. However, late in July some controls were reinstated, among them wheat and flour ceilings, but not the subsidy program. All mill business was paralyzed for a week while two government departments engaged in a public quarrel over what to do. New ceiling levels were finally established, but on August 20 the wheat order was annulled and with rising wheat prices the flour ceiling became unmanageable and it was ended on October 23. It was a period of almost incredible confusion, frustration and perplexity.

Late in 1947 the industry was badgered by a furor over Agene, a bleaching and maturing substance that was in general use (Chapter X). More than a year was required to establish that this product had no deleterious effect upon humans, and meanwhile the opponents of white bread as well as the faddists had a field day at the expense of the industry. A suitable alternative for Agene was not available until 1948, and the industry then took the lead in seeking and obtaining a change in the flour standards that prohibited the further use of Agene.

As if in response to the pleas of a hungry world, the American wheat harvest of 1947 was more than 200,000,000 bushels greater than that of any previous crop. Of the total of 1,-359,000,000 bushels, half-a-billion went abroad. Both these figures were towering records that stood for some years. The size of the 1947 crop was a boon to sorely-pressed areas of the world, and it was probably also the deciding factor in ending the various types of regimentation that the mills of this country had endured and in forestalling others that were being urged.

The great 1947 wheat crop was one of a long series that exceeded billion-bushel size. This era was ushered in by 1944, when 1,060,000,000 bushels were harvested—only the second time that the billion-bushel mark was exceeded. However, from 1944 to 1962, inclusive, in only four years has the wheat crop dropped below a billion bushels and then only by relatively small amounts. The average of the second half of the 1940's was 1,202,000,000 bushels, and in the 1950's it was 1,095,-000,000 bushels despite severe restrictions upon acreage. The secret of the great increase is in yields per acre, which in recent years have run more than 75 per cent higher than their levels a quarter of a century ago.

These huge wheat crops led to a third period of burdensome wheat supplies, the first having been ended by the drouths in the mid-1930's and the second by world scarcities a decade later. Carryover in June 1948 was 196,000,000 bushels, and it went up to 425,000,000 bushels in two years, then fell back a bit but by 1954 had reached 933,000,000 bushels, and after remaining around that general level for several years it swept up to a mountainous 1,295,000,000 bushels in 1959. The carryover has been at that point or higher ever since even though hard-driving and heavily-subsidized export programs have moved tremendous quantities abroad in every year since 1949.

Government loans on wheat began with the 1938 crop at 52 per cent of parity. The rate was elevated to 90 per cent in 1941 to stimulate production, and although Congress authorized a sliding scale in 1948 the effective date was extended from year to year and wheat was supported at 90 per cent until 1955. Supports thereafter were 82½ or 75 per cent until the 1962 law returned them to 90 per cent. These government loans are non-recourse in nature, and consequently most wheat on which

loans were taken became government property except in periods
when the free market rose above support levels. In some years
the government body became the chief owner of the carryover.

The long shadow of the support program has fallen upon
the milling industry in a variety of ways. Chief among them
were the creation of artificial scarcities of wheat from time to
time, due to huge accumulations in government hands usually
not being available for mill use; perpetuation of a market pattern based upon historic performance, thus not taking account
of changing conditions; no discrimination against inferior milling wheats until late years, even though excessive production
took place; maintenance of wheat prices at levels not justified
by economic conditions; and the development of a tremendous
system of storage for wheat held by the government agency.
Many milling companies participated in the storage business,
at first to the extent of their available space and then through
the construction of additional facilities. In some cases the storage of wheat for the government became so extensive over a
period of time that it dwarfed milling activities.

Wheat Flour Institute was expanded in 1947 for the purpose of conducting a national advertising program in behalf
of the products of wheat flour. Almost two-and-a-half million
dollars were raised to defray advertising and other costs, and
an advertising program was launched in national magazines
and other periodicals in mid-1948 and continued for more than
a year-and-a-half. The undertaking was suspended in the summer of 1950 but its non-advertising features were absorbed into
the Institute's work program. Thus came to an end an idea
that had been discussed at intervals from 1903, but two of its
by-products remained—the sandwich time program, which has
grown into the largest food promotion of the year, has been

continued to the present; and use of bread in weight-reduction diets, based on research at the University of Nebraska.

Competition for flour business existed all through the period of peak production—a rather surprising circumstance considering the ease with which orders were obtained—but it became exceedingly keen by the mid-point of 1948 when the precipitate decline in overseas business occurred, amounting to a reduction of 4,000,000 cwt. per month. For the first time in four-and-one-half years millers had trouble keeping their plants in operation, and this was reflected in distinctly narrowed margins. Many mills had been running largely on export orders and when this business disappeared they were without enough domestic trade connections to enable them to operate to advantage. A number of mills closed almost at once, others followed at intervals and in the course of about two years, 82 plants of commercial size ceased to produce flour. The process continued, and another 50 mills were also closed by the end of 1953. Thus in about five years the milling industry lost 132 plants, the total capacity of which was 245,905 cwt. daily. The decline was partially offset by increases in the capacities of other mills, amounting to 70,000 cwt. in all. From 1941 to 1953 the industry's facilities were scaled down more than 107,000 cwt. net.

An effort has been made in some quarters to picture the loss of mills in 1948-53 as a great milling debacle. Actually, it was nothing of the sort, for practically all of the plants that went out of production were old, inefficient and obsolete. There were not as many as half-a-dozen good mills among all the 132 that were closed. Many of them had remained in use only because of the great demand for flour and when that was over they quit. The closings were spread over the entire industry, from the largest to the smallest and in all areas although proportionately there were more in the Southwest than elsewhere.

Flour production in the United States fell to 225,000,000 cwt. in 1950, and remained at substantially that level until 1957, when the total rose to 239,000,000 cwt. Each successive year thereafter an increase has taken place, practically all of it due to greater exports. Overseas business was in the general range of 20,000,000 cwt. annually from 1949 to 1956 inclusive, but it then grew steadily until it reached 47,000,000 cwt. in 1962, the gain coming in large part from expansion in government wheat disposal programs after the enactment of P. L. 480 in 1956. Domestic usage of flour has remained at roughly the same total for more than 30 years—about 210,000,000 cwt. annually. Per capita consumption fell 16 pounds in a decade to 119 pounds in 1960, but for the past seven years it has been practically constant. Commercially baked goods, which required 60 per cent of the flour at war's end, now use more than 75 per cent.

Among the other events of importance in milling in late years was the establishment of the International Wheat Agreement in 1949 and its excellent administration by Arnold A. Garthoff of the Department of Agriculture; the loss of the China trade in flour at the Communist takeover, a business that had been sizable through eight decades; the construction of mills in many wheat-deficit nations, resulting in the loss of American export outlets of consequence, the most notable being the Philippines; the plant sanitation program and later the grain sanitation program, which resulted in great improvement in the conditions under which flour is milled and handled; a recurring shortage of durum wheat because of the ravages of rust; concentration of family flour business in relatively few hands; development of bulk transportation of flour in trucks and rail cars; rejuvenation of water traffic in flour; a partial breakup of the time-honored rail rate structure as it applies to wheat and flour; installation of pneumatic conveying systems in more than 40 flour mills; and launching of such innovations as air classification and the Bellera process.

Numerous improvements took place in milling techniques after steel rolls and the purifier came into general use (see page 49). However, the basic process itself remained essentially the same until recent years, when two companies announced departures from tradition and once more aroused interest in the potentials of further changes in the basic process. The Pillsbury Co. presented certain air classification developments in 1957, and General Mills announced its Bellera process in 1960. Air classification developed by Pillsbury was said by that company to enable almost revolutionary changes in the separation of flour streams. General Mills stated that Bellera is a simplified process with a short flow which produces a higher extraction of flour earlier in the reduction stage than in the conventional gradual reduction process. Economic and usage values of these developments are still being explored.

By the middle 1950's flour milling capacity and flour outlets were in approximate balance in most of the major milling areas. The mills that went out of production after 1948 were only partly offset by enlargement of the surviving plants, and the increased production due to export business caused many additional mills to be increased in late years and also caused new mills to be built. Net capacity of the industry has grown more than 75,000 cwt. since 1953.

The approximate balance between capacity and demand the past seven years or so has not significantly ameliorated the sharpness and vigor of competition in flour. There have been few occasions in this period when mills were not booked well ahead, considering the season, and yet every flour order that came into view was pursued as if the mill had nothing on which to operate the next day. The hard pursuit of business has not been appreciably different in recent years, when no excess capacity as a practical matter existed, then it was in the period before that when facilities exceeded needs by as much as 15 per cent. It is a condition that puzzles many millers who have long believed that the disappearance of unneeded mills would enable earnings to increase. In general, mill earnings the past decade and a half have not been unsatisfactory at least half the time; that has been the case in the seasons when millfeed prices advanced perceptibly after flour was booked. Another important source of earnings is revenue from storage of government wheat, but net income from flour milling itself has been quite light.

Milling consolidations have continued at a steady pace throughout the past two decades, stimulated to some degree by more and more bakery mergers but also being based upon the desire of elderly owners to retire. Most extensive in this period were the purchases of 14 plants by International Milling Co.— the mills in Wabasha, St. Paul, Detroit, New Ulm, Ponca City, Baldwinsville and the Midland and Shellabarger properties. Next largest was a series of steps by the Bresky interests whereby Rodney Milling Co. acquired several interior Kansas plants, the purchase of Consolidated Flour Mills Co. and the eventual merger of these companies and Ismert-Hincke Milling Co. into Seaboard Allied Milling Corp. Another large deal resulted in the consolidation of two Peavey-owned companies as Russell Miller-King Midas Mills and a later change of name to Peavey Co. Flour Mills. Colorado Milling & Elevator Co. bought mills in Omaha, El Reno, Beardstown, St. Louis and Knoxville and ceased to use most of its small plants. Ross Industries, Inc., was the product of consolidation of American Flours, Inc., Hunter

Milling Co., and Kansas Milling Co. John Vanier's milling properties went up from three to six when he acquired Inland Milling Co., Fuhrer-Ford Milling Co., and Red Wing Milling Co. The Pillsbury Co. bought Ballard & Ballard Co., Inc., and Bay State Milling Co. did likewise with the Lysle mill and La-Grange Mills. Dixie-Portland Flour Mills disposed of its country plants and leased and enlarged the Chattanooga mill. Archer-Daniels-Midland Co. acquired Atkinson Milling Co. On the other hand, Standard Milling Co. chose to dismantle its two largest plants and sold another. Flour Mills of America, Inc., sold one of its two chief plants and has operated the other somewhat irregularly.

Mills of the Atlantic seaboard were dominant in the business until after the halfway stage of the 1800's. First New York, then Philadelphia, next Baltimore and Richmond and finally Rochester were the chief milling centers, each becoming important through abundance of nearby wheat supplies and through transportation facilities. The eastern mills were less important relatively as the focus of wheat production moved westward, but Rochester, Baltimore and Richmond continued to be milling points of consequence well into the twentieth century. Mills in these and other cities did a surprising amount of export business throughout their existence. A general decline in eastern milling set in by the first World War, and there are now only a few commercial mills in that area, except in Buffalo, which did not become important millingwise until after 1900.

The Central States came to the fore during the second quarter of the nineteenth century and were the leaders from the 1850's until 1880. Volume of flour production in the area from Ohio and Michigan to Missouri, inclusive, has continued to increase, even though it has long been overshadowed by other regions. This is the chief soft winter wheat district, and its mills long ago turned largely from the household trade to flour for such products as cookies, crackers, pastry and cake. Central States mills are the largest suppliers of soft wheat bakery flour, but beginning chiefly after the first World War they also became substantial producers of hard wheat flour as well.

South and southeast of the Ohio River is a secondary soft wheat district comprising Kentucky, Tennessee, Virginia and the Carolinas. Mills there very largely have catered to the southern family trade. Recent years have witnessed a change in that several hard wheat mills have been established along the Tennessee River waterway.

World-wide demand for spring wheat flour and fame for Minnesota mills were the immediate results of the great milling revolution, and Minneapolis was the milling capital for a half a century from 1880. A third of the spring wheat flour was exported during most of this period. Secondary milling points of importance were Superior, Milwaukee and several Minnesota towns. Changing transportation conditions and the milling of Canadian wheat in bond caused a shift of a considerable amount of spring wheat capacity to Buffalo and it has been the first milling city since 1930. In recent years milling of bonded wheat has fallen to insignificance, but Buffalo has retained its preeminence because of its convenient location with respect to eastern metropolitan areas. Spring wheat milling has remained at about the same level for many years but hard winter wheat milling has forged well ahead in total volume.

Hard winter wheat milling is a relative newcomer to the milling scene, having appeared not much before 1880 and not becoming important until near 1900. Thereafter it moved up rapidly, and for the past 30 years the volume of flour production of the five southwestern states of Texas, Oklahoma, Colorado, Kansas and Nebraska, plus the cities of St. Joseph and Kansas City, has exceeded that of any other milling section. Southwestern flour was not generally accepted by the bakery trade until around first World War days, but in the course of another decade it became widely established. Kansas City has been the largest point of hard winter wheat flour production since the section became important, and other milling cities of considerable consequence in the area are Wichita, Arkansas City, Salina, Dallas, Denver, Omaha and Fort Worth. The Southwestern district has also provided a large share of the export flour of recent years.

California's Forty-Niners created such a demand for flour that wheat growing and milling soon got under way, and it is said that flour did not sell for less than $10 per cwt. in San Francisco for more than ten years and often commanded a price of twice that amount. The Oriental flour trade began in the 1860's and for a large part of the next 75 years it absorbed a third of Pacific Coast flour production. After 1900 it was mainly supplied by Oregon and Washington rather than California, because wheat was no longer widely grown in the Golden State. After the market in China was lost in 1949, and that of the Philippines went to its own mills in recent years, the mills of the Northwest have had to find new outlets; these have been in other parts of the Orient and in California with its tremendous gain in population. New mills in late years in Los Angeles have projected that city to first place among Pacific milling centers, followed by Seattle, Spokane and Portland.

Durum milling began in 1904 in a small North Dakota mill, and after a few years it began to grow considerably in volume as macaroni manufacturers turned from imported semolina. There are ten durum mills operated by seven companies, and their aggregate capacity is 33,000 cwt. All but one of these plants is in or near Minnesota, reflecting the fact that the bulk of the durum crop is produced as a rule in North Dakota. Consumer use of macaroni and other products made from durum wheat is on the rise, having increased from five to almost eight pounds per capita in the postwar period.

Rye milling, the smallest segment of the industry, is also largely concentrated in the Northwest. There are only seven rye mills of commercial size in the nation, their total capacity being about 12,000 cwt. Usage of rye flour has fallen during the past 40 years from about 3,500,000 cwt. annually to 1,-600,000 cwt.

Pioneer America was dotted with a host of grist mills; next there arose the early merchant mills in the little cities; flour milling was long the most important industry in the nation; mills increased in size and efficiency, first via Oliver Evans' inventions and then by the steel roll revolution; areas of wheat production and flour milling were vastly extended by the railroad network that covered the nation; mills grew into substantial business enterprises in large numbers; commercial baked products largely supplanted household use of flour over a period of time; numerous changes inherent in the American way of life transformed flour milling, causing disappearance of grist mills and greatly reducing the number of smaller units; growth and consolidations created large companies, so that presently one-third of the commercial milling capacity is operated by three concerns, 60 per cent by ten, more than 75 per cent by 20. That, in kaleidoscope brevity, is the milling history of the past two centuries.

CHAPTER TEN

Aspects of Milling History

Certain important phases of American milling history have received inadequate attention in the preceding eight chapters, primarily because the chronological theme would have been unduly diverted had they been developed as their importance deserved. In some cases they have extensive backgrounds that should be related and in others detailed facts are necessary for their proper presentation. The device has therefore been adopted of giving an independent account of each of these significant aspects of the progress of the milling industry.

Wheat Production

Wheat is grown on more of the earth's surface than is any other crop. Almost one-fifth of the 2,600,000,000 acres of cultivated land in the world is used for wheat. This proportion also held true in the United States before acreages were limited, but in recent years the American total has dropped to about one-sixth.

More than 80 per cent of the wheat harvested is utilized

for the production of flour after seed requirements are met—poultry and livestock feed and breakfast cereals being the other outlets of most consequence.

Soft red winter varieties comprised nearly all the wheat grown in the United States before about 1860. These were the common wheats of Western Europe whence came the early colonists, and they were brought along to the New World. Soil and climatic conditions in the eastern seaboard area resemble those on the other side of the Atlantic sufficiently so that wheat characteristics did not undergo major changes. This is borne out by the fact that wheat grown today in such states as Pennsylvania and Virginia bears a considerable likeness to that produced in Western Europe.

The somewhat delicate flour that was milled from soft wheat was quite well suited for the hand procedures of early times. That was so not only in the home kitchens where a very high proportion of the flour was used, but it was equally true in the handcraft bakeries. When stronger flours made their appearance after the middle of the nineteenth century, they were disliked both by consumers and bakers. This was due in large part to most of these flours then being mottled and gray in color.

Hard spring wheat was grown to a very limited extent from colonial times, but production was not consequential until after the Civil War. Soft wheat did not do well in Wisconsin and Minnesota, but the spring varieties that came in from Ontario gave an excellent account of themselves. However, they were discounted severely in the markets until the milling revolution of the 1870's pointed up their superiority for bread making. Although the production of spring wheat has been attempted elsewhere on many occasions, it is not usually successful south of the Minnesota-Iowa line, and it has therefore been confined chiefly to Minnesota, the Dakotas, Montana and Washington, with a few pockets of production in other states.

Russia was the country of origin of hard red winter wheat, which in later years has comprised about 60 per cent of the United States wheat production. It was brought to America in the 1870's by the Mennonites who emigrated from the Crimea to the Newton-McPherson area in Kansas. This wheat was called Turkey Red. Despite its superiority over soft wheat for southwestern conditions, Turkey Red spread rather slowly and it was not until the 1890's that it became the principal wheat of the states from Nebraska to Texas. The production of hard red winter varieties increased year after year and since before the first World War the volume of this wheat has led that of all the other classes by a wide margin.

Soft wheats are divided between red and white varieties, the former being largest in total production. From the North Atlantic area the soft red moved westward across the Ohio and Mississippi valleys and penetrated well into Kansas and Texas. However, the soft red class retreated from the points of farthest advance, and this has continued to the point that it now comprises little more than a third of the production of Missouri and Illinois. However, it predominates from Indiana to the Atlantic and throughout the border states. Soft white wheat is largely confined in the eastern states to Michigan and New York.

Early wheat production in the Intermountain and Pacific states was chiefly of soft red and white varieties, but later on both hard winter and spring wheats were also introduced. Several of the leading wheats of the Pacific area were imported from Australia. The wide variation in climatic conditions in the western states makes possible the production of all classes of wheat. However, the largest volume is of the soft white class.

Durum wheat was brought to the United States from Russia before 1900. Major production is in North Dakota.

More than 200 recognized varieties of wheat are grown in the United States. A few have been known for long periods, but a large majority were developed within recent years. Although botanists have been studying wheat intensively for several centuries, scientific breeding of new varieties did not get under way to any extent until about 1900 and it first attained importance two decades or so later. Since that time great numbers of new strains have been developed by the agricultural experiment stations and some by individual breeders. New and improved wheats have been released in a steady procession, as indicated by the fact that no less than two-thirds of the 1962 harvest consisted of varieties that were not even in existence ten years earlier. These new and improved varieties are probably the largest factor in causing acre yields to increase more than 75 per cent during the past quarter of a century.

For some years the objective sought by the wheat breeders was high yields and other desirable agronomic factors—short and stiff straw, resistance to insects and diseases, etc. Scant attention was given at that time to milling qualities, with the result that some of the new wheats proved to be inferior for the purpose for which wheat was grown. This condition existed to some degree in all the major classes of wheat, but it was most acute with hard red winter. For about a decade the problem threatened to get out of hand, but the high-yielding varieties that had poor milling values received a mortal blow in 1955 when the Department of Agriculture began to discount them severely in the price support program. During the past quarter of a century milling value has received more and more attention from breeders as a characteristic that must be taken into account in developing a new variety.

Transportation in Milling

Many of the main segments of the American railroad system were built in the quarter century that ended about 1875. This brought into being a mode of transportation that was so incomparably superior to anything previously known in all human history that it had a revolutionary effect upon the economic development of the nation. Before railroads the means of transportation were limited to water carriers and primitive roads, and the boundaries of commerce were circumscribed within extremely small areas.

Although the establishment of the railroads was a tremendous stimulus to the growth and conduct of business, vast new problems were created. By any standard with which our generation is familiar, service was undependable and inefficient. Moreover, railroad officials were often arrogant and arbitrary; on one occasion when Gen. Washburn protested too vigorously over a charge to his mill, the Milwaukee Railroad responded by tearing out the switch tracks and leaving the mill stranded, and the general was obliged to organize a new railway in order to remain in business.

What was even worse than the inefficiency and the arrogance was the fact that no system of rates existed for many years. The cost of shipping a carload of flour or other merchandise was the subject of negotiation, and often one shipper was charged twice as much as another for the same service. Railroad officials thus had it in their power to make or break companies or even cities and states. For almost a decade the Northern Pacific refused to extend its tracks into Seattle, which had no railroad, as the company directors owned most of Tacoma and were determined to make it the great city of the Northwest. Publications of that era recounted great numbers of discriminatory practices by the carriers, many of which were initiated by shipping interests that were powerful enough to exact special rates.

Many of the railroad abuses were corrected by the adoption in 1887 of the Interstate Commerce Act and by the amendments of 1906. These statutes prohibited unreasonable discriminations and required the publication of rates available to all shippers. In the wake of published rates there gradually developed a grain rate structure that in time covered the entire nation. In somewhat oversimplified terms, it may be described as a set of rates that began at the wheat fields and extended to the seaports, with a series of rate-break points at important terminals along the way.

Implicit in the grain rate structure was the transit privilege, by which is meant that the entire movement from the point of origin of the wheat to the final destination of the flour was one movement and entitled to the same rate no matter where milled. This had the effect of largely equalizing the mills that were located along the way. More than any other factor, transit permitted the establishment of mills near the wheat country. Transit was first devised at Nashville about 1870 by the Nashville & Chattanooga Railway, and in time it was adopted elsewhere. It became the accepted principle that governed the shipment of wheat and flour and was repeatedly approved by the Interstate Commerce Commission.

From the time that the grain rate structure began to take form in the 1890's many of the individual rates have been the subject of controversies within the milling industry. On some occasions it has been section against section, in other cases a more localized issue. It has become almost traditional for millers to object even to small concessions that may be sought by competitors or to ask for revisions favorable to themselves. This is a constant process that is still going on after three-quarters of a century, a fact that illustrates the sharp competition within the industry and the importance of transportation advantages and disadvantages, even if they are measured only in pennies. However, a difference of a few cents per unit of product adds up to many dollars in the course of a year.

The transit system has been almost universal, if one overlooks the fact that the central and eastern carriers have long made a small charge for transit. However, a series of events that have taken place mostly in recent years throw considerable doubt upon its continuance into the indefinite future. These are the use of motor trucks in hauling grain, particularly for long distances; perfection of the bulk flour truck; resurgence of barge transportation of both wheat and flour on the inland waterways; development of bulk railroad cars for transporting flour; and special rates on wheat that are not applicable on flour, made in an effort to recapture traffic lost by the railroads. The movement of grain down the Great Lakes might well be added to the list were it not of long standing.

Motor vehicles have taken away a great deal of wheat traffic from the rail carriers, and more than a third of the grain shipped by country elevators goes by truck in addition to the huge amounts that move direct from farms to terminal or mill points. This process seems destined to continue except in the improbable event that these carriers are brought under effective regulation. Bulk flour trucks make deliveries at long distances. Around half of the bakery flour moves in special bulk cars, by which the cost of shipping is substantially higher than by standard boxcars. Barge shipment of flour is not large thus far, but it is growing rapidly. For the most part, these developments are based upon the premise that wheat can be moved more economically than flour, as are the proposals by the railroads for special low rates on wheat that they are unwilling to extend to flour. The net effect of the innovations in transportation is to erode the entire time-honored transit system and to threaten its existence.

Mills locations are inevitably associated with the transit system, and should it be ended or seriously impaired many mills are likely to be obliged to move.

Flour Containers

Goatskins and earthen jars were probably the first containers for flour. Occasional references in ancient writings seem to establish that the former was usually employed when the product was transported and the latter was the conventional means of storage in those times. There is no way of determining, however, when these practices began nor how long they continued.

Wooden flour barrels were common in Western Europe, long before the settlement of America, and that they were English in origin is suggested strongly by their standard size of 196 pounds, the equivalent of 14 English stone. The early millers of the New World brought with them the English barrel. For perhaps two hundred years no other flour container was known here, although an English historian notes that during the reign of Charles II (1660-85) sacks were adopted to some extent for flour but the practice seems to have lapsed for several generations. These early flour sacks contained 140 and 280 pounds (10 and 20 stone, respectively), sizes that are in common use to this day in the United Kingdom.

Just when textile bags for flour were introduced in America is somewhat uncertain, but the event evidently took place in the first half of the nineteenth century. These pioneer bags, being hand-sewn, were expensive and were not widely adopted. Soon after Elias Howe perfected the sewing machine in 1846, Henry S. Chase and John Batchelder began experimenting with a machine to sew bags and they developed one by 1849. Although the use of cotton flour bags increased considerably as a result, wooden barrels predominated in the ratio of more than ten to one in Minneapolis as late as 1880. In those days practically every flour mill also had a cooper shop, and the number of coopers often exceeded the number of millers. How many million feet of fine oak, maple and cherry wood went into the manufacture of flour barrels is almost beyond calculation.

The first cotton and burlap flour bags contained 98 pounds, or a half-barrel, and the barrel thus became a measure of quantity as well as a container. Cotton sacks of the 98-pound size, usually called halves cotton, grew rapidly in popularity after 1880, and before the end of the century they had surpassed barrels in importance and by the first World War period less than 10 per cent of the flour was packed in wood. In fact, by that time the 196-pound barrel had all but disappeared and it was replaced by the 98-pound half barrel. This container is still in use in a small way in the mountain areas of the border states.

Cotton sacks of lesser sizes than 98s made their appearance in the 1870's. The first were 49's and 24½'s—for the household trade only. Their convenience gained an instant popularity, and in the course of a decade or two even smaller sizes had become fairly common in the cities. About that time paper began to dispute with cotton for the flour sack trade, at first for the small sizes but by 1940 the predominant volume of flour packed in containers below the half-barrel level was in paper. Along the way a great multiplicity of sizes proliferated. In the North the custom was to use even fractions of the barrel down to 24½ pounds, then jump to 10's and 5's. For the South and the border states mills packed a schedule consisting of 96, 48, 24, 12 and 6 pounds. The Pacific area followed the barrel fractions to 24½, thereafter going to 9.8 and 4.9 pounds. In many spots there were special sizes, New York City taking 7 and 3½ pounds, with such irregular packages as 45, 22½, 20 and 8 pounds also being known along with others. Very small packages, such as 3 and 2 pounds, came into being in later years, and the production of two-pound bags has been extremely large in recent times.

A device called the package differential was propelled into being by the variegated sizes of flour packages. It dates from about 1881, when the Michigan Millers' Association recommended a price differential for halves cotton and quarters cotton over wooden barrels. The amounts were to cover the additional cost of the smaller containers and the additional cost of packing and handling them, as compared to the then standard barrel. During the next 35 years or so, various differential schedules were issued, but beginning in 1902 the others largely faded out when Millers' National Federation brought out the first national schedule. In 1917 the U. S. Food Administration required Federation differentials to be followed, and thereafter until 1944 they continued to have nearly universal adherence. The differential schedule was a convenience both to millers and their trade, as it enabled a merchant to make a purchase at a basis price (delivery in halves cotton after 1917) and then work out his package assortment as he ordered shipments from time to time. The package differential did not attempt to fix or regulate the price on the basis package, but it was a table that indicated the amount that would be charged over basis for any smaller package.

Although the federal government had required on three distinct occasions the Federation package differential to be employed (in 1917 and 1942 under wartime controls, in 1934 under the mill code) and had specified in its own purchase contracts for flour that it be followed, the Department of Justice brought price-fixing charges in 1943 that resulted in criminal indictments of Millers' National Federation, 13 individual members of its package differential committee and the 16 milling companies with which they were affiliated. An eight-day trial in Chicago in June 1944 ended in a guilty verdict by the jury, but this finding was immediately set aside by the presiding judge on the ground that no law violation had taken place. Although vindicated by the outcome, the Federation discontinued publication and distribution of the schedule soon after. Various companies worked out their own differentials for a few years, but even before that time the sale of household flour had been shifting to a bale basis, somewhat like other grocery items, and a differential schedule ceased to be necessary.

In 1943 the War Production Board ended the hodgepodge of flour packages by a conservation order that prohibited the packing of flour in other than six sizes—100, 50, 25, 10, 5 and 2 pounds. This was a boon to the industry as it enabled mills of moderate size to reduce their inventories by as much as $100,000 each—and others in proportion. Before the federal order lapsed in 1945, the industry made the reform permanent through state legislation that limited flour packages to the wartime list (often called the decimal schedule). A uniform statute developed by Millers' National Federation and endorsed by the National Association of State Commissioners of Agriculture was adopted in 37 states, most of the enactments taking place in 1945.

Bakery flour was packed universally in barrels until textile containers came into vogue; and thereafter in cotton 98's and burlap 98's and 140's. Around the first World War period a cotton grain bag similar to the osnaburg widely used for exports was introduced, and it brought with it the practice of reusing cotton and burlap bags. This practice grew until from 1935 to 1945 it was estimated that two-thirds of the bakery flour went out from mills in used containers. This was something of an economy to the buyer, but it was a headache to the miller as in many cases bags had not been cleansed properly and more than a few were torn or weakened by wear. A survey in 1938 showed that more than a third of the bags returned for refilling were in unsanitary condition and that almost 15 per cent could not be made fit for further use. Oklahoma Board of Health in 1939 prohibited the repacking of flour sacks for shipment to Oklahoma destinations, and after the wartime shortage of containers ended a number of other states proceeded along lines that were patterned after the Oklahoma order. In several areas, notably Buffalo and the Pacific Coast, millers refused to pack used containers, taking this stand a year or more before the sanitary authorities acted. Refilling of flour bags was practically ended by 1949.

Multiwall paper sacks suitable for flour were developed about 1933 but were used only to a very limited extent until 1946. During the next three years or so, these containers not only replaced a large share of the used flour sacks for bakeries but they also reduced the number of new cottons of large size. Earlier use of paper sacks for flour had been confined to smaller sizes, the materials employed being kraft or rope paper.

Bulk shipments of flour in railroad cars began in 1948,

but did not become important until after General American Transportation Corp. brought out the Airslide car in 1954. At the end of eight years, approximately 5000 Airslides were being used exclusively for the shipment of flour. This form of transportation now accounts for more than half the bakery flour and semolina being moved by the railroads, and thus the period of multiwall supremacy in flour proved to be quite brief. In 1953 the first commercial delivery of flour by bulk truck was made by an affiliate of Atkinson Milling Co., and this method of transportation of mill product also forged ahead rapidly during the first decade of its existence.

In the light of vast improvements that have been generated in flour packages, it is a curious fact that many old-time millers objected vigorously to packing flour in anything but wooden barrels. Several attempts were made to prevent the use of cotton sacks. A great debate on this issue took place in the early 1880's at a convention of Millers' National Association. On that occasion Charles B. Cole declared bluntly that "a man who won't buy a barrel of flour ought to go without bread!" Before the beloved Uncle Charley was gathered to his fathers, in 1928, the Cole mill packed barrels only on rather rare occasions; and nowadays the same mill produces, among others, a vast steady stream of 2's. How times change!

Flour Enrichment

Enrichment of flour with vitamins and iron has repeatedly been termed by authorities on human nutrition as the most important step in that field in many years. The consensus is that, in the words of a past president of the American Medical Association, "the more buoyant health and the increased mental and physical vigor of the American people can be attributed in considerable part to cereal enrichment."

The milling industry played a vital role in the development of the enrichment program and making it a reality in an incredibly short time. The addition of thiamine to white flour was first advocated in a scientific meeting in Toronto in May 1938, but it was not until September 1940 that the idea was amplified to include riboflavin, niacin and iron. A proposal to this effect was made by Dr. Russell M. Wilder (b. 1885 Ohio, d. 1959) of Mayo Clinic in the course of the federal flour standards hearings, and it was based upon evidence that the average American diet was then deficient in these substances.

The principle of the Wilder plan was quickly accepted by the milling industry; by November an agreement had been reached by the scientists as to the amount of the ingredients in the enrichment formula; and at the end of January 1941 practically all commercial flour mills began producing enriched flour more or less simultaneously. Four months later a survey showed that nearly 40 per cent of household flour was being enriched and within a year this had almost doubled. Enriched flour was not used in bakery bread to any considerable extent, because of the duplication in riboflavin values when bread is made with milk solids, but enrichment is obtained through wafers that contain the enriching ingredients, with allowance for the riboflavin content of milk.

South Carolina enacted a statute in 1942 requiring flour and bread offered for sale in that state to be enriched. Others took similar action, and within a decade or so enrichment laws were in effect in 29 states.

The most dramatic evidence demonstrating the fundamental merit of flour enrichment was developed in Newfoundland. Following a medical survey in 1944 in what was then a crown colony, all flour was enriched for four years. A second survey in 1948 disclosed a sensational improvement in public health and greatly reduced mortality rates. In the United States, medical observers noted that within a few years after enrichment began there was a virtual disappearance of deficiency diseases as well as a general improvement in health. These results were obtained from an annual expenditure of only a few cents per person.

In one sense, flour enrichment had its roots in a century of agitation against the use of white flour. This propaganda was largely originated by Rev. Sylvester Graham (b. 1794 Conn., d. 1851), a natural foods crank and supporter of a long list of "isms." Graham asserted that he would live to be a hundred by following his food regimen, but although he missed this goal by more than 40 years his food theories became the gospel for several generations of food faddists. Foremost among them was the idea that white flour is harmful, and that only whole wheat flour should be used. This came to be known as Graham flour, but in late years the term has fallen into partial disuse.

Graham followers covered a wide range—from deep-dyed fanatics to persons who have a taste preference for whole wheat over white bread, from those who embraced the Graham theories as a means of selling books, so-called health foods, etc., to those who somehow had only a vague distrust in the products of white flour. Their ranks were augmented considerably as a result of a long-continued campaign, begun in the 1890's, by several breakfast cereal companies to downgrade foods made from white flour as a means of establishing their own products.

The fund of scientific knowledge of nutrition increased greatly after the beginning of the twentieth century. After the discovery of vitamins and their role in nutrition circa World War I, the fact was gradually established that the American diet was somewhat lacking in certain of these substances. Many reputable nutritionists began to look askance at white bread because a considerable share of the vitamins present in wheat were lost in the milling process. After a generation of urging the public to turn to whole wheat and making no progress of consequence, all except the doctrinaire whole wheaters supported the enrichment of white flour through the restoration of nutrients lost in milling. The step that made this program possible was the synthesis of thiamine in 1936 by Dr. Robert R. Williams (b. 1886 India).

Whole wheat usage in the United States never exceeded three per cent of all wheat flour despite long and vigorous preaching in its behalf and currently the proportion is less than half that much. This leads to the suspicion that the principal effect of the criticism of white flour has been to reduce its use without much compensating increase in the use of dark flour.

Per capita consumption of flour in the United States has declined almost 45 per cent since the beginning of the present century. Obviously, a great deal of the decline has come from the changing pattern of American life and by the greatly increased availability and improvement of other foods, but food faddist doctrine and scientific criticism are also undoubtedly factors in the reduction. No other food has been subjected to such long-continued criticism, much of it abusive and slanderous. Only in recent years have authorities begun to challenge the attacks on breadstuffs and to denounce as false many of the statements that have been made.

Launching of flour enrichment did not by any means end faddist propaganda against breadstuffs. What it did was to lead to a gradual recognition, on the part of leaders in the nutrition field, of the dietary worth of cereal products. This recognition benefits all, especially in view of the widespread popular interest in human nutrition.

Baking Industry

Commercial bakeries use more than 75 per cent of the flour milled in the United States, exclusive of exports. Baking and milling are interdependent to a degree that prevails in the case of few other industries.

The predominance of commercial bakeries as the chief customers of flour mills is of comparatively recent origin. At the beginning of the twentieth century, little more than 10 per cent of the flour milled for domestic use went to bakeshops. This proportion doubled by the end of the first World War. It continued to increase, except through the depression years, and it reached 40 per cent before the second war. At the end of that conflict the baker's proportion was nearing 60 per cent. The war period may therefore be regarded as the time when bakers first became the major factors in the production of wheat foods.

Although the chief growth of the baking industry has taken place within the past two generations, there were baking establishments in America from earliest colonial times. They were located only in the larger towns, and it was not until late in the nineteenth century that bakeries began to develop elsewhere to any great extent. In fact, the display of bakery equipment at the World's Columbian Exposition in Chicago in 1893 is credited with being a most important stimulus in the subsequent expansion of the baking industry.

The American baking industry did not follow the pattern of baking in Europe, even though nearly all the early bakers came from that continent. There the baking business was largely under the control of guilds and had been so from far back into medieval times. The guilds were small-scale trusts, with more than a slight resemblance to labor unions; they regulated prices and production, determined who might enter the business, trained apprentices and decided where they might work and how much each workman could do. Many of the bakeries and flour mills of Western Europe were under the same roofs, in that respect being similar to the combination establishments that existed in Rome, Carthage, Babylon and other ancient cities.

One of the proudest traditions of the baking business relates to Christopher Ludwick (b. 1720 Germany, d. 1807), who had the title of baker general in George Washington's patriot army. A self-styled gingerbread baker from Philadelphia, Ludwick devised the equipment and made the bread for Washington's men and refused all compensation for his services.

The milling revolution of the 1870's laid the foundation for bakery expansion. Until shortly before that time the only flour available was milled from soft wheat. It worked well in the hand shops of those days, but the introduction of hard wheat and the improvement that was wrought in hard wheat flour by the purifier and the roller mill opened the way to bakeshop mechanization. Machine bakeries first appeared in 1862, but they did not make much headway until the 1880's. High speed mixers and the other equipment came into general use around 1920.

Wholesale bakeries had operated far back in the preceding century, but they first became really important during the rapid growth of commercial baking that got under way about 1900. Until that time baking had been primarily a trade, but wholesale plants required considerable capital and baking became a business in addition to being a trade. The first large companies were established in that period, and a series of mergers took place in the middle 1920's. The first milling mergers were in considerable part a reflex from the bakery mergers.

Few bakers seem to have been intrigued with having their own mills, as was the common situation in the ancient world and in comparatively modern times in Europe. The few ventures of that sort that have taken place in the United States have not turned out well, except perhaps in the case of the two large cracker manufacturers.

The commercial baking business stands first among all the segments of the food industry in value of product and in number of employees. Bakers made almost $4,750,000,000 worth of goods in 1958, the latest year for which official figures are available, and they employed more than 327,000 persons. These represent the highest totals ever attained up to that time. The 1958 total of less than 18,000 bakeries is, however, a substantial decline from that of earlier years. Forty years ago, when the baking business did considerably less than half as much business as it has recently, there were almost 26,000 shops. The trend toward larger production units that began with bakery mechanization is still under way.

Millers and bakers are on opposite sides of the bargaining table when flour is bought and sold. During a large majority of the time since commercial baking became important, bakers have proved to be better buyers than millers are sellers. Bakery flour margins for the miller have been narrow except for rather brief periods and on more than a few occasions have actually been non-existent, so intense is competition in flour milling.

Because various issues arise in which the two closely associated industries have a common interest, millers and bakers formed an inter-industry conference committee in 1944. This committee has been in existence more than 18 years. Its purpose is to provide a means of free exchange of views on questions that are of importance to the members of the two industries. It meets as occasion seems to require, usually once or twice annually. The joint committee is not an action body, but it nevertheless has dispelled many points of possible contention. As good an example as any was the complex situation that developed a decade ago in connection with wheat protein quality which bakers, not being wheat men, did not understand. The problem was cleared up in the course of a full discussion. The joint committee, which is one of very few bodies of its kind, has been of great service to both industries.

Flour Bleaching and Maturing

For a long time the most controversial phase of milling was chemical treatment of flour for the purpose of color removal and maturing. The practice was strongly opposed by the United States Government, and years of litigation ensued before mills won the right to make use of certain processes in the production of flour. It is only in recent times that the issue has apparently been settled.

Until the advent of chemical oxidation, freshly-milled flour often misbehaved in the oven. From time immemorial, bucky and sticky doughs and inferior baked products were frequently encountered at the harvest season and occasionally later in the year, both in home kitchens and in commercial bakeshops. Although it had been observed for centuries that these baking troubles disappeared as a rule after flour had been stored, it was not until about 60 years ago that cereal chemists were able to perfect a method of instant oxidation that made lengthy storage unnecessary—and simultaneously remove from flour the color to which consumers objected.

First of the American flour bleaches was nitrogen peroxide gas obtained from an airstream passing over flaming electric arcs. It was developed in 1903 at Cape County Milling Co., Jackson, Mo., by James N. Alsop, and it came into rather general use in a short time. The Alsop process ran into conflict with a somewhat similar method known as the Andrews process, devised in Scotland in 1901; but after litigation the Alsop owners bought the American rights to the Andrews system.

Dr. Harvey W. Wiley, chief of the U. S. Bureau of Chemistry and renowned crusader for pure food, challenged flour bleaching, charging that it injured the baking quality of flour and concealed inferiority; that bleached flour therefore was adulterated and in violation of the Food and Drugs Act. After several years of acrimonious controversy, an interstate shipment of flour by Lexington Mill & Elevator Co., Lexington, Neb., was used as a test case. The government won in the trial court, but this finding was reversed upon appeal; and in 1915, seven years after the beginning of the dispute, the United States Supreme Court sustained the appellate decision and held that Dr. Wiley had not proved any part of his contentions. Another four years passed before the government relented sufficiently to issue regulations that permitted bleached flour to be shipped in interstate commerce when it was properly labeled as such.

Dr. Wiley was enraged over the outcome of this case, and for the remainder of his life he fulminated against bleached flour. It is not improbable that a considerable share of the criticism of bleached flour stemmed from his antagonism.

Several states had anti-bleaching laws, and some of them remained in effect until the latter 1920's, while an ordinance in New York City that prohibited the sale of bleached flour remained on the books until 1939.

The Lexington decision was vital to the hard winter wheat industry, as flour made from that wheat had a distinct yellowish tint and was discriminated against both by consumers and commercial users for that reason. Southwestern millers needed the right to bleach flour in order to keep their place in the sun, whereas other millers were divided in their opinions about bleaching. The smaller spring wheat mills and a majority of the soft wheat mills sided with the government because of their limited usage of chemical treatments. This created a schism in the industry that was not healed for a decade or two. The Lexington case defense was largely provided by a group of Nebraska and Kansas millers headed by Frederic D. Larabee.

In 1914 a mixture of chlorine and nitrosyl chloride for treating flour was introduced and was used chiefly on soft wheat bakery flour. The effect was to mellow and mature the product.

Nitrogen trichloride, usually referred to as the Agene process, was perfected in 1921 by Dr. John C. Baker, and because of its outstanding performance in maturing flour it was widely adopted. Agene was followed in 1922 by the importation from Holland of benzoyl peroxide, a superior agent for color removal; it was known as the Novadel process, and some years later it was also sold under the name Oxylite. Novadel and Agene were the standard treatments for hard wheat flours for more than 20 years, and chlorine and Agene were used on soft wheat flours.

Before the federal flour standards were established in 1942, the Food & Drug Administration made an exhaustive study of bleaching and maturing agents for flour, and the conclusion was that their use would be in the interest of the consuming public. It then approved for use the several treatments then available.

Late in 1946 a storm broke out over the findings of Sir Edward Mellanby, an English scientist, that Agene induced running fits in dogs. This generated a great hue and cry against all chemical treatments of flour. The University of Wisconsin established that although Agene induced running fits in dogs it had no deleterious effects upon human beings, even when fed in heavy doses to those with epileptic tendencies. Agene was vindicated, but as soon as a satisfactory substitute was found the milling industry asked the government to withdraw its sanction for the use of Agene on flour. This action became effective in 1949.

Chlorine dioxide was authorized for use in 1948. It is generally similar to Agene in its action on flour, but it has no deleterious effects upon animals or humans, and it quickly supplanted Agene for mill use.

Two new treatments were authorized in 1962 — acetone peroxide and arodicarbonamide—and are replacing the older treatments to some extent.

Milling Schools

Kansas State University is the only institution in the Western Hemisphere that offers professional training to millers. A course in operative milling was inaugurated there in 1909 and has been considerably amplified in the course of time. The number of students in the milling department has never been very large, but an impressive share of the production executives of the industry is numbered among its graduates.

Research in milling problems has gone hand in hand with student training. The first experimental mill was built in 1914, and after being rebuilt on several occasions and then being destroyed by fire, it was replaced by a new and modern establishment in 1961.

Louis A. Fitz was the first milling department head, serving in 1909-23. Dr. Charles O. Swanson (b. 1869, d. 1948), internationally known chemist, was professor of milling industry in 1923-1938. He was succeeded by Dr. Edwin G. Bayfield (b. 1900 Nova Scotia) in 1938-43, and the department head for the past 20 years has been Dr. John A. Shellenberger (b. 1900 Ill.).

Pennsylvania State University had a milling school at one time, and the University of Minnesota also had a course in milling engineering. Both these curricula were discontinued some years ago.

Mill Labor Unions

Chief labor union in the milling industry is American Federation of Grain Millers. Its first locals were formed in 1933, and the new body was called National Council of Cereal Workers. In 1940 it became American Federation of Grain Processors, consisting of 125 locals with about 25,000 members. It operated until 1948 as a federal union under the supervision of the American Federation of Labor, but it received its international charter and adopted the present name at that time.

Total membership is about 48,000, affiliated through 312 locals. Around 40 per cent are production workers in flour mills. The remainder are chiefly in feed mills, cereal plants, grain elevators and sugar mills. In a few flour mills the employees belong to other unions, and there are also members of craft unions in many mills.

The mill union came into being on the wave of industrial organization that flourished in the 1930's. Its formation touched off a series of strikes that were especially severe in the Pacific Northwest. By 1937 it had sufficient strength so that the larger milling companies recognized it as the bargaining agent for plant employees, and master agreements were devised between the union and the companies that governed all working conditions except wage rates. The latter was left for negotiation at the local level, a pattern that has continued to the present. There have been no industry-wide negotiations, but bargaining on an area basis has been taking place for Buffalo, Minneapolis, Kansas City and the Pacific Northwest.

Minneapolis became union headquarters in 1936 and has remained such. Samuel P. Ming (b. 1891 Kan.) was president in 1940-60, being followed by Roy O. Wellborn (b. 1910 Okla.). William A. Younker (b. 1900, d. 1946) was secretary-treasurer in 1940-46, and was succeeded by the present officer, Harold A. Schneider (b. 1909 Kan.). A somewhat unusual union provision requires all officers to have worked in flour mills for three years before becoming eligible for election.

American Federation of Grain Millers is a comparatively small international labor organization, particularly among the industrial unions. It has a much larger proportion of members among flour mill employees than it does of the other groups in its field. It is generally regarded as a democratic organization, and its activities are largely confined to trade union matters and do not go much into political affairs. Its wage demands have not been exorbitant for the most part, although some mill owners doubtless think otherwise. Mill wages have advanced tremendously since the union was formed, but it is impossible to say how much is due to the union and how much to inflationary conditions that have prevailed throughout that period. The fringe benefits that mill employees enjoy are equalled in few other industries. Along with many but not all other unions, the mill union has stubbornly opposed most labor-saving techniques. It has called strikes on some occasions that nonpartisan observers would call unjustified, but it has not been at fault in all cases by any means.

The present union was preceded by several earlier attempts to organize mill workers. On one occasion the bakery union tried to enroll them as members, and on another the brewery union sought to do so, but both efforts failed. The Flour Packers' and Nailers' Protective Union struck 17 mills in Minneapolis in 1903, but the strike failed and the organization collapsed. There were also strikes in that city on various earlier occasions for higher wages, notably in 1884 and 1894 when gains resulted. By 1910 several of the larger milling companies sponsored company unions, but most of them were disbanded by the middle 1930's. However, they were responsible for establishing the eight-hour day in the larger plants, but it was not until 1933 and later that this became standard in medium-sized and smaller mills.

Miller Presidents

Five American presidents were proprietors of flour mills. They were George Washington, John Adams, Thomas Jefferson, James Madison and Abraham Lincoln. It may be that others had some connection with milling, but if so the fact seems to have escaped historians.

Washington was one of the foremost millers of his time. His reputation as a miller was so well established that flour barrels stamped "G. Washington, Mount Vernon," were exempt from inspection at British ports in the West Indies. This was a distinction from which he derived satisfaction almost as great as his military and national honors. When he had a bookplate made in his later years, the family coat of arms was supplemented with heads of wheat as symbolic of his favorite business of growing wheat and milling flour.

Washington's principal mill was on his Mount Vernon estate. It was built before 1739 by his father. The property came into Washington's hands in 1752 and the mill was operated by him the remaining 47 years of his life. It was enlarged and improved in 1770. Washington owned another mill, built in 1776 near Perryopolis, south of Pittsburgh, and it was operated intermittently until 1795. The Mount Vernon mill was idle for about 70 years until restoration in 1930.

Little is known about the flour mill built by John Adams on his farm near Braintree, Mass. It was not in a wheat-growing area of any importance and it is likely that it was a very small grist mill.

Thomas Jefferson's mill near Charlottesville, Va., was apparently used only to supply those who lived at Monticello, but he took a lively interest in its operation and in his writings are many references to the importance of milling.

James Madison built a mill on his plantation near Orange, Va., in 1795. It was probably typical of the mills that were common at that time on the larger land holdings in the Old Dominion.

Abraham Lincoln managed a mill for one season for his visionary cousin, Denton Offutt. This mill was located at New Salem, Ill., about 20 miles northwest of Springfield. It has also been restored.

The roll of millers who have held other high offices is quite extensive. It includes fourteen Governors, seven United States

Senators, ten Congressmen, one cabinet officer and several who served in other positions. How many have been elected to state legislatures is not known, but it is doubtless rather lengthy.

Producer Relations

Controversies between producers of farm commodities and traders in and processors of these commodities, generated by differences in the market place, have been common for hundreds of years. Sometimes they have led to violence, as in milk strikes and movements to prevent the sale of livestock or produce. In other cases they have brought on political repercussions of a varied sort. In many other instances they have caused the formation of cooperative associations to supplant conventional systems of marketing.

In very large measure the milling industry has somehow avoided major troubles in the area of producer relations. This is in sharp contrast with the experience of the meat packers, grain dealers and milk distributors, and of other agricultural trades. Anyone who studies the long and variegated course of farm movements in the United States will find only slight reference to friction between flour millers and wheat growers—it has been so slight as to be almost negligible.

The first important national farm movement was launched in 1867 by the organization of the National Grange. Its prime targets were the railroads, grain dealers and farm implement companies. During the heyday of the Grange, in the 1870's, there were flour mills in practically every wheat growing community from Pennsylvania to and beyond the Missouri River, and it is beyond belief that antagonism was non-existent in all these places, yet the only acrimony of consequence in that period was of non-Grange origin. It was occasioned by the operation of the Minneapolis Millers' Association, organized in 1875 by Charles A. Pillsbury to assure a sufficient wheat supply for the Minneapolis mills. It was not only the sole purchaser of wheat there, but it sent out agents to acquire large amounts of wheat at country points. Farmers did not like this situation, even after it was established in an investigation by state authorities that prices were as high as or higher than they were elsewhere, considering freight differences. However, the association was dissolved when a public market was created in 1881 by the organization of the Minneapolis Chamber of Commerce (now the Minneapolis Grain Exchange).

The Farmers' Alliance, which flourished briefly in the late 1880's, was antagonistic to all the agricultural trades and it sponsored several mills in North Texas. Two of them were forerunners of well-known mills in later years.

Millers were involved to some extent in the backwash of the Chicago market boycott of farmer-owned grain elevators in 1902-04 and in a somewhat similar situation in the spring wheat states a decade or more later. These activities were instigated by the state grain dealers' associations, the members of which refused not only to trade with the farmer groups but also with anyone who did. Great bitterness between these groups remained long after the boycotts were broken, but mills generally escaped opprobrium as in most cases they were only secondary participants.

The cooperative grain movement included several terminal marketing organizations, one of which dates back to 1915, and in the 1920's state-wide wheat pools were formed. Some of them were expanded in the Federal Farm Board period. Several of the terminal organizations have attained considerable size during the past 25 years. No major issues have arisen between these groups and the mills, nor between the mills and local farmers' elevators. As far as most mills are concerned the grain cooperatives are simply sources of supply of wheat, the same as other dealers in grain.

The Farmers' Nonpartisan League of North Dakota, which reached its zenith around 1920, was violently anti-business. Many of its leaders were doctrinaire Socialists who believed that the state should own all the means of production, farm lands excepted, and one of their pet projects was a large flour mill. In order to get this idea across they carried on a lengthy hate campaign against the milling business. North Dakota Mill & Elevator went into operation in 1922, and although it paid no taxes, nearly 20 years were required to reach a consistent breakeven basis. The heavy losses taken for years by this concern put an effective damper upon similar projects that were being urged in Oklahoma, Nebraska and elsewhere. Much of the antagonism toward flour milling that was whipped up by the leaders of the League has died out, but not all of it.

It may primarily be a reflection of the low earning record of milling companies that very few cooperative mills have been launched at any time. Small enterprises of this kind have been started, but usually have not been long-lived. The only cooperatives now in the industry are branches of much larger organizations that acquired mills after becoming established in some related line.

Through most of the four decades of national farm legislative programs the milling industry has remained out of the limelight. Few millers have had faith in the ideas upon which these programs were based, but the industry has usually preferred a neutral position to one of overt opposition. It has thus avoided becoming the whipping boy of the program promoters, but more importantly it has remained in a position where it might have a voice in shaping the program details that would weigh heavily in the day-to-day operation of flour mills.

The development of high-yielding but inferior milling wheats caused millers to redouble their efforts to promote wheat improvement, and this led into another phase of producer relations. Some years of educational work brought home to growers the facts that their chief market is the flour mill, and that wheat has little intrinsic value unless it is suitable for making flour. The result of this work is that the objectives of wheat improvement now have the hearty support of growers' organizations and the agricultural colleges as well as of the milling industry.

Formation of the National Association of Wheat Growers in 1953 brought into existence a wheat organization set up on commodity lines. In the varied activities of this Association and its state units and regional marketing agencies there are many points of common interest with the milling industry. In many of these areas the two have found similar points of view and harmonious relations have been developed even though in other respects there are divergences between them. These differences are no more extensive than, for example, those between millers and the grain trade. In both instances, as well as with other interests, the occasions on which common action can be taken are much more numerous than where they are obliged to agree to disagree.

Relations between the milling industry and the American Farm Bureau Federation, largest of the farm organizations, have usually remained cordial over a long period of time.

It seems quite remarkable in view of the nature of the milling business and the extensive ramifications of farm organizations and diversity of ideas among the members of these

organizations that so few points of differences have arisen between them.

Government Relations

Some sardonic soul has declared that most American businessmen did not discover the existence of a national government until the federal income tax became effective in 1914.
There is a grain of truth in this observation even though it is
apocryphal.

The miller of a century ago had only the most fleeting
contact with the United States government. He may actually
have had none at all unless he happened to be selling a little
flour to an army post. Of course, various actions of government affected all citizens in those days, but one looks in vain
for things that related directly to the conduct of the milling
business.

The miller of a half-century ago had begun to make the
acquaintance of his government. There were laws that regulated
such things as freight rates, purity of food, ocean shipping conditions and a few shoddy business practices. He was then preparing to pay a small tax on his personal earnings as well as on
corporate profits. He was on the verge of having wheat graded
under the supervision of a government agency. The states were
deciding the size of packages that might be used for flour and
they were also regulating the sale of millfeed. Most of these
things he had welcomed but none except the brand new tax
on incomes was regarded as much of a burden.

By contrast, the miller of 1963 is guided or regulated in
literally scores of respects. The wheat he grinds is not only
graded according to government standards but its price is virtually determined by government support programs. If it was
purchased on a grain exchange floor, the deal was made under

rules sanctioned by a government agency, and if hedged in a futures market a government supervisor checked the transaction. The railroad on which it was shipped charged a freight rate that was subject to approval by a government commission. His grain storage operations are under contract with Commodity Credit Corporation, and the government pays the charges. His mill conforms to numerous sanitary standards. He is required by law to negotiate over wages and working conditions with a union that represents a majority of his employees. In the event of a strike a government conciliator steps in. There are numerous restrictions upon his employment practices and a sizable premium is required to be paid to anyone who works overtime. He may not discriminate in price to competing customers, and it is unlawful to have any kind of an understanding with his competitors, even of an implied nature. His export sales are made possible by a government subsidy; a large majority are made to an arm of the government. His flour is subject to standards created by government edict. At the end of the year he pays more than half his company's net to the federal treasury, after which his personal earnings are taxed at a graduated rate that in many cases may exceed the corporate rate.

The above does not by any means exhaust the areas of government regulation. A complete list would encompass several additional pages.

The old-time miller would have been horrified at first at the thought of such regimentation of his business, but despite his rugged individualism he was also a realist. His freedom to operate a business virtually without restraint created few if any problems in the relatively simple agrarian society of which he was a part. As his business grew and especially as new means of transportation and communication enlarged his world, he encountered new problems with which he could not cope—practices by railroads and ocean carriers, lack of standard grades, methods of competition, adulterated product and so on—and for which he could obtain relief only through public authority. Step by step the process of regulation grew, accelerated by the tremendous complications of the industrial society that relegated the simple conditions of our grandfathers' era to the scrapheap.

The old-time miller would scarcely have comprehended what is meant by government relations, but it is a term that is of the utmost importance to his grandson. So many phases of the business are affected by government programs or are regulated by law or administrative action that it is literally a fact that few things are done nowadays in milling without first taking account of government position and policy.

Everything considered, the milling industry has managed in reasonably good fashion to make the far-reaching adjustments to the changed conditions that were created by the growth of government. This process really had its inception in World War I, when milling was almost the first industry to be regimented and when few other lines of business were subject to such tight controls. Had it not been for the patriotic motive there might have been a lot of resistance, but the job was done in superb fashion under the leadership of industry men. Perhaps that precedent enabled the industry to rationalize its subsequent course of action in cooperating with government officials to the extent of their ability, even on some occasions when millers felt that the program was not a sound one.

Over the years the industry has built up a superlative standing with many government departments. That is especially true of the long-established agencies as distinct from the newer and political bureaus, although this standing is not restricted to the former group. For years the industry followed the practice, when an issue of some importance arose, of sending a small committee of millers well-informed on that particular problem to confer with the agency that had jurisdiction. It learned long ago that far better results could usually be obtained in this manner than through political pressure. The word gradually got around in Washington that millers did not generally seek anything unreasonable and that they usually presented sound reasons for what they wanted. It wasn't a very spectacular system, but the industry gained an acceptance, even in circles that might have been unfriendly, that was exceeded by no other.

About 1948 the method that had been employed for some years was systematized by the formation of the committee on agriculture of Millers' National Federation and charging it with the responsibility of representing the industry in all negotiations that related to the administration of agricultural laws. This program has been attended with a high degree of success even in the face of obstacles. In fact, as time passed it became the practice of many officials to solicit the committee's views, so highly were they regarded.

The industry has rarely been engaged in a public controversy over a government policy. Perhaps the most notable exception was on the occasion of the adoption of the ill-advised program of long-extraction flour in 1946. Now and then it appears before a Congressional committee that is considering legislative proposals, but contrary to the practice of many industries it does not do so with any degree of frequency.

A large majority of bureaucrats are dedicated persons who are trying to do a conscientious job for their country. With that type of official the milling industry has encountered comparatively little difficulty; when troubles have arisen they have usually grown out of insufficient information. There are, of course, some officials who become arbitrary and antagonistic. As far as millers are concerned, they have experienced that attitude mainly in three periods: During the late 1930's when the Department of Agriculture was carrying on a vendetta against the agricultural trades as a whole; in 1946, when the professional price controllers sought to make their program permanent; and in the strong anti-business atmosphere that has pervaded Washington throughout the past two years or more.

The Milling Press

Milling publications have served purposes that have ranged from dissemination of trade news and technical information to advising owners on management policies. A close relationship has existed between millers and their trade papers, although the milling press has been independently owned. For the most part the milling papers have been well edited and they do not suffer in that respect and in objectivity by comparison with the journals that are associated with other industries.

There presently are four trade papers that serve the milling field. Such papers were relatively numerous at one time, especially during and after the milling revolution of the 1870's when the demand for information on New Process milling was extensive. Some states had several milling papers in that period. They seem to have been largely organs of opinion and experience. Most of them were short-lived and even the names of a majority have been lost.

American Miller & Processor, published in Chicago, is a monthly that specializes in mill equipment and operating procedures. The present publication is a lineal descendant of *American Miller,* founded in 1873 in Ottawa, Illinois, and for two or three generations the bible of small millers. Its antecedents also include seven other papers, the largest of which, *National Miller,* was merged in 1930. *American Miller & Processor* has been owned since 1960 by *National Provisioner.* H. Kenneth Ferguson (b. 1900 Iowa) has been its editor for many years.

Modern Miller & Bakers' News was established in 1888 in St. Louis by Parker H. Litchfield as *Modern Miller.* It was moved to Chicago in 1913 and to the suburb of Prospect Heights in 1952. It was a weekly until 1948, when the present name was adopted, a bi-weekly until 1963 and now a monthly. *Modern Miller* was largely devoted to soft wheat milling and to export trade for years, but in later periods its field has been enlarged. Charles M. Yager (b. 1872, Ill., d. 1955) was owner and editor in 1903-48, and was succeeded by Charles M., Jr.

Northwestern Miller was founded in 1873 in LaCrosse, Wisconsin, by Amasa K. Ostrander, and was moved to Minneapolis in 1879. During its first quarter-century it was largely concerned with spring wheat milling but thereafter it became national in scope and it maintained several branch offices, including one in London. Under William C. Edgar (b. 1856 Wis., d. 1932), who was its owner and editor in 1895-1923, *Northwestern Miller* attained great prestige and influence and it had an international following. It was perhaps best known for its vigorous editorial policy and its service to exporting millers. Control passed to staff members in 1923 and has since remained in the hands of successive staffs. Beginning in 1928 the owners established several other publications, and in later years some were more successful than the parent. *Northwestern Miller* was a weekly in 1875-1960, and then a bi-weekly. After Edgar, its editors were Robert E. Sterling (b. 1876 Kan., d. 1951) in 1923-49; Carroll K. Michener (b. 1885 Minn.) in

1949-57; and George E. Swarbreck (b. 1914 England) since 1957.

Southwestern Miller, now the only weekly milling journal, was established in Kansas City in 1922. It was originally an organ for the hard winter wheat millers, but after the first years its coverage became national in scope. Throughout its history, *Southwestern Miller* has been noted for its exhaustive coverage of grain and flour markets and in later years for its extensive reporting of news that relates to grain and milling. This publication was founded by three brothers—David N. (b. 1895 Mo.), Samuel (b. 1890 Russia) and Sanders Sosland (b. 1899 Mo.)—who have continued to own and edit the paper during the entire 41 years of its history.

CHAPTER ELEVEN

Millers' Associations

Trade associations have played a conspicuous part in miller's affairs throughout the past century. Even when flour milling was largely a local business, common problems arose now and then that made consultation desirable and on occasion led to action.

Local associations of millers existed in several milling centers as early as 1800 and perhaps even before that. New York, Philadelphia and Baltimore had such organizations and probably there were others then or later. What their extent and purposes were have been lost through absence of surviving records, but one suspects that they may have been responsible for such things as compulsory inspection of flour coming into their cities from outside, local mills being exempt.

Trade organizations in great numbers were formed during and soon after the Civil War, and milling followed the trend. State associations of millers were established in 1873 in Georgia, in 1874 in Illinois, Iowa, Kansas and Missouri, in 1875 in

Michigan, in 1876 in Wisconsin and Minnesota, in 1877 in Indiana, Ohio, Maryland, New York, Nebraska and Texas, in 1878 in Pennsylvania, and in 1881 in California, Arkansas and Dakota Territory. These bodies had membership rolls that averaged more than a hundred each, and at times they were much larger.

Meanwhile, in 1873, Millers' National Association was organized at a mass meeting in Cleveland, largely under the leadership of Michigan millers. Headquarters was established in Milwaukee. The impetus for the national body, and for a majority of the state groups, were the royalty claims that were being made by the owners of the Cochrane patents on purifiers, and later the Association defended millers against the owners of meal drier patents. For the most part, the Association was successful in these efforts, the Cochrane claims being settled for a small fraction of the amounts originally demanded.

The national association worked at times on other problems, but it was primarily a one-issue organization and it became moribund when that issue was no longer of great importance. After 1891 the national conventions were attended only by a corporal's guard each year and the association was of small consequence.

For a decade or more, beginning in 1889, regional associations of considerable strength moved to the fore. First of these was the Hard Wheat Millers' Association, organized that year in Milwaukee and consisting of spring wheat millers. At about the same time the millers in the central states met in Indianapolis and set up the Winter Wheat Millers' League. These groups were created primarily to regulate the output of flour and to establish prices, but attempts along these lines met with little success and were continued for temporary periods only. Five years later two other similar organizations were formed for the same purposes—Southwestern Winter Wheat Millers' Association, created in Kansas City in 1894, and Southern Millers' Association, put together the same year in Nashville. The most conspicuous accomplishments of these associations were in export issues.

Over the years, the state associations of millers had three main lines of activity. First was social, centering in annual conventions of several days' duration at which many enduring friendships were forged; second was educational, consisting of convention discussions of milling methods and other subjects; third was the action field. Freight rates, which at that time were largely negotiated, were a favorite target for joint effort; for example, the St. Louis millers followed a plan of pooling their shipments for a year at a time and awarding all business to the railroad that made the lowest rate to each destination. The state associations fathered a number of mutual insurance companies, some of which are still operating, to counter the rates that were charged on mill property by stock companies. The varying systems of wheat grading in the different markets was a recurring subject for complaint. Now and then efforts were made to regulate prices for flour, usually on a local basis, but these were sporadic and do not seem to have been effective.

The tendency for mill problems to cross state lines and affect wide areas as well as for an increasing number of them to have national aspects resulted in a major overhaul of millers' organizations in 1902. Delegates from 26 local, state and regional associations met in Chicago and created Millers' National Federation. As the name indicates, it was a federation of state and other associations of millers. Individual millers were urged to join the associations in their respective states, but in the absence of such they could become direct members. Millers' National Association and Winter Wheat Millers' League were disbanded, and the new organization took over their functions and acquired new ones. Headquarters was established in Chicago.

Several state associations gained new vigor from the formation of the Federation. This was notably the case in Pennsylvania, Ohio, Michigan, Kansas and Oklahoma, and their associations employed full-time secretaries, whereas up to that time the duties of that post had usually been handled by a miller as a sideline to his own business. However, in three important areas the state associations were supplanted a decade or so later by regional groups of considerable importance.

For the most part, state and regional associations devoted themselves to transportation and state legislation. Conflicts of interest between sections prevented the Federation from dealing with more than a few transportation problems, and in the course of time the importance of these issues made them practically the sole program of work for most of the smaller organizations. However, the declining number of mills gradually reduced the membership rolls, and one after another the state and regional associations either disbanded or merged with feed dealers or continued on a nominal basis. Of the many that formerly were active, only the Michigan association is presently functioning, although several others are amalgamated with other bodies in their respective states. Texas Millers' Association, which had a spectacular career, was dissolved in 1914 through anti-trust proceedings brought by the state.

Millers' National Federation is now in its sixty-first year. Its membership at the end of the first year was more than a thousand out of ten times that many mills in the nation, but it was estimated that this represented nearly half of the capacity. In 1929 it had 220 members and about 60 per cent of the capacity. At the end of 1933 the Federation had 595 members and 90 per cent of the industry. Since that time the roll of members had shown a decline practically every year, and in 1962 it was 132. During the past 30 years the volume represented has fallen below 80 per cent only in two brief periods, and currently it stands at 86 per cent.

The Federation has been a useful organization throughout its history and on more than a few occasions it has performed services of a distinguished character. These services have not been limited to the industry but the government and people of the United States have also often been beneficiaries to an equal degree. Familiar illustrations of the latter kind are found in the industry's assistance to and cooperation with the authorities in dealing with vital problems during both of the World Wars.

During its early years the Federation was most prominently concerned with such things as arbitration of trade disputes, establishment of flour package differentials, registration of flour brands, enactment of uniform state laws on feeds, development of a uniform sales contract and formulation of federal wheat grades. Each year the docket of important undertakings was a little longer than the year before. Some of the projects were on the active list for years; the proposal for a federal system of wheat grades to replace the hodge-podge that resulted from every market having its own grades is a good case in point. Uniformity of grades had been advocated in millers' meetings from the early 1880's. It was urged in the organization meeting of the Federation and each year thereafter for more than a decade. When enabling legislation was before Congress in 1914 and 1915, the Federation was the only trade body to give wholehearted support. Perhaps even more important was the technical assistance that was rendered to the Department of Agriculture as the standards were being worked out.

The milling industry enlisted in the national service the day war broke out in 1917. This story is told in detail elsewhere (Chapter VII), but it should be noted here that of the nine millers whose services were requisitioned by the government to administer the food control law as it applied to flour milling operations, three were past presidents of the Federation, one was the current president and two were called to serve as presidents within the ensuing three years. This was eloquent testimony to the standing that had been attained.

Fostering export trade in flour became the outstanding activity through the early 1920's, a special department being created for that purpose. Also during those years the organization considered an advertising program for wheat products, it made trade practices a major activity and developed a code of ethics, it prepared cost accounting manuals and campaigned for uniformity in accounting procedures and it began to take an active interest in national legislation that dealt with farm marketing. It was one of the foremost opponents of McNary-Haugen proposals in 1925-28 but thereafter its leaders tended to concentrate their efforts on modifying legislative ideas so as to soften their impact upon milling. They felt that it would be futile in most cases to oppose measures that had the support of whatever administration was in power. This policy was initiated when the Hoover farm board plan was offered in 1929 and was followed relative to most farm legislation until the Freeman program of rigid controls was launched in 1961.

All through the kaleidoscope of the 1930's, the Federation served as information agency and advisor to millers as well as being the industry's advocate. This policy was ushered in when the farm board program got under way just as the decade dawned; it was continued through Red Cross flour distribution in 1932; and it reached full flower in the impact of such New

Deal innovations as the wheat processing tax, the code of fair competition, social security and wage-hour regulation. Not the least of the complications that occurred grew out of court findings that the processing tax was unconstitutional. This precipitated the adoption of the tax on unjust enrichment and led to controversy and litigation that continued to some degree for years. Just before the second global war, the Federation played the leading role in the formulation of federal flour standards and in the development of what came to be known as the flour enrichment program.

In 1938 the uniform sales contract was modified so as to establish a basic 120-day booking period, with carrying charges or an equivalent price increase to apply on deliveries after that length of time. The adoption of this principle made carrying charges generally collectible. A survey showed that in one year the total carrying charge collections amounted to more than $2,000,000, covering costs that previously had not been compensated for. Even exceeding this in importance was the fact that carrying charges kept contract files in current condition and ended the old state of affairs in which some contracts were not delivered for many months and sometimes for several years. The 1938 contract was the most important reform ever brought about in flour merchandising.

Directly after Pearl Harbor the milling industry again enlisted for the duration. It was confronted with vastly different problems from those of the earlier conflict and the Federation served as buffer for the industry as well as information channel and counselor. Serious and complicated as were the wartime problems, they were much less troublesome than were the perplexities of delayed decontrol. Outstanding in the latter period was the ill-advised requirement of long extraction that was in effect during half of 1946. Before the end of the 1940's the industry launched an advertising campaign for its products, financed for more than $2,000,000, but its effect was nominal and the project was discontinued in 1950. Another major event of the 1940's was the standardization of flour package sizes, accomplished through uniform state legislation.

Events of the past decade or so are highlighted by such occurrences as the controls that came in during the Korean War, the grain sanitation program, the international wheat agreement, the flour export subsidy, establishment of the Federation's export program, organization of wheat growers' associations, revision of grain grades, administration of the mounting complex of agricultural laws and a variety of new legislative ideas.

Wheat Flour Institute was organized in 1935 as a department of the Federation. Its purpose was to conduct educational efforts in behalf of wheat products, chiefly among members of the medical, public health, home economics and teaching professions. It absorbed a smaller organization of like kind but more limited objectives—National Food Bureau, founded in Wichita in 1928. The Bureau was managed in 1928-35 by Harley T. Corson (b. 1871 Kan., d. 1960), who continued in the Institute until 1940.

At the discontinuance of the long-range program, as the millers' advertising program was called, the scope of the Institute was expanded considerably. Its most extensive activities in later years have been the sandwich time promotion, which is generally regarded as outstanding among all food promotions, and by an advertising program in medical and public health journals. Wheat Flour Institute has been directed since 1950 by Howard Lampman (b. 1912 Ore.). Executives who served the Institute earlier included W. Floyd Keepers (b. 1896 Ill.) and Clara G. Snyder.

Millers' National Federation continued as a federation of local and state associations until 1924, when the increasing weakness of the subordinate groups caused the national body to go to a direct membership basis. However, somewhat illogically the old name was retained, although it was no longer a federation. The 1924 reorganization brought in a full-time president as executive head, and a branch office was opened in Washington the following year. In 1929 the top post was changed to executive vice president, in 1935 a full-time president came in for two years, in 1939 the executive vice presidency was abolished and a unique system of co-management by two vice presidents of equal rank began and it continued until 1958. The following year the executive vice presidency was revived, and the holder of the office became president in 1962.

Except for the periods named above, the presidents of Millers' National Federation have been industry leaders who have held office for not more than two years each, chosen by the membership from among their own number. When a full-time employee was designated as president, the industry leader has been known as chairman. This individual presides over conventions, board and executive committee meetings, is often the spokesman for the industry and in general has the duty of seeing that official policy is followed.

Harry L. (Larry) Kennedy (b. 1856 Minn., d. 1941) was the first Federation secretary. In 1904 he was succeeded by Louis T. Jamme (b. 1870 N. Y., d. 1924). Third secretary was Albert L. Goetzmann (b. 1869 Iowa, d. 1941), who held office in 1905-12. Alonzo P. Husband (b. 1868 Pa., d. 1934), who had been secretary of Pennsylvania Millers' Association, was Federation secretary in 1912-29. Sydney Anderson (b. 1880 Minn., d. 1948), who had a distinguished career in Congress for fourteen years, became full-time president in 1925-29. First executive vice president was George Livingston (b. 1886 Ohio, d. 1954), who was a bureau chief in the Department of Agriculture before organizing Livingston Economic Service in 1924. He held office in 1929-39.

Herman Steen (b. 1893 Iowa), formerly a newspaper man, became secretary in 1929 and retained this position for 29 years, also being elected vice president in charge of Chicago headquarters in 1939. At that time also, Herman Fakler (b. 1897 Minn., d. 1958), who had been vice president from 1935, became head of the Washington office. This dual system continued for 19 years; Steen then had charge of the entire organization for about six months. Casper L. Mast, Jr. (b. 1910 Ill.), also a newspaper man, came in as secretary in 1958, was elected executive vice president in 1959 and president in 1962. John J. Sherlock (b. 1923 Ill.) became secretary in 1959, when Fred H. Mewhinney (b. 1932 N.Y.) was named Washington representative.

Flour export promotion became a major Federation activity in 1952, when the export department was established. It has been managed by Gordon P. Boals (b. 1905 Neb.).

Sectional rivalries impelled the formation of several regional organizations of considerable importance. Southeastern Millers' Association was organized in 1914 by soft wheat family flour millers whose trade area was principally in the Middle South. For a time it was able to regulate trade practices, and it was active in traffic and legislative matters as well as being a vigorous proponent of soft wheat interests. J. Briggs McLemore was secretary during the first decade, and his successors were, in turn, John W. Sample, Wallace H. Strowd, Gustave A. Breaux and Ralph H. Missman. Headquarters was in Nashville until 1933, and then in Louisville and Evansville. The association became inactive in 1944.

Sectional issues also caused Southwestern Millers' League to be established in 1908, its members being hard winter wheat millers. On occasion the league pursued an independent policy, notably in the controversy over milling-in-bond. It was, however, principally a traffic organization and became one of the best known in that field. The league was headed by Lincoln E. Moses in its first years, and he became full-time president after his retirement from Flour Mills of America, Inc., in 1923. He was followed in 1928 by Ernest H. Hogueland. Headquarters was in Kansas City. The league disbanded in 1937, and was succeeded by Associated Millers of Kansas Wheat, which devoted its major efforts to wheat improvement. Jess B. Smith was full-time president of the latter until 1949, when it also disbanded.

North Pacific Millers' Association, formed in 1918 with offices in Tacoma, was not only a traffic bureau of importance but it also became prominent in flour export issues that affected the Pacific area. Its secretaries were Rodney D. Lytle, George V. Hayes, Earl C. Corey, William C. Theda and Howard W. Taylor. It became inactive in 1962.

Millers in the Minneapolis area have not had a regional organization of comparable nature. For years they had Spring Wheat Millers' Club, a social body with no office nor employees, but it withered away before 1950.

Organizations that were wholly engaged in traffic matters have included Kansas and Missouri River Mills, still in existence, and Southern Minnesota Mills and Southern Kansas Milers Club, both dissolved several years ago.

American Millers' Association was an organization of small

millers, chiefly in Kentucky and Indiana. It was called American Custom Millers Association when it was organized in 1926. It was dissolved in 1947.

National Soft Wheat Millers' Association came into being in 1924, primarily as a promotional agency for soft wheat flour. After an advertising and publicity program on a large scale, it became inactive but was revived in 1933 as a militant crusader for the soft wheat industry. Wallace H. Strowd (b. 1889 N. C., d. 1946) was its secretary for 24 years. In 1947 it was reorganized, and it also absorbed remnants of the Southeastern, Piedmont and American associations. Since that time its annual conventions—in Louisville, Roanoke and a Carolina point—have served as rallying points for millers in those areas. Paul M. Marshall (b. 1890 Pa., d. 1957) was executive officer in 1947-57, his successor being Rondal M. Huffman (b. 1914 Ind.). Nashville was headquarters until 1947, Chicago thereafter.

Flour Millers' Export Association was founded in 1943, under the Webb-Pomerene Act, chiefly to allocate ocean shipping space, which was scarce at that time. Offices were in Washington. Later it undertook to deal with many other export issues. William T. McArthur was executive secretary during its most active period. Since the export program of the Federation was initiated in 1952, it has absorbed many of the functions of the export association. However, the latter remains in existence in order to take care of activities that are reserved to Webb-Pomerene organizations.

Association of Operative Millers is a professional and technical organization, the membership of which embraces nearly all those whose responsibilities are in flour production above the manual level, in the United States and Canada. It also has members in 28 other nations. It was organized in 1895 as the Fraternity of Operative Millers by Benjamin W. Dedrick (b. 1860 Ill., d. 1946), an Illinois miller who later became professor of milling at Pennsylvania State College. The present name was acquired in 1919. Main activities of AOM are the annual technical conference and trade show, periodic meetings in the fourteen districts of the association, correspondence courses in milling and the publication of technical bulletins. Offices are in Kansas City. Donald S. Eber (b. 1904 Ore.) has been executive officer since 1947, having been preceded by W. E. McCraith, Charles W. Partridge, Hugo Roos and Matthew F. Dillon.

National Association of Flour Distributors is not a milling organization but is closely related to the industry. It was formed in 1919 as National Federated Flour Clubs, the units of which were groups of flour merchants in several large cities. Membership consists chiefly of brokers, jobbers and mill representatives. The flour clubs are primarily social organizations, although to some extent they have participated in business affairs. Both in the New Deal years and during the second world war period, the national body took an active part in issues that arose in these emergencies. Name was changed in 1942 to the present form.

American Association of Cereal Chemists is likewise not a millers' organization, although it is closely related to the industry. It is a professional society that is devoted to the science of cereal chemistry. AACC was formed in 1915 by mill chemists, principally in Kansas, for the purpose of standardizing the methods used in mill laboratories. In the course of time, it grew into a scientific body of international scope and reputation, and its publications have worldwide standing and use. About one-third of the present membership is identified with milling companies in the United States, but it also has members in 26 foreign countries. Until 1950 the editorial and other work of AACC was done on a volunteer basis, and it had no office. At that time Raymond J. Tarleton became secretary and editor, and offices were established in St. Paul, an arrangement that has continued to the present.

CHAPTER TWELVE

Flour Milling Economics

Flour millers' favorite tradition seems to be that the business was highly lucrative in the past, in contrast to meager current earnings. This intriguing idea has been commonly believed for no less than 75 years, each generation giving its predecessor credit for great affluence.

Various data may be cited in support of the tradition. Development of New Process milling produced a bonanza for the Minnesota mills for a time around 1880. Handsome earnings were realized industry-wide for three or four seasons during and just after each of the two World Wars. Exceptional profits have been garnered now and then—sometimes by a few companies, on other occasions by many.

Despite the legend, the condition that has prevailed for several generations in flour milling has been for a very large majority of companies to earn only modest profits each year. The amount of these profits has varied considerably from season to season and from company to company, but except for a few brief periods such as were noted above earnings have been less than sensational.

On the other hand, years in which a majority of companies have suffered losses are quite rare; during this century, only the fiscal periods that ended in 1921 and 1938 belong in that category. In several other years, considerable numbers of companies required red ink to close their books but that was not the general rule. However, more than a few companies have had the experience of never going through a losing year in their entire history.

During the developmental period of the American merchant milling system, which in a broad sense coincided with the nineteenth century, the most successful and outstanding millers were those for whose flour there existed a domestic consumer demand or who had export outlets of considerable consequence, or both; in either case, product quality was a paramount consideration. In those days there was tremendous variation in flour quality, and millers who made a consistently good flour seldom lacked a ready market. Although competition was usually brisk and sometimes sharp, such millers generally were able to obtain prices that were distinctly better than the levels that prevailed in the city flour markets upon which many of their contemporaries were dependent.

It is decidedly probable that the profits of millers of premium grade flour in the era just referred to were considerably greater per unit of product than those obtained in later years. However, these millers were a minority of the industry, and there were only a few large mills, so the earnings level was of less significance than it would otherwise have been. Although data on the earnings of other millers are now largely unavailable, analysis of prices that prevailed leads to the belief that not many of them could have been really prosperous.

The evolution of merchant milling from several thousand plants, most of them small, to about four hundred considerably larger plants, which occurred between the beginning of the present century and the outbreak of the second World War, was marked by several developments of a major character. Chief among them were the perfection of merchandising techniques that created and established consumer preferences for branded goods; a general improvement in flour quality, along with a great increase in the number of companies able to produce flour acceptable to discriminating customers; and the growth from obscurity to great size of the commercial baking industry. These factors were not necessarily working in harmony; for example, a miller who had built up a great consumer following found that this meant practically nothing to the bakery trade.

During those years, milling was being transformed from the production and merchandising of consumer goods, at least in large part, into becoming the maker of raw materials for secondary processors. That this course was against the better judgment of its principals is not especially pertinent—they were carried along by external forces that they could not control.

When superior quality flour became the conventional product, the premium that it formerly commanded simply disappeared. This was the natural result of competition, which became increasingly keen as total output reached a level of stability and as more and more mills improved their production techniques. Growth of the baking industry and consolidation of baking companies also had the effect of sharpening the competition among mills. The net result was a trend toward narrower margins over material costs, but this was minimized by the increased average size of milling companies.

The milling pattern of the past quarter of a century had its roots much farther in the past. The trend toward increased plant size and fewer mills has continued unabated—the four hundred mills that operated on the eve of the last war are now only a bit more than two hundred in number. This trend has been accompanied by a quickening tempo of milling company mergers, and no less than 85 per cent of the hard wheat bakery flour is now produced by the 25 largest suppliers. The family flour business is also concentrated to approximately the same extent.

Latter-day milling is characterized by extensive diversification, nearly all of it in lines that are closely related to milling. The widespread diversification that exists generally among companies above average size includes vast amounts of grain storage facilities; country elevator lines; grain merchandising; formula feed manufacturing; breakfast cereals; flour mixes of a great variety; refrigerated doughs; soybean processing; chemicals derived from farm products; and even some foreign enterprises. In most cases these lines mesh well into mill operation because of the similarity of source materials.

Throughout the fifteen years that began in 1948, a substantial part of milling company earnings has been received from sidelines and from other non-milling activities, of which the most important is the speculative gain on millfeed after flour sales are booked. The main business of the industry—the production of bakery flour—has supplied a relatively small part of the earnings. In fact, income from milling flour is invariably a disproportionately small part of company income, and not infrequently a loss is incurred in this phase of the business. Were it not for reasonably good revenue from diversified lines, and particularly for income resulting from millfeed inventory advances, more than a few companies would have had decidedly unflattering results in recent years.

During these late years, milling company earnings in total

have not been unsatisfactory a majority of the time. However, the fact that such a preponderant share of income is produced by non-milling lines and by market gains on a by-product of milling has been giving deep concern to the industry's executives. It is not generally regarded as a healthy situation for a business. Indeed, it would be difficult to find another industry that relies primarily upon sidelines for its earnings and obtains only nominal profits from its principal service and activities.

Although for almost three-fourths of a century there was a significant excess of flour milling facilities in the United States (except during the two World War periods), that condition came to an end nearly a decade ago in the major milling region that runs from Minnesota to Texas and from Illinois to Colorado, inclusive. Since 1955 few mills of commercial consequence in that area have suffered from light running time; on the contrary, practically all have experienced the heaviest output in years. This state of affairs has nevertheless had little or no effect upon milling margins and upon competitive practices. For several generations it was confidently believed in the industry that milling would become more profitable if the capacity excess were to come to an end, but this idea has been discredited by events of the past eight years in which plant capacity and available business have remained in practical balance.

Another belief long held by some millers that competition would be less rugged when a major share of the industry's capacity went into a few hands has also been confounded by the performance in recent years. In this time a fairly small number of companies have controlled a large share of the industry's facilities, and yet flour orders were never more eagerly nor more persistently solicited. However, this result was forecast for years by conditions in rye and durum milling, in which only a few companies have ever been engaged; there the rivalry for business has long been as keen as in any other segment of the industry.

American food industries in general operate on small profit margins, the chief exceptions being on minor items that are controlled or dominated by a single interest. Even on most trademarked items, the tendency is toward large volume and narrow margins. The markup is of course smallest on products that cannot be identified to the consumer and therefore are not subject to consumer demand. Flour sold to secondary processors comes in this category, as when bread or crackers or other bakery goods appear on the retail shelf there is no possible way for the prospective buyer to determine whose flour they contain.

Milling has thus progressed from a business that produced consumer goods to a business that is largely devoted to producing flour for another industry to fabricate. This was a familiar role in the distant past, as invariably when ancient and medieval cities grew to great size the production of breadstuffs was transferred from homes to commercial establishments. However, there is this significant difference: Ancient and medieval mills were as often as not integral parts of baking establishments, but that is not the case in present-day America. Although there is some amalgamation of mills and bakeries in modern Europe, this condition is by no means general.

Several baking companies have moved into milling in this country, but such ventures have proved to be costly and have been abandoned. Even in the case of the two large cracker companies that have had their own mills for many years, there is well-reasoned belief that they might have invested their funds and their energies to much better advantage elsewhere than in their milling properties. The common saying among millers that bakers can buy flour cheaper than they can make it may be only a partial explanation why bakers have shunned mill ownership. The baking business has become so complex and has so many serious problems of its own that it could hardly expect to become expert in the intricacies of another complicated enterprise.

Household flour volume has diminished more than half during the past two decades, and this trade has also undergone fundamental changes. Only in the South and Southeast does flour for the home continue to be a major grocery item, and in that area the use of self-rising flour has remained almost steady while other flour has declined tremendously. Both there and elsewhere, flour mixes have gained greatly in popularity; first introduced in 1928, they came into much wider use about 1946, and subsequently the kind and variety of prepared flours has proliferated. In many metropolitan areas the tonnage of mixes exceeds that of conventional flour for home use. Merchandising costs, and especially the use of television, have tended to concentrate the mix business in a small list of companies.

Concentration is also the rule in family flour, except in the states south of the Ohio and the Potomac, where about 25 companies have a significant volume of business. Several of them have totals in excess of what they had two or three decades ago, a fact that points up the disappearance of many once active and prominent family flour mills. In all phases of the family flour business, intense competition has been the prevailing condition for years, much of this stemming from the determination on the part of participants to hold their own volume constant in the face of the downward course of the total market.

A shrinking total market obviously intensifies competition among those elements that elect to remain in the picture, and that is the basic fact about the household trade in recent years. The problem of the bakery flour miller is, however, of a wholly different nature, as his total market has been expanding and the facilities for supplying the market are all regularly employed. His chief quandary is that of discovering a way to obtain a slightly higher wage for his services and for his dollars. An increase of only a few pennies for each cwt. of product would turn the trick, but he has not as yet learned how to market his goods that well. Until he does, he will be obliged to live in large measure from revenues generated by secondary parts of his business complex.

Considering all the perplexities that contribute to the uneasy existence of present-day millers, it is not surprising that they have a tendency to think of the business experiences of their forebears as having been in aureate epochs. Possibly the flight of time has obscured or obliterated troubles that must have been monumental in those days—primitive transportation, limited trade information, gross discrimination in freight rates, prevalence of mill fires, rigged markets, unreliable banking, to name only a few things of the many that must once have been prime causes of miller insomnia. Rewards there doubtless were, but they were by no means universally distributed, as shown by the high proportion of mills that went out of business—and mills were seldom closed as long as they were able to earn anything of consequence.

Rather than accept the thesis that milling has been in a descending earnings spiral for several successive generations— a thesis for which no real proof has been adduced—it seems more realistic to believe that each of these generations has had its share of troublesome experiences as well as its rewards. It is just possible, after all, that millers in some future age may look back to the present and say wistfully that it must have been wonderful to have been in the milling business in America in 1963!

Company Histories

On the following pages there appears the history of 408 American milling companies. This number includes all that have operated a plant or plants with 1000 cwt. or more milling capacity at any time after the end of the first World War. The essential facts in the history of each company are included, insofar as it was possible to obtain the information.

Each company account appears under the city in which main offices were located. In the case of a company that moved, the history will be found at the last location. Separate accounts are given for each of the participants in mergers that took place after 1918.

Names of individual millers are indexed in the back of the volume, as are all companies and company predecessors.

ARIZONA

Corn was doubtless ground for hundreds of years by the Indians of Arizona, and the first flour mills in the state were built when the mining industry was established after the Civil War. These mills were small in size and few in number, but in two cases they were the nucleus for companies that have continued to the present.

Phoenix

Arizona Milling Co.—Four small flour mills in Arizona were purchased in 1926 by Joe T. Melczer (b. 1889 Calif.) and associates from the Viaults. They were merged into Phoenix Flour Mills Co., which was founded in 1871, and the company name was changed in 1933 to Arizona Flour Mills Co. The Phoenix mill was enlarged to 1200 cwt., and the other mills were closed. Great growth of the feed business in later years overshadowed flour operations, the company name was changed in 1960 to Arizona Milling Co., and flour milling ceased in 1961. Melczer was president in 1926-58, his son, Louis A. (b. 1914 Ariz.) since 1958.

Tempe

Hayden Flour Mills operates a new 1000-cwt. pneumatic flour mill in Tempe, 20 miles east of Phoenix. It replaced a plant built in 1872, or 40 years prior to statehood, by Charles T. Hayden (b. 1825, d. 1900), who was its proprietor for 28 years.

The founder's son, Carl Hayden (b. 1877 Ariz.), managed the business in 1901-06 and was a sort of overseer until 1915. He left the mill to enter political life, was a member of Congress in 1912-27 and has been United States Senator since 1927—the longest Congressional service in American history.

Hayden Flour Mills was incorporated in 1915, and William T. Studer (b. 1880 Kan.) was manager from that time until 1955. He was succeeded by Hayden C. Hayden (b. 1922 Ariz.), grandson of the founder and nephew of Senator Hayden.

ARKANSAS

Although wheat production never attained much importance in Arkansas, there were a good many grist mills and in 1881 the Arkansas Millers' Association was formed. The 1900 census reported that the state had 173 mills that ground wheat. Nearly all were in the northern and central parts. In 1958 only three mills were remaining.

Arkadelphia

Arkadelphia Milling Co.—Halfway between Little Rock and Texarkana, in the foothills of the Ouachitas, was the largest flour mill ever operated in Arkansas. Arkadelphia Roller Mills was organized in 1902, and it was later called Arkadelphia Milling Co. Capacity was 1200 cwt. flour and 1600 cwt. corn meal. The company was controlled by the Adams family, and Joe M. Adams was president through most of its history. His nephew, William N. Adams (b. 1880 Tenn., d. 1942), was manager in 1902-29, leaving to become head of a railroad. The mill was closed in 1932, J. E. Herbert being the last manager.

Mammoth Spring

Mammoth Spring Milling Co.—Within a mile of the Missouri border is Mammoth Spring, where a flour mill of 1000 cwt. was named for the town. Edward C. Bellamy was the last manager. The business was liquidated in 1925.

CALIFORNIA

The padres who ran the chain of missions that dotted the

coast line were California's first millers. It is believed that the
first flour mill in California was built in 1781 at San Gabriel
Mission, near what is now Pasadena, by Father Jose Zaloiden.
Within a few years there were mills also at San Diego, Santa
Cruz and San Luis Obispo, and eventually nearly all the missions had mills. During the Mexican era, many of the great
ranchos had their own grist mills.

Gold was discovered in 1848 by men employed by John A.
Sutter to build a flour mill near Coloma, in the Sierra foothills
east of Sacramento. The tremendous influx of population created a demand that caused flour to sell at fantastic prices. The
San Juaquin and Sacramento valleys were turned into great
wheat fields, and within a decade California was one of the
chief states in wheat production. First mill of much consequence was in Stockton, built in 1852 by Austin Sperry, and
it was followed by others in Oakland and San Francisco. Although there were mills in Los Angeles from pioneer days, it
is only in the past year that this city has taken first place among
Pacific Coast milling centers.

California flour production was 6,533,000 cwt. in 1961.

Alhambra

El Molino Mills is in a Los Angeles suburb. It was founded
in 1926 by Edward A. Vandercook (b. 1883 Mich., d. 1955)
and operated by his sons, Edward W., Clare R., and Gene. The
concern has a 1200-cwt. whole wheat mill, built in 1947, in
which the grinding is on stones. It does business all over the
nation, predominantly with bakers.

Los Angeles

California Milling Corp. facilities comprise a flour mill of
4200 cwt., feed mill of 400 tons and 635,000 bushels of grain

storage, all in Los Angeles, and a 400-ton feed mill in Cor-
coran, Calif. Flour business is chiefly with the bakery trade of
Southern California. Ownership and management of California
Milling Corp. have been in the hands of the Viault family
throughout company history, which began in 1923.

The first Viault mill was in Phoenix, where Valley Flour
Mills was established in 1903 by Emile Viault (b. 1855 France,
d. 1928). He had learned the trade in Minnesota and continued it after going to Arizona in 1894. Between 1912 and 1920
his sons built three other small units in Arizona, but these properties were sold soon after they embarked upon their California
venture. Their first Los Angeles mill of 700 cwt. was increased
to 1400 cwt. in 1928 and to 2100 cwt. in 1945. A pneumatic
unit was added in 1956, doubling the size of the mill.

Four brothers and a sister were associated originally in California Milling Corp., but in 1933 Max and Arthur withdrew
and formed V-O Milling Co. in Los Angeles. Frank and Albert
continued to operate California Milling Corp. Frank (b. 1885
Minn.) was president of the company in 1923-56 except for
two years in the late 1920's when Max held the office. Frank,
Jr. (b. 1916 Ariz.) has been president since 1956, and Clifton B. Capps (b. 1910 Mont.), son-in-law of Frank, Sr., became general manager in 1940 and executive vice president in
1956.

Capitol Milling Co.'s plant is near downtown Los Angeles,
and but half a mile from Father Junipero Serra's historic mission which became the nucleus for the great city named for the
queen of the angels. The trade of the company is primarily
with the bakers of Southern California. A mill has stood on
the site since 1840. The pioneer mill was built by Abel Stearns,
a New England sea captain who became a Mexican don and

the largest land owner in California prior to American sovereignty.

Capitol Milling Co. was formed in 1883 by Jacob Loew (b. 1848 Germany, d. 1921), and he was its president for 38 years. The mill was rebuilt in 1886, and in 1921 it was replaced by a new mill of 1050 cwt. From 1885 Loew's nephew, Herman Levi (b. 1870 Germany, d. 1948), was in the business and was president in 1921-45. Head since 1945 is Stephen N. Loew (b. 1891 Calif.), son of the company founder; his company connection began in 1909. John N. Levi (b. 1905 Calif.), son of Herman, and Stephen N. Loew, Jr. (b. 1914 Calif.) joined the company in the early 1930's.

Globe Grain & Milling Co.—Largest milling company based in Southern California was Globe Grain & Milling Co., which was acquired in 1940 by Pillsbury Flour Mills Co. The Globe purchase made Pillsbury a truly national company for the first time.

This enterprise traces to 1892, when McDonald Grain & Milling Co. established a small mill in Los Angeles. It was reorganized in 1902 as Globe Grain & Milling Co., and mills were built in Colton, San Diego and San Francisco. The San Francisco mill was rebuilt after being lost in the 1906 fire and earthquake. The Los Angeles mill was increased to 2000 cwt., and in 1914 a mill in El Paso, Texas, was purchased but later was spun off. In 1919 a mill was built in Ogden and in 1920 Phoenix Milling Co. in Sacramento was acquired. The company then had about 10,000 cwt. capacity. Globe also had extensive interests in cotton gins, cotton oil mills, cattle feeding yards and feed milling.

Just before Globe became a Pillsbury property, the Colton and San Diego mills were closed, the non-milling businesses were sold soon after, and in 1945 and 1948 the San Francisco and Los Angeles mills ceased to make flour. The Globe business operated as Pillsbury-Globe division until 1952, and then was integrated into the parent company.

William E. Keller (b. 1860 Texas, d. 1926) organized Globe Grain & Milling Co., and was its president in 1902-26. O. H. Morgan (b. 1885, d. 1941) was president in 1926-40, with Clifford C. Hine (b. 1889 Ont., d. 1952) as general manager. Hine continued in an executive position after the merger. Patrick J. McKenney (b. 1888 Ohio, d. 1952) was Globe division president in 1940-48, succeeded by Benjamin J. Greer in 1948-52. Greer was later Pillsbury executive vice president.

V-O Milling Co.—After disposing of their interests in California Milling Corp., Max Viault (b. 1879 Minn., d. 1953) and his brother Arthur established V-O Milling Co. They opened a new 2,000-cwt. plant in 1934. Max was president and manager. The business continued until 1945, when the mill was sold to Quaker Oats Co., which has continued it in operation.

Max Viault was associated with mills in Arizona for 25 years before becoming a co-founder of California Milling Corp. in 1923.

San Francisco

Sperry Flour Co.—Fourth largest milling company in the United States in the middle 1920's, Sperry Flour Co. had a history that went back to gold rush days. In fact, its founder, Austin Sperry (b. 1818 Vt., d. 1881), was a gold miner, but only for three weeks. He was a flour miller almost 30 years.

The first Sperry mill, built in Stockton in 1852, was famous in early California history, and served as a bank for the gold miners. It was operated by Sperry and his heirs for 70 years, and ultimately it attained 5000 cwt. capacity.

Golden Gate Flouring Mills, established in San Francisco in 1860, was Sperry's chief rival. It was controlled by Horace Davis (b. 1831 Mass., d. 1916), who also served two terms in Congress (1877-81) and was president of the University of California. Golden Gate, Sperry and four smaller companies in Central California were consolidated in 1892 under the Sperry name but under the leadership of Davis. Mills were established in Tacoma and Los Angeles in 1903, the Porta Costa Milling Co. in Vallejo (up the bay from San Francisco) was acquired in 1910 and mills were built in Ogden and Spokane in 1919. By the latter year the company's eight mills had 26,900 cwt. capacity. For half a century before that a third of the output went to the Oriental market.

Severe financial reverses in the early 1920's brought bankers into control of Sperry, and in 1922 they merged with it a concern in like plight—Portland Flouring Mills Co., which had 21,300 cwt. capacity in Oregon and Washington. Most of the smaller plants were closed during the next few years, and by 1928 Sperry capacity had been reduced to 29,000 cwt.

Sperry Flour Co. was acquired in 1929 by General Mills, Inc., and became a division a few years later. However, Sperry's identity was preserved much longer and to a greater degree than was the case with other divisions. Headquarters, which had been in San Francisco from 1892, went to nearby Palo Alto in 1961. The division operates five flour mills—in Ogden, Spokane, Tacoma, Vallejo and Los Angeles—with 31,600 cwt. total capacity. The Los Angeles mill was built in 1949, the first Sperry mill in that city having been lost to fire 25 years earlier. The present Los Angeles mill was the first pneumatic plant in the United States.

Sperry presidents: Davis in 1892-1910; John E. Rossetter in 1910-22; Seward B. McNear (b. 1874 Calif., d. 1959), who had been president of Porta Costa Milling Co., in 1922-24; William H. Joyce in 1924-26; Roy N. Bishop (b. 1879 Ill., d. 1938) in 1926-29. Division presidents, termed general managers in recent years, have been Frank B. Burke (b. 1880 Kan.) in 1929-46; Edward O. Boyer (b. 1894 Calif.) in 1946-58; Burton W. Roberts (b. 1916 Utah) since 1958. Boyer became executive vice president of General Mills, Inc., in 1958-61.

COLORADO

Colorado milling history is dominated by John K. Mullen and the company he founded, since for 75 years it has comprised the predominant part of the industry of the state. In that time only a few other mills have existed there.

First flour mill in Colorado was apparently a small mill at Guadeloupe, in the San Luis Valley, built before the Civil War. First mill of consequential size was built in Pueblo in 1862.

Colorado mills produced 4,033,000 cwt. of flour in 1961.

Denver

Colorado Milling & Elevator Co. is fifth in size in the nation's milling industry and the largest company with headquarters outside of Minneapolis. It operates fourteen milling plants in nine states, their aggregate capacity being 58,500 cwt. It is also engaged extensively in the grain business, with 81 country elevators and 22,000,000 bushels of storage space, and the company's feed milling capacity is 1000 tons per day. It does business in every state, and it is a large supplier to the hard and soft wheat bakery trade as well as having sizable outlets in household flour.

The first 44 years of Colorado Milling & Elevator Co. are really the story of John K. Mullen (b. 1847 Ireland, d. 1929). With a partner named Theodore Seth, he leased a small mill in Denver in 1875. A year later he was sole owner. In 1882 he built the Hungarian mill in Denver, so named after the roller process that was just coming in vogue. In 1885 Mullen led in forming a consolidation of four mills in Denver—Hungarian, Eagle, Excelsior and Crescent—and mills in Fort Collins, Longmont and Greeley, thus launching Colorado Milling & Elevator Co. As time went on, mills were built in Loveland and Berthoud in Northern Colorado; in Lamar, LaJunta and Pueblo in the Arkansas Valley; and at five points in the San Luis Valley. By the first World War era, the company had four mills in Denver, with total capacity of 5300 cwt., and fourteen mills at other Colorado points with 9600 cwt. capacity.

Early in this century Mullen entered Kansas with a mill in Hays. Later other Kansas plants were acquired in Wilson, Dodge City and Claflin. Beginning in 1907, the company built five mills in Idaho—in Caldwell, Weiser, St. Anthony, Twin Falls and Burley. In 1905, the company acquired Husler Flour Mills in Salt Lake City. During the latter part of the Mullen regime, the company had 28 mills, with aggregate capacity of about 30,000 cwt. Each mill had its own manager, and all operated independently. The company was in reality a chain of small country mills.

The founder was president in 1887-1922. He was succeeded in 1922-29 by his son-in-law, Oscar L. Malo (b. 1877 Ill.), and in 1929-43 by another son-in-law, John L. Dower (b. 1867 Conn., d. 1943). Herbert E. Johnson (b. 1862 Wis., d. 1952), long Mullen's right-hand man, had the title of general manager in 1917-21, as did Clyde E. Williams (b. 1880 Colo., d. 1940) in 1927-37.

The Mullen heirs sold their predominant interest in 1943, and the company has since been publicly owned. Guy A. Thomas, who had been president of Commander-Larabee, headed Colorado Milling & Elevator Co. for a year. Later presidents were Fred W. Lake (b. 1888 Mo., d. 1955), one of the industry's foremost grain men, in 1944-55; Robert M. Pease (b. 1900 Mo., d. 1962) in 1955-60; and Earl F. Cross (b. 1900 Kan.) since 1960. George M. Hopfenbeck (b. 1900 Utah, d. 1963), the company's financial man, was elected board chairman in 1960, J. Lawson Cook (b. 1906 Ga.) becoming executive vice president at the same time.

During Dower's time the company remained as it had been under Mullen—a chain of country mills—but several of them were closed in the late 1930's. At that time occurred the first new purchase of consequence, the Meyer-Blair mill in Springfield, Mo., acquired in 1939 and operated until 1951. It was during the Lake administration that a fundamental change took place in the company. Six more mills were closed (two lost through fire), a series of mill purchases were consummated and the principal plants were enlarged extensively. The purchases consisted of Omar, Inc., in 1949, Canadian Milling & Elevator Co. in 1951 and Schultz, Baujan & Co. in 1953. Four years later the Valier & Spies plant of Flour Mills of America, Inc., also was purchased. Still later four more of the country mills were closed. Early in 1963 the company acquired J. Allen Smith & Co., Inc.

Colorado Milling & Elevator Co. now has its major milling facilities in seven cities—Denver (three mills) 11,150 cwt., Salt Lake City 5000 cwt., ElReno, Okla., 4300 cwt., Omaha 7250 cwt., Beardstown, Ill., 6300 cwt., St. Louis 13,000 cwt., and Knoxville 5000 cwt. There remain only five of the big chain of country mills; they are in Monte Vista, Colo.; Burley,

Twin Falls and Weiser, Idaho; and Claflin, Kan. Their total capacity is 6500 cwt., about one-eighth of the company's total.

Longmont Farmers' Milling & Elevator Co.—About 1890 J. A. Forsythe and associates built a 600-cwt. mill in Longmont, 25 miles north of Denver. It was not a cooperative, as the name might indicate. Ten years later the concern added a 1200-cwt. mill in Denver and moved its office there. George Russell was general manager for many years. The Denver mill was destroyed by fire in 1920 and was replaced by a new plant of 2400 cwt. The company was overtaken by financial troubles during the 1920's, and the Denver mill was leased to Dixie-Portland interests in 1931 but was closed the following year. The Longmont mill, which had been idle, was sold to Golden West Milling Co., and was operated until 1948.

DISTRICT OF COLUMBIA

Washington

Wilkins-Rogers Milling Co. is located in the Georgetown district of the nation's capital. It has an 800-cwt. flour mill and 500-cwt. corn mill, and it is probably the largest producer of water-ground corn meal. Flour business is with the family trade in and near Washington. The company is owned by the four Rogers brothers, headed by Samuel H., Jr. (b. 1922 D.C.), president since 1954.

The business was established by Howard L. Wilkins (b. 1865 N. J., d. 1949) and Samuel H. Rogers (b. 1877 Va., d. 1954). Wilkins had been a feed merchant and Rogers a flour broker whose father and grandfather had been Virginia millers. They joined forces first in a flour and feed company, and in 1914 they bought the old Cissel mill which had been in use from 1849. The plant burned in 1922 and was replaced by the present facilities. The company has continued to job hard wheat flour in the Washington area in addition to operating the soft wheat and corn mills.

Wilkins was president in 1914-49, and his partner then became sole owner and president in 1949-54.

GEORGIA

The first state association of millers of which there is any record was organized in Georgia in 1873. The state then had a considerable number of flour mills, and in 1900 there were 433 mills that ground wheat, nearly all of which were grist operations. In 1958 there were 54 mills in the state, all but a few being very small.

Atlanta

Atlanta Milling Co.—Georgia's metropolis was the site of a 3000-cwt. mill established in 1898 by John B. Whitman (d. 1920) and William C. Mansfield (b. 1856 Ga., d. 1929). With them was associated William F. Hutcheson, who controlled Mountain City Mill Co., and Mansfield owned an interest in Hutcheson's company. Whitman was president in 1898-1920, Mansfield in 1920-29, and Charles N. Dannals (d. 1955), son-in-law of Whitman, in 1929-55. The mill was destroyed by fire in 1933 but the company continued flour distribution until 1961.

Dalton

Barrett, Denton & Lynn Co.—The Owensby mill in Dalton was purchased in 1882 by the firm of Barrett, Denton & Lynn. Some years later the 800-cwt. mill was increased to 1200 cwt. William M. Denton was the long-time manager. The plant was closed in 1930.

Macon

Birdsey Flour Mills for the past decade or more has concentrated on the cracker trade in the Southeast. The business was established in 1913 with a 150-cwt. mill that was enlarged in 1919 to 1450 cwt. In the late 1920's the company began operating its own retail stores that handled feed, flour and a few other staples, and in time there were a hundred stores in the chain. After 1950 the stores were closed or sold.

The founders of the business were J. Sandford Birdsey (b. 1872 N. C., d. 1952) and his brother Ralph T. (b. 1875 N. C., d. 1936), and later two more brothers, Samuel R. and Angus B., joined with them. Company presidents: J. Sandford Birdsey in 1913-37; his son, B. S. (b. 1912 Ga.) in 1937-49; and Herbert F. (b. 1909 Fla.), son of Ralph T., since 1949.

Rome

Southeastern Mills, Inc. is the largest mill now in Georgia, with a flour unit of 1500 cwt. and corn mill of 1000 cwt., along with grain storage of 500,000 bushels. The company's trade territory is chiefly within the state, and the business is divided between family and bakery flour. Fred R. Johnson (b. 1897 Ga.) has been president and manager since 1941.

After Theo. E. Stivers (b. 1895 Tenn., d. 1963) lost his mill in East Tennessee through fire, he went to the Northwest Georgia town of Rome and established Theo. Stivers Milling Co. in 1929. After about ten years, the concern became insolvent. It was operated as Rome Milling Co. for a year, and in 1941 the property was purchased by a group of Rome business men headed by Johnson, who had been a produce merchant. Southeastern Mills, Inc., was launched at that time.

HAWAII

Maui and Oahu began to grow wheat in the 1840's, and in the gold rush days when food was scarce and dear in California a mission mill in Wailuku shipped flour regularly to the Golden State. Mills were then built in Makawao and Honolulu. The California trade continued for more than a decade. Pineapple production was more profitable than wheat, and the mills of Hawaii were gone by the late 1870's.

IDAHO

Moscow

Mark P. Miller Milling Co.—The Caruthers mill that began in the 1890's in Moscow, 90 miles southeast of Spokane, was acquired in 1902 by Mark P. Miller and rebuilt with 1200 cwt. capacity. It was managed by Miller during his lifetime and thereafter by Terminal Flour Mills Co. The mill was closed in 1949.

ILLINOIS

Illinois superseded Ohio as the premier wheat state several years before the Civil War and it retained first place for more than 20 years. During this period, and in earlier times as well, a sizable milling industry developed. There were 443 flour mills in Illinois reported by the 1900 census, and probably nearly as many had been in existence through most of the preceding half century. A large majority of them were located within an arc of 75 miles from St. Louis, this being the chief area of wheat production in the state. The Illinois milling industry is now concentrated in half a dozen large plants and as many more of moderate size, and the 1958 census reported a total of 26 mills in the state. Illinois flour production in 1961 was 17,282,000 cwt., its rank being fifth among the states.

French settlers at Kaskaskia, on the Mississippi 65 miles or so southeast of St. Louis, operated the first flour mill in Illinois. It was established about 1712 and was the first mill west of the Atlantic Seaboard.

Abraham Lincoln was a miller, at least for one season. He managed the grist mill of his visionary friend, Denton Offutt, in 1829-30. It was located on the Sangamon, 20 miles northwest of Springfield, at the village of New Salem. The mill has been restored and it stands in the state park.

Alton

Sparks Milling Co.—Largest mill owners in Illinois in 1869 were Captain David R. Sparks (b. 1823 Ind., d. 1907) and Wesley Best. The partnership then operated five mills, the last having been established that year in Alton. The first Sparks & Best mill had been built in 1855 in Staunton, 25 miles northeast; the others were in nearby towns. Aggregate capacity was 2000 cwt.

The other mills were closed in the course of time, the Alton mill was rebuilt in 1881 and 1922 and it attained 4000 cwt. capacity. In 1893 a mill of 2000 cwt. was acquired in Terre Haute, Ind.

Sparks Milling Co. was incorporated in 1887, and Captain Sparks was its president for the next 20 years. His successors were his son, Hosea B. (b. 1858 Ill., d. 1951) in 1907-29; his grandson, George S. Milnor (b. 1880 Ill., d. 1959) in 1929-30; and another son of the founder, William L. (b. 1867 Ill., d. 1952), in 1930-36. The mills were closed in 1936 and the company was liquidated. Part of the Alton mill was re-opened and used in 1943-45 for making alcohol grits by a partnership of George S. Milnor and Edwin M. Sparks (b. 1889 Ill., d. 1950), nephew of H. B. and W. L. Sparks.

Hosea B. Sparks was president of Millers' National Federation in 1911-12. George S. Milnor was general manager of Farmers' National Grain Corp. and other agencies created in 1930 for wheat market stabilization.

Stanard-Tilton Milling Co.—Eagle Steam Mill in St. Louis was purchased in 1857 from the Plants by Edwin O. Stanard (b. 1832 N. H., d. 1914). A few years later he also bought Alton City Mills, 20 miles up the Mississippi on the Illinois side.

The St. Louis mill was operated 18 years. The Alton mill was enlarged considerably and in 1902 a new plant of 4000 cwt. replaced the old mill. In 1892 Empire Mills of 500 cwt. in Dallas was purchased from the Alexander Cockrell estate and enlarged. In 1914 it was also replaced by a new mill of 4000 cwt. Headquarters was in St. Louis until 1934 and then was moved to Alton.

E. O. Stanard Milling Co., incorporated in 1882, became Stanard-Tilton Milling Co. in 1904, the Tilton being Edgar D. (b. 1852, d. 1917), son-in-law of E. O. Stanard. Presidents: E. O. Stanard in 1882-1914; his son, William K. (b. 1861 Mo., d. 1934) in 1914-34; the latter's son, Edwin T. (b. 1886 Mo.) in 1934-38; and Joseph R. Brown (b. 1881 Tenn.), son-in-law of W. K. Stanard, in 1938-41. The Texas mill was virtually a separate enterprise except for ownership, its management the last 20 years being vested in Brown and Daniel S. Donovan (b. 1873 La., d. 1953).

E. O. Stanard was Lieutenant Governor of Missouri in 1869-71 and a member of Congress in 1873-75.

Russell-Miller Milling Co. purchased Stanard-Tilton Milling Co. in 1941. The Dallas and Alton mills have continued in operation, the Alton mill being rebuilt after destruction by fire in 1946. Present total capacity of these plants is 21,400 cwt.

Aviston

Aviston Milling Co.—At Aviston, about 30 miles east of St. Louis, a small flour mill was built in 1866. Aviston Milling Co. was incorporated in 1894, and the mill was later enlarged to 1200 cwt. Paul C. Guignon (b. 1877 Mo.) joined the company in 1909 and obtained control ten years later. He was president in 1919-50. The mill was destroyed by fire in 1929, but the business has continued to the present through the distribution of flour milled by others.

Beardstown

Schultz, Baujan & Co.—Beardstown is on the Illinois River, 45 miles northwest of Springfield, and it was the site for a 400-cwt. flour mill built in 1875 by John Schultz (b. 1849 Germany, d. 1932). Another mill of about 800 cwt. that had preceded him in Beardstown became Schultz property about 1890. This was the Hagener Bros. mill which stood on the present plant site. After the purchase the original mill was abandoned.

The flour mill was doubled in size in 1910, and another unit was added in 1916. Fire destroyed a large part of the mill in 1917, and a new mill of 4000 cwt. was completed in 1918. Present capacity is 7500 cwt. The feed mill was opened in 1929 and its size is now 400 tons.

The business was a partnership for 64 years. It was known as J. Baujan during the early years and as Schultz, Baujan & Co. thereafter. John Baujan was Schultz' father-in-law; his sons Louis and Edward were in the business until 1910, when

their interests were purchased by Schultz. The principal partners for many years were Schultz, his sons, Edward E. (b. 1880
Ill., d. 1936) and Alfred G. (b. 1886 Ill., d. 1961), and his
son-in-law, Clarence J. (Deacon) White (b. 1880 Ill., d.
1937). Schultz, Baujan & Co. was incorporated in 1939, A.
G. Schultz becoming president.

The company was consolidated with Colorado Milling &
Elevator Co. in 1953, and the flour and feed mills have since
been operated under the name of Beardstown Mills. This unit
of the Colorado company is jointly managed by John J. White
(b. 1909 Ill.), son of C. J., and Robert H. Hommel, Jr. (b.
1912 Ind.), son-in-law of A. G. Schultz.

Chester

H. C. Cole Milling Co. holds the banner for longest continuous operation of a flour milling enterprise in the United
States by members of one family. The mill site in Chester, 70
miles southeast of St. Louis on the Mississippi, has been occupied by Cole mills since 1839. The 3000-cwt. mill produces
soft wheat flour chiefly for the southern family trade. Grain
storage is 850,000 bushels.

The original mill was enlarged to 500 cwt. in 1855 and
was rebuilt in 1883. The mill was destroyed by fire in 1915
and was replaced by a 1500-cwt. plant. This was doubled in
size a decade later.

Nathan Cole (d. 1840) was the founder. His son, Hermon
C. (b. 1814 N. Y., d. 1874) managed the business in its most
critical years, and when the company was incorporated in 1888
it was named in his honor. Company presidents: Harry C. (b.
1852 Ill., d. 1924), son of Hermon C., in 1888-1924; another
son, Charles B. (b. 1845 Ill., d. 1928), who managed the
business for almost 50 years, in 1924-28; their nephew, Aus-

tin Cole (b. 1876 Ill., d. 1957) in 1928-57; Austin, Jr. (b. 1902 Calif.) since 1957. Emery E. May (b. 1912 N. C.) has been general manager from 1955.

Gilster Milling Co., an affiliate of Martha White Mills, has a 1400-cwt. mill in Steeleville, 70 miles southeast of St. Louis, a 1500-cwt. mill in Trenton and a cake mix plant. Offices are in Chester. It is a family flour business. Grain storage totals 425,000 bushels.

The Steeleville mill dates back to 1859, and in 1875 H. F. Stinde became the owner. Twenty years later he sold the property to Albert H. Gilster (b. 1873 Ill., d. 1946), who organized Steeleville Milling Co. in 1900 and became its president. The mill was increased to 800 cwt. about that time and to 1400 cwt. in the late 1920's, when Gilster Milling Co. became the name. Gilster headed the business for 51 years, and his brother, Adolph L. (b. 1885 Ill., d. 1961), who had been associated from 1900, was president in 1946-61.

Major interest was acquired in 1961 by the Cohen Williams group, William H. Welge (b. 1902 Ill.) becoming president. The Gilster company acquired Trenton Milling Co. in 1962.

Chicago

Eckhart Milling Co. produces hard and soft wheat flour and rye flour. The mill is located on Chicago's West Side. Pneumatic conveying equipment was installed in 1961, and plant capacity is 7000 cwt. wheat flour and 1200 cwt. rye. Grain storage is 1,000,000 bushels. The company's flour business is chiefly with cracker and bread bakers in northern cities from Chicago eastward.

This enterprise had its origin in a wholesale flour business that was established in the early 1870's by Bernard A. Eckhart

(b. 1852 Germany, d. 1931) and James Swan. In 1884 they built a 1000-cwt. flour mill, and in the 1890's the mill was moved to its present location and increased in size. It was operated as a partnership until 1909, when B. A. Eckhart Milling Co. was incorporated. Eckhart had previously purchased the Swan interest from the latter's estate.

Eckhart was a noted figure in the milling industry. He led the movement which resulted in the organization of Millers' National Federation in 1902, and he was its first president, serving in 1902-04. He was the author of what was called the Eckhart plan, which set a safety factor on the millfeed allowance in computing flour prices. He also received many honors for services rendered to city, state and nation, and he had extensive interests in real estate and finance in Chicago.

The business was personally managed by Eckhart for many years. Edgar A. Weaver (b. 1876 Ind., d. 1958) served as general manager in 1914-41. Alfred Simandl (b. 1897 Wis.) succeeded to many of these duties in 1941-49. Donald H. Wilson (b. 1899 Neb.) has been executive vice president and general manager since 1949. Wilson served as president of Millers' National Federation in 1958-60.

Eckhart was company president in 1909-31. His son, Percy B. (b. 1877 Ill.), who headed one of the city's great law firms, was president in 1931-38 and board chairman since that time. Frank E. Church (b. 1882 Mich.) was president in 1938-50, and Thomas R. Coyne (b. 1908 Ill.), son-in-law of P. B. Eckhart, has held the office from 1950. Company name was changed in 1955 to Eckhart Milling Co.

Quaker Oats Co. operates world wide, and has plants in eleven nations on four continents. Best known as the premier producer of oat cereals, it is also one of the largest factors in formula feeds with four plants that have 4400 tons capacity, it is foremost among pet food makers, is first in pancake mixes and is the leading manufacturer of the furan group of chemicals which are derived from farm wastes such as corn cobs and straw. The company is the largest corn miller, operating five plants with 17,200 cwt. aggregate capacity, and in flour milling it has four plants—in St. Joseph, Los Angeles, Cedar Rapids and Sherman, Texas—that can produce 11,600 cwt. It has mill storage for 14,000,000 bushels of grain.

Quaker Oats Co. was chartered in 1901 as successor to American Cereal Co., which was formed twelve years earlier in a merger of several oatmeal companies. One of these was North Star Mills, Cedar Rapids, founded in 1873 by John Stuart and his son, Robert, and a Stuart has been at the Quaker Oats helm more than half the time since it was formed. Another of the merging units was German Mills American Cereal Co., established in 1856 in Akron by Ferdinand Schumacher, who became known as "The Oatmeal King." He had introduced oatmeal to the United States through his Akron grocery. Two years later he had an oatmeal mill in Akron, and in 1876 he began the production of animal feeds.

Schumacher's first plant was the Stone mill, built in 1832, and it was used for the production of both oatmeal and flour throughout its history. The original mill was replaced in 1909 by a new mill of 4000 cwt. The latter was used until 1926 when it was dismantled. Meanwhile the company had expanded its flour operations by adding a unit of 3000 cwt. to the Cedar Rapids cereal plant in 1917. Aunt Jemima Mills, its St. Joseph mill and famous brand for pancake flour, were purchased in 1925. G. B. R. Smith Milling Co. in Sherman was acquired from Commander Larabee Milling Co. in 1941, and V-O Milling Co. in Los Angeles from Max Viault in 1945. A considerable part of the company's flour output is used in the formulation of mixes, and it is also a substantial participant in the bakery and family flour trade.

Donold B. Lourie (b. 1899 Ala.) is chief executive officer. He was president in 1947-53 and in 1954-62, and is now board chairman. He served as Undersecretary of State in 1953-54. Colin S. Gordon (b. 1904 Ill.), who was executive vice president in 1952-62, is vice chairman. Robert D. Stuart, Jr. (b. 1916 Ill.), great-grandson of the North Star founder, was elected president in 1962. R. Douglas Stuart (b. 1886 Ill.), the new president's father, was president in 1942-47; he was Ambassador to Canada in 1953-56. His brother, John (b. 1877 Iowa), was president in 1922-42.

Star & Crescent Milling Co.—Within two blocks of Chicago's loop a flour mill stood until early in the twentieth century. This was the 2000-cwt. plant of Star & Crescent Milling Co., built in 1867 on the west bank of the Chicago River between Randolph and Washington Streets. The business was established and the company largely owned by Clinton F. Briggs.

The mill was torn down in 1902 when the city took the site as part of a river-widening project. Briggs then built a new Star & Crescent mill of 6000 cwt. on the Calumet River, about 10 miles south of the loop. The mill was purchased in 1922 by Washburn Crosby Co., and has been operated for the past 40 years by that company and its successor, General Mills, Inc. Present capacity is 8200 cwt.

Briggs was president of Star & Crescent Milling Co. until 1904, followed by Robert S. Johnston, a Pittsburgh steel man, to 1912. William L. Phelps (b. 1868 Ohio, d. 1923), son-in-law of Briggs, was president in 1912-22. Frank B. Rice (b. 1860 Wis., d. 1939) was vice president and general manager in 1906-22.

East St. Louis

Hezel Milling Co.—First built in 1865 and rebuilt after destruction by tornado in 1896, Hezel Milling Co. operated a 1000-cwt. mill in East St. Louis. It was family-owned, and Charles J. Hezel (d. 1932) was the last president and manager. The mill was closed in 1931 and the property foreclosed in 1932.

Edwardsville

Blake Milling Co.—As early as 1832 there was a flour mill in Edwardsville, about 25 miles northeast of St. Louis, and four mills operated there simultaneously for a time after the Civil War. During the early years of this century, Charles J. Rock was president of Edwardsville Milling Co. This company's plant was sold in 1914 to Thomas F. Blake (b. 1872 Kan., d. 1918), who had been associated with the Maneys in Oklahoma and Omaha. He organized Blake Milling Co. and enlarged the plant to 1600 cwt. Frank T. Jacobi was manager after Blake's death. The mill was burned out in 1926.

Evansville

Sauers Milling Co.—The first mill in Evansville, a village 50 miles southeast of St. Louis, was built in 1854 by John Wehlheim and Cadwell Evans. It became the property a few years later of Philip Sauer, and still later of his son, William (b. 1845 Ill., d. 1921). It was rebuilt and enlarged to 1400 cwt. by William's sons, Philip E. (b. 1873 Ill., d. 1940) and George N. (b. 1879 Ill., d. 1946). The mill was dismantled in 1949.

Freeburg

Reichert Milling Co.—Joseph Reichert (b. 1830 Germany, d. 1903) established a flour mill in 1862 in Freeburg, 25 miles southeast of St. Louis. Reichert Milling Co. was incorporated in 1887. The original mill was destroyed by fire in 1898 and was replaced by a plant of 1400 cwt.

The founder headed the company until shortly before his death, and he was succeeded as owner and president by his son, William J. (b. 1864 Ill., d. 1943). After the latter's time, his son, William C. (b. 1897 Ill., d. 1959) was president. The flour mill was increased to 2300 cwt. in later years, but was closed in 1949.

Highland

Highland Milling Co.—Charles H. Seybt (b. 1840 Germany, d. 1918) was president of Millers' National Insurance Co. for 42 years, and was a leader of national stature in mill mutual insurance. He entered the milling business in 1875 by buying the mill of his father-in-law, Joseph Suppiger, in Highland, 25 miles east of St. Louis. He operated this 1000-cwt. plant the remainder of his days. Martin Huber (b. 1877, d. 1932) followed Seybt, but his attempt to launch a household cake flour business ended in bankruptcy in 1931.

Lebanon

Pfeffer Milling Co.—The Pfeffers were distillers in Lebanon, 25 miles east of St. Louis, until 1889. They then acquired the 800-cwt. plant of the famous Veranda Milling Co., founded in 1857, and Pfeffer Milling Co. was formed. The mill was later enlarged to 1000 cwt. and 900 cwt. corn meal. It operated until 1956.

Christian Pfeffer (b. 1824 Germany, d. 1896) was president in 1889-92; his son, Louis L. (b. 1862 Ohio, d. 1924) in 1892-1919; another son, Edward S. (b. 1871 Ohio, d. 1932) in 1920-32; and Harold S. (b. 1889 Ill.), son of Louis L., in 1932-56. In this concern, the secretary-treasurer was virtually the manager, and the post was held in 1889-1924 by Christian J. Pfeffer (b. 1857 Ohio, d. 1924), the founder's son; and in 1924-56 by William C. Pfeffer (b. 1882 Ill.), son of Christian J.

Mascoutah

Ph. H. Postel Milling Co.—About 75 years ago there were seven flour mills in Mascoutah, all operating on local wheat, and no less than 250 men in the town were employed as teamsters to haul flour to boat landings on the Mississippi River whence it was shipped south. Mascoutah is 25 miles southeast of St. Louis, in the heart of the great wheat country of Southern Illinois.

Conrad and Philip Eisenmayer took in a new partner in their Mascoutah grist mill in 1841—their cousin, Philip H. Postel (b. 1818 Germany, d. 1907). Seven years later Postel and another cousin, Andrew Eisenmayer, formed the partnership of Postel & Eisenmayer, and in 1851 they completed a new and larger mill. In 1873 Postel became sole owner.

Ph. H. Postel Milling Co. was organized in 1886, and the founder was president the remainder of his life, but management was in the hands of his sons—Philip H., Jr. (b. 1850 Ill., d. 1916), George (b. 1852 Ill., d. 1915) and Julius (b. 1862 Ill., d. 1933). Philip H., Jr., and Julius headed the company for a few years each, and George's son, Philip H., III (b. 1890 Ill., d. 1948), was president and manager in 1921-48.

The company attained great prestige in the soft wheat trade in the lower Mississippi Valley. The mill was of 1000 cwt.

capacity in later years. After the elevator was damaged by fire in 1948 the mill was closed.

Conrad Eisenmayer, who operated a mill in nearby Summerfield for many years, beginning in 1848, became the father-in-law of the famous Bernhard Warkentin, and much later was identified with mills in Kansas.

Murphysboro

Reliance Milling Co.—The great tornado of 1925 destroyed the 1000-cwt. mill of Reliance Milling Co., in Murphysboro, 85 miles southeast of St. Louis. It had been owned from 1912 by Murry M. Dean and his four sons, who also had a mill in nearby Ava. Homer K. Dean was head of the business, James L. (b. 1890 Ill.) the manager of Reliance. The mill was built before 1900 and was operated as Jackson County Milling Co., first by a Mr. Clay and then by Sauer Bros.

Southern Illinois Milling Co. — Production of flour by Southern Illinois Milling Co. ceased in 1940, and its 1200-cwt. mill was turned into a feed plant by Samuel O. Bizzell (b. 1905 Ill.) who had managed the flour mill through the 1930's. This mill stood on a site where Philip Eisenmayer ran a mill from 1843 to 1884; his nephews later became prominent in Missouri milling. Some years after Eisenmayer's time his mill was owned and operated by Charles A. Wall (b. 1868 Ill., d. 1924) and his son, Willard, and then it was acquired by the owners of Pinckneyville Milling Co.

Nashville

Huegely Milling Co.—One of several flour mills in Nashville, 50 miles southeast of St. Louis, was that owned by the Huegely family. It reached 1000 cwt., and was managed in later years by J. Homer Huegely. After the early 1930's the mill operated only intermittently and was destroyed by fire in 1936.

O'Fallon

Charles Tiedemann Milling Co.—The mills in O'Fallon and Collinsville, towns about 20 miles east of St. Louis, were established in the 1880's by Charles Tiedemann, and had total capacity of 1600 cwt. They were operated in later years by George J. Freivogel (b. 1866, d. 1932) and George W. Tiedemann (b. 1874, d. 1951), the latter a son of the founder. The mills ran but little after 1930 and became idle by 1940.

Pinckneyville

Pinckneyville Milling Co.—City Flouring Mills, founded in 1871 by John Schulze, later became Pinckneyville Milling Co. At one time it was owned by the Ismerts and the Hinckes, who became famous in Kansas milling. The mill had 1000 cwt. capacity. It was managed for years by Henry Dreimeyer. At that time it was owned by the Zacher family, and Arthur Zacher was the last manager. The mill ran sparingly after the middle 1930's and ceased to operate by 1950.

Pittsfield

M. D. King Milling Co.—Pike county had 17 flour mills in 1873, largest of which was the 200-cwt. plant built four years before by Clark P. Chapman (b. 1824 Mass., d. 1898). The business was conducted as C. P. Chapman & Co. until 1898, and as Dow & King to 1909. Augustus Dow was a partner for 37 years, beginning in 1872.

Myron D. King (b. 1849 Mass., d. 1931), son-in-law of Chapman, entered the firm in 1876. The first mill was destroyed by fire in 1898, and a new 1200-cwt. mill was built. M. D. King Milling Co. was incorporated in 1909. Its presidents: M. D. King in 1909-31; his son, Lyndle C. (b. 1879 Ill., d. 1955) in 1931-37; his grandson, Vinton S. King, Jr. (b. 1907 Ill., d. 1942) in 1937-42; the latter's brother, Myron D. King II (b. 1912 Ill.) since 1942.

The flour mill was closed in 1950, and the company has continued in feed manufacturing and the grain business.

Red Bud

C. Becker Milling Co.—The partnership of Eggers and Becker first had a mill in St. Louis, and then one also in Red Bud, 40 miles southeast. In 1894 the partnership was dissolved, and Conrad Becker (b. 1850 Germany, d. 1912) became sole owner of the 400-cwt. Red Bud mill. It was enlarged about 1905 to 800 cwt., about 1915 to 1200 cwt., and to 1600 cwt. in the early 1940's. The mill operated until 1952.

Presidents of C. Becker Milling Co. were Conrad Becker in 1894-1912; his son, Herman C. (b. 1876 Mo., d. 1947) in 1912-47; the latter's son, Conrad F. (b. 1905 Ill.), in 1947-52. Conrad F. Becker served two terms as Illinois State Treasurer.

Teutopolis

Siemer Milling Co. is now the only flour mill between St. Louis and Indianapolis on the Pennsylvania Railroad, although at one time there were nearly two score. The business began in 1882 as Hope Roller Mills, owned by Clem Uptmor and managed by his son-in-law, Joseph Siemer (b. 1855 Ohio, d. 1927). In 1906 Siemer bought out the other Uptmor heirs, and the enterprise has since been known as Siemer Milling Co. Siemer's son, Clem J. (b. 1884 Ill., d. 1960), became the owner in

1927, and in 1944 he formed a partnership with his children. Siemer Milling Co. was incorporated in 1960, with Quintin A. Siemer (b. 1914 Ill.), son of Clem J., as president. The company operates a feed mill of 100 tons and a 900-cwt. pneumatic flour mill.

Trenton

Trenton Milling Co.—Centennial Mills was established in 1874 by Peter Emig in Trenton, 30 miles east of St. Louis, and the mill was later operated by John Dugger and then by Joseph Hanke. Trenton Milling Co. was incorporated in 1895, with Sebastian Hammel (b. 1840 Ill., d. 1932) and Louis C. Reimann (b. 1866 Ill., d. 1956) as the principal owners. The mill then had 500 cwt. capacity, which was increased to 1000 cwt. in 1911 and to 1500 cwt. in 1947.

Hammel was president to 1920, followed to 1934 by Reimann. A. Brink Hammel (b. 1874 Ill., d. 1939), son of the co-founder and general manager from 1911, became president in 1934-39, and his son, Richard K. (b. 1911 Ill.), was president in 1939-62. Harold E. Yoder (b. 1913 Ind.) was general manager in 1957-62.

The business was acquired in 1962 by Gilster Milling Co., an affiliate of Martha White Mills.

Waterloo

Monroe Milling Co.—Waterloo, 25 miles south of St. Louis, was a flour mill town for 93 years, and for two-thirds of that time the Koenigsmarks were the mill operators. A succession of small mills, beginning in 1858, was followed by the 2000-cwt. Chouteau & Edwards Co. plant, built in 1881, but it was destroyed by fire three years later.

Thomas Koenigsmark (b. 1835 Austria, d. 1911), who had been running a small mill in nearby Columbia for a decade, then bought the site and built a 1000-cwt. plant. Koenigsmark Mill Co. was organized in 1904, with the founder as president and his son, Jacob J. (b. 1858 Ill., d. 1924) as vice president. The latter became president a few years later.

Monroe Milling Co. was a merger of Koenigsmark Mill Co. and two smaller neighboring mills in 1924, a third being added later. Total capacity was about 2400 cwt. The smaller plants were used only a few years, the Waterloo mill remaining in production until 1948. Milling manager of the company through most of the intervening years was Conrad H. Koenigsmark (b. 1885 Ill.), son of Jacob. His brother, Alois J. (b. 1883 Ill.), was president, but was largely occupied with other business.

INDIANA

Wheat production in Indiana began with the first settlers, and it is believed that grist mills were established in the Ohio River country not long after the dawn of the nineteenth century. Wheat has continued to be grown in a substantial way in practically every county of the state. This was also true in pioneer days, and in consequence Indiana had a large number of mills. The 1900 census reported 645 wheat flour mills in the state. Their number was 24 in 1958.

Hoosier flour mills produced 4,753,000 cwt. of flour in 1961.

Evansville

Akin-Erskine Milling Co.—William A. Akin, a meat packer, and his son-in-law, Wilbur N. Erskine (b. 1863 Ind., d. 1933), bought a small mill in 1897 and formed Akin-Erskine

Milling Co. The plant was soon enlarged to 1300 cwt., and rebuilt larger after it was burned in 1906. Size was increased in 1914 to 5000 cwt., making it one of the largest mills then in the southern family trade.

The great wheat market decline in 1920-21 carried the company into bankruptcy. Two years later Erskine resumed milling in one unit, but only for a short time. The plant was sold in 1924 by creditors to Kelsay-Burns Milling Co., a concern organized by men of those names, but within their first month of operation the mill was destroyed by fire.

Igleheart Bros., Inc.—For two full generations the Igle-hearts did the predominant volume of cake flour business throughout the nation. They were the first to put cake flour on the market, and their successor is still the largest producer of cake flour, exclusive of mixes, for the household trade.

Levi Igleheart built a 400-cwt. mill in Evansville in 1856. From a local trade it expanded gradually into southern markets, but for almost 40 years it had little to distinguish it from most other soft wheat mills. In 1895, Levi's son, Addison W. (b. 1852 Ind., d. 1927), launched the product that made the company famous. The very short patent flour was marketed in small packages—an unusual thing for flour at that time. It was first advertised nationally in 1898. The volume grew steadily, and the original plant was replaced by a 1000-cwt. mill in 1905. When this mill was destroyed by fire four years later, it was succeeded by a mill of 3000 cwt.

The sons of Levi Igleheart ran the business for many years. The company was incorporated in 1892. Addison W. was president in 1892-1904, and Leslie T. (b. 1848 Ind., d. 1930) in 1904-26. John L. (b. 1863 Ind., d. 1933) was general manager for many years prior to his presidency in 1926-33.

Igleheart Bros., Inc. was acquired by General Foods Corp. in 1926. Management of the company (later converted into a General Foods division) continued in Igleheart hands, with Edgar A. (b. 1891 Ind., d. 1962), son of Leslie T., as president in 1933-43. He was followed in 1943-54 by Earl J. Heseman (b. 1899 Ind.), the title being changed in 1950 to general manager. Then followed Raymond P. Ramming (b. 1896 Ind., d. 1962) in 1955-59 and William B. Dress (b. 1905 Ind.) since 1959. Austin Igleheart (b. 1889 Ind.), son of John L., was president of General Foods Corp. in 1943-53.

A series of mill purchases added to the company's plant capacity. Phoenix Flour Mill, Evansville, 2000 cwt., was acquired in 1926; Atlas Mills, Vincennes, 800 cwt., in 1927; Dunlop Milling Co., Clarksville, Tenn., 2400 cwt., in 1930; and Collins Flour Mills, Pendleton, Ore., 1500 cwt., in 1940 (leased 1937). The Phoenix and Atlas mills were closed in 1949, Dunlop in 1956. Present capacity: Evansville 4300 cwt., Pendleton 2800 cwt. Elevator storage is 4,000,000 bushels.

Charles Nunn & Sons Milling Co. is a family enterprise owned by a father, two sons and two daughters. All four members of the second generation are active in the management of the business. In such respects it resembles many flour mills of several generations ago, but it most others it is wholly unlike them.

Charles E. Nunn (b. 1874 Ky.), who had been a miller in his home state, took over a small idle mill on the outskirts of Evansville in 1926. This has grown into an establishment that embraces a flour mill of 800 cwt., corn mill of 600 cwt., and feed plant of 250 tons. It serves the family trade exclusively, chiefly in an area within a radius of a hundred miles. The business is a partnership of Nunn and his sons, Lockett C. (b.

1905 Ky.) and Dorris J. (b. 1907 Ky.), and his daughters, Aline Renner and Rebecca Couth, with D. J. Nunn as the manager.

Phoenix Flour Mill.—On the Evansville waterfront was Canal Mills, owned by Nicolas Elles, and in 1875 Jacob L. Knauss (b. 1850 Ill., d. 1937) bought a half-interest. When Elles died in 1885, Knauss organized Phoenix Flour Mill to take over the business. He headed this enterprise more than 40 years. In 1895 a new 500-cwt. mill was built on rail trackage, it was increased in 1911 to 2000 cwt., and Phoenix became a prominent factor in the southern family trade. The mill was sold in 1926 to Postum Cereal Co., which became General Foods Corp. It was operated until 1949. Otto A. Knauss (b. 1890 Ind.), who had been associated with his father, was in the Igleheart Division of General Foods until 1944.

Sunnyside Milling Co.—George T. Brose (b. 1847, d. 1918) was in the milling business for 50 years in Evansville, having an interest in several mills there. In 1918 he sold a 1000-cwt. mill to August Ellerbush and Eugene Pfafflin, who operated it only a year or so before it became idle.

Charles T. Johnson and associates bought the former Brose mill in 1922 and organized Sunnyside Milling Co. Johnson was president, and the manager was his son-in-law, Ralph H. Missman (b. 1889 Ill.). The mill operated for more than 20 years, but was closed in 1943.

Fort Wayne

Mayflower Mills operates a 2800-cwt. plant that is used chiefly for the production of soft wheat bakery flour. The com-

pany has 250,000 bushels of elevator space. It has been managed by members of the Bash family throughout its history.

The first mill had 200 cwt. and was built in 1887 by Solo-
mon Bash. It was increased to 600 cwt. in 1908, but was destroyed by fire in 1911. It was rebuilt with 1000 cwt. capacity,
and increased in 1956 and 1961 to the present size.

Mayflower Mills was incorporated in 1889. Harry Bash
(b. 1871 Ind., d. 1936), son of the founder, became president
and manager in 1895. His son, Edward (b. 1907 Ind.) took
over in 1936, and was followed by another son, David W. (b.
1910 Ind.) in 1958. Robert Bash (b. 1918 Ind.), also a son
of Harry, is secretary-treasurer.

Goshen

Goshen Milling Co.—Goshen, near South Bend, had a
1400-cwt. flour mill that was operated by F. E. C. Hawks for
many years. His connection with it began about 1888. The mill
was known as Hawks & Gartner before Goshen Milling Co.
was incorporated in 1923. The mill was closed two years or
so later.

Grandview

Cadick Milling Co.—Denby E. Cadick (b. 1861 Ind., d.
1953) had a business career of 71 years, all but five in flour
milling. His father, William (b. 1833 Jamaica, d. 1912),
bought a grist mill in 1881 in Grandview, 35 miles east of
Evansville. The mill was later enlarged, and for a time it
was operated by the partnership of Cadick & Craig. Incorporation of Cadick Milling Co. took place in 1900, and Denby
E. Cadick was president for the next 53 years. The Ohio River
was the means employed during the early years to ship flour
to southern markets, and it was not until 1911 that a railroad

reached the plant. At that time the mill was rebuilt, with 1000 cwt. The company ceased to mill flour in 1948.

Greensburg

Garland Mills, Inc.—Greensburg, between Indianapolis and Cincinnati, has had a flour mill on the same site for 94 years. The first mill had 400 cwt. capacity when erected by Isaac Emmert in 1869. It was rebuilt in 1883 and again in 1920, when it was rated at 1000 cwt. It was enlarged in recent years to 1500 cwt.

Garland Milling Co. was incorporated in 1898 by R. P. Moore. In 1908 John F. Russell (b. 1870 Ind., d. 1943) began 35 years of service as president. Will H. Lanham (b. 1882 Ind., d. 1957) was president in 1943-48, but had been manager during the preceding decade.

Garland Mills, Inc. was formed in 1948 by Orland A. Church (b. 1895 Ill., d. 1955) and Ray F. Sopher (b. 1890 Pa., d. 1962), who purchased the business at that time. Church was president in 1948-55 and Sopher, who was an operative miller for 50 years, in 1955-57. The plant was sold in 1957 to Nebraska Consolidated Mills Co., and is operated by that company.

Indianapolis

Acme-Evans Co., a division of General Grain, Inc., operates a flour mill of 7000 cwt., corn mill of 1000 cwt., feed plant of 500 tons and 1,750,000 bushels of elevator space. Its parent company has 16,750,000 bushels. Acme-Evans is a leading miller of soft wheat bakery flour but mills other types as well.

First flour mill in the vicinity of the present Acme-Evans site, near the historic National Road crossing over White River, was built in 1821 by Isaac Wilson, a Revolutionary soldier.

In 1832 James Blake built a mill on the present site, but the Blake mill later burned. Hoosier State Mill was erected on the same ground in 1852, and it was acquired in 1878 by George T. Evans and D. A. Richardson. Evans purchased the Richardson interest in 1893 and operated as George T. Evans & Son.

John Carlisle built a mill in 1841 near the Blake mill. It passed through several hands before its purchase in the 1870's by Samuel F. Robinson, who organized Acme Milling Co. His heirs sold the company in 1898 to Arthur Gillett.

The Evans and Gillett properties were consolidated in 1909 as Acme-Evans Co. The combined plants had 4000 cwt., which was increased to 7000 cwt. after the Acme unit was destroyed by fire in 1917. Other companies were absorbed— Blanton Milling Co. in 1924, Noblesville Milling Co. in 1941 and Blish Milling Co. in 1949, but only the Blish plant was operated and that for but two years. Acme-Evans interests acquired several large grain companies in the 1940's, and all were merged in 1962 as General Grain, Inc.

George T. Evans and Arthur Gillett lived only a few months after the consolidation. Edgar H. Evans (b. 1870 N. Y., d. 1954), son of George T., was president in 1909-33; he was the last surviving founder of Millers' National Federation and was its president in 1931-32. Later Acme-Evans presidents were Isaac E. Woodard (b. 1883 Ind., d. 1958) in 1933-45, Evans' son-in-law, Samuel R. Harrell (b. 1897 Ind.) in 1945-49, and William H. Bowman (b. 1900 Mo.) since 1949. John A. Reis (b. 1881 Ohio, d. 1949), vice president, also attained industry prominence.

Blanton Milling Co.—Members of the Blanton family established a mill in Indianapolis in the 1890's, and the business was incorporated in 1906 as Blanton Milling Co. The mill eventually reached about 1000 cwt. capacity. The business was sold in 1924 to Acme-Evans Co., which did not operate the mill but retained Blanton as a trade name. The last officers were Alexander J. Blanton, president, and Forrest W. Blanton, secretary-treasurer.

Lawrenceburg

Lawrenceburg Roller Mills Co.—The first Indiana town downriver from Cincinnati had a bankrupt mill that was purchased in 1897 by a Boston group headed by Bernard J. Rothwell. They organized Lawrenceburg Roller Mills Co., and for six years the 2400-cwt. plant made shipments exclusively to Great Britain and Ireland. In 1903, the company entered the domestic market, principally New England and the South. The mill was enlarged to 3600 cwt. before 1900 and to 5000 cwt. in 1930. It was destroyed by fire in 1941.

John T. Sheriff (d. 1930) was manager in 1897-1903. His successor was George H. Lewis (b. 1866 Wales, d. 1921), an operative miller who became prominent in the industry. Frank Hutchinson (b. 1886 Ind.) was manager the last 20 years, and after the fire he purchased the elevators and engaged in the grain business. He was also prominent, and served as president of Millers' National Federation in 1932-33. Rothwell, who kept his office in Boston, was president for all but one year of the company's history; in 1940, he was succeeded by his son, Paul T.

The first Lawrenceburg mill was established in 1852 by Lewis & Eikelburger. This firm was succeeded some years later by G. Y. Root Co., which was wrecked by wheat speculation.

Ligonier

Lyon & Greenleaf Co. is in Ligonier, midway between Fort Wayne and South Bend. The soft wheat mill of 1800 cwt. serves bakery trade in the Middle West. The company also has 600,000 bushels of grain storage. It originated in Wauseon, Ohio, about 1870, and the mill there was operated until 1928, Ligonier being acquired meanwhile. Head for many years was Graham S. Lyon (b. 1887 Ohio, d. 1951), whose father founded the business. He was succeeded by his son-in-law, Lyle E. Schuman.

Mount Vernon

Fuhrer-Ford Mill Co., Inc. is farthest east of the Vanier milling enterprises. The 2000-cwt. pneumatic mill stands on the bank of the Ohio River, and much of its product moves to market via water transportation.

The present concern dates only to 1958, but Fuhrer milling history goes back to the late 1870's, when William C. Fuhrer (b. 1837 Pa., d. 1916) established Mount Vernon Mill & Elevator Co. It was lost to fire a few years later, and in 1890 a new mill was built by Fuhrer and Frank E. Kauffman of St. Louis. It, too, was lost to fire in 1898, and the following year Fuhrer-Ford Milling Co. was organized and a 1000-cwt. mill erected. This is the present plant, but enlarged after the business was purchased in 1958 by John J. Vanier.

Fuhrer-Ford presidents: W. C. Fuhrer in 1899-1916; William C. Ford in 1916-23; Eugene H. Fuhrer (b. 1863 Ind., d. 1943), son of the founder, in 1923-43; Harry C. Ford in 1943-52; Malcolm W. Fuhrer (b. 1892 Ind.), son of Eugene H., in 1952-58; Vanier since 1958. The business was managed for many years by M. W. Fuhrer before his retirement. Manager since 1960 is James V. Otto (b. 1923 Kan.).

Home Mill & Grain Co.—Adding calcium phosphate to flour was devised about 1915 at Home Mill & Grain Co., the first mill to employ a practice which soon became widespread for the southern family flour trade.

Charles T. Johnson (b. 1866 Tenn., d. 1933) had several grain-buying stations in the Mount Vernon area before he established a mill there in 1899. Ownership of the mill was shared by Johnson and several men in the town. Johnson managed the 1200-cwt. mill, and also later for a time the smaller Sunlight Milling Co. In 1922 he became president of Sunnyside Milling Co., Evansville, the manager of which was Ralph H. Missman. Johnson was one of the best-known soft wheat millers of his era. His successor at the Home mill was Ivan Q. Field (b. 1888 Ky., d. 1943) and then Carl L. Blesch. The mill was closed in 1950.

Noblesville

Noblesville Milling Co.—Nordyke & Marmon Co., mill builders and Equipment Manufacturers, put a 200-cwt. mill in Noblesville, 20 miles north of Indianapolis, in 1892. It was used for experimental and demonstration purposes, attracting engineers and students from many countries. Early in this century the mill was enlarged to 2400-cwt., and became a commercial enterprise although still used experimentally until into the 1930's.

Noblesville Milling Co. was owned largely by Nordyke & Marmon Co. until after the latter disposed of its mill business. Daniel W. Marmon and then Walter C. Marmon (b. 1872 Ind., d. 1940) served as presidents, followed by Orland A. Church, a relative of W. C. Marmon, in 1939-41.

John Hollowell was the first company manager. David C. Anderson (b. 1867 Ireland, d. 1942) held sway in 1895-1909, before going on to manage and eventually control National Milling Co. He was followed in 1909-31 by Charles B. Jenkins (b. 1866 Ohio, d. 1956), and he by his son, Don B. (b. 1888 Ohio) in 1931-41.

The mill was closed in 1941, after its sale to Acme-Evans Co. Don B. Jenkins and Church became Acme-Evans executives.

Seymour

Blish Milling Co.—Two centuries and seven generations after Abraham Blish ran a grist mill on Cape Cod, John H. Blish entered into a milling partnership in 1858 with his father-in-law, Captain Meedy W. Shields, in Seymour, midway between Indianapolis and Louisville. The mill had been built more than 40 years earlier, in 1816, by the captain's father, James Shields. It continued in Blish hands until 1885, when the 200-cwt. mill was destroyed by fire.

Blish Milling Co. was incorporated in 1886 to operate a new 300-cwt. mill. This plant grew rapidly and it attained 2400-cwt. size after the turn of the century. It was a prominent factor in soft wheat milling. The company head for 36 years was Meedy S. Blish (b. 1859 Ind., d. 1922), son of J. H. Blish, followed by his longtime associate and brother, Tipton S. (b. 1865 Ind., d. 1927) in 1922-27. A distant cousin, J. Lewis Davis (b. 1876 Mont., d. 1942), was president in 1927-42, then John L. Blish (b. 1901 Ind., d. 1945), son of M. S., in 1942-45, and Edwin A. Blish (b. 1908 Ind., d. 1960), son of Tipton S., in 1945-49. Tipton S. Blish was president of Millers' National Federation in 1924-25.

The plant reached 4000 cwt. capacity in its later years. The business was sold in 1949 to Acme-Evans Co., which operated the plant about two years. It has been idle since 1951.

IOWA

Jefferson Davis, then a lieutenant in the United States Army, built the first flour mill ever to operate in Iowa. That was in 1831, the locale being on the Yellow River in the extreme northeastern part of the state. The first privately-owned mill in Iowa was established in 1833 at Millville, also in the Northeast. Grist mills were common in Iowa before the Civil War and increased rapidly in the 1870's when for four years the Hawkeye State was first in wheat production and in one year harvested more than 44,000,000 bushels. Iowa had 502 mills of all kinds in 1870, two-thirds of which may have produced flour; and as late as 1900 there were 379 mills that ground wheat, even though meanwhile corn had taken over nearly all the Iowa wheat acreage. In 1958 the state had 10 mills.

Two of Iowa's most famous governors were millers. Samuel J. Kirkwood (b. 1813 Md., d. 1894) ran a community mill near Iowa City; he was governor in 1860-64 and 1876-77, United States Senator in 1866-67 and 1877-81 and Secretary of the Interior in President Garfield's cabinet. William Larrabee (b. 1832 Conn., d. 1912), whose mill was at Clermont, Northeast Iowa, was governor in 1886-90 after serving 20 years in the state senate.

Iowa flour production in 1961 was 6,231,000 cwt.

Des Moines

Inland Mills, Inc., a member of the Vanier chain of companies, is located within a mile of the Iowa State House. The plant of 6000 cwt. produces hard wheat bakery flour. Elevator space totals 2,500,000 bushels.

The early history of this mill reads like a series of heartbreaks. The 600-cwt. mill of Shannon & Mott was enlarged fourfold in 1919. During the next nine years the business operated under five names and ten managements and survived two receiverships and two other reorganizations. From Shannon & Mott it went through Bast-Fogarty Milling Co. and Falcon Milling Co. and Red Crown Milling Co., until in 1928 it became Inland Milling Co. That was after its purchase by the Hubbells, Des Moines capitalists. Albert L. Goetzmann was manager in 1928-30.

J. Dolliver Kent (b. 1892 Iowa), a Hubbell associate with grain experience, became president and manager in 1930, leaving ten years later to head an insurance company. His successor was Clarence S. Chase (b. 1886 Kan., d. 1958), long engaged in milling in his native state. Guy C. Grimes (b. 1902 Iowa, d. 1953) followed Chase in 1942 and continued in charge after the Vanier interests bought the property in 1945. Aubrey A. Cavey (b. 1906 Neb.) has been manager since 1953.

LeMars

Plymouth Milling Co.—LeMars is in Northwestern Iowa, close to the South Dakota border, and a couple of generations ago it was the location of an active flour mill. Plymouth Roller Mills opened for business in 1884, and was managed for many years by William L. Smiley (b. 1859 N. Y., d. 1914). The Wernli family was one of the principal owners, and Charles A. Wernli (b. 1863 Wis., d. 1935) then became head of the business, which meanwhile had become known as Plymouth Milling Co. Milling of flour came to an end in 1920, and the company operated a corn mill thereafter.

Sheldon

Scott Logan Milling Co.—The mill established about 1885 by Scott Logan (b. 1851, d. 1922) had 1400 cwt. capacity. He sold the property in 1920 to Charles E. Richards, who operated the mill until the latter part of the decade.

Sioux City

Mystic Milling Co.—A flour mill of 1000 cwt. was built in Sioux City about 1890 by Great Western Cereal Co., and was operated by that company, by Sioux City Milling Co., and later by Mystic Milling Co. The plant was purchased in 1920 by International Milling Co. The mill ran until 1947, when it was destroyed by fire.

Waterloo

Waterloo & Cedar Falls Union Mill Co.—Two mills in Waterloo—the Cedar, dating from 1868, and the City, built a few years later — and two in adjoining Cedar Falls — the Miner, founded about 1856, and the Dayton, built in 1871— all became the property of Waterloo & Cedar Falls Union Mill Co., which operated them for many years. Their total capacity was about 3000 cwt. Roger Leavitt (b. 1860 Iowa, d. 1935) was president, and until 1920 William J. Peddicord was manager. The latter was succeeded by Glenn C. Bown (b. 1890 Iowa), who became a feed manufacturer when the mills were closed in 1924.

KANSAS

Kansas leads all the states in flour production by a wide margin, just as it does in wheat. The 1961 output of Kansas mills was 42,395,000 cwt., almost 50 per cent more than New York, the second state.

First mill in Kansas was a primitive affair, built in 1852 near Kansas City by Matthias Splitlogs, an Indian. First mill in which flour was bolted was built near Lawrence in 1857 by John Willey, Jr.

Mennonite settlers who came to Kansas in large numbers from Russia, beginning in 1873, brought with them the Turkey Red wheat that made the Sunflower State famous both in wheat and in milling. Until then hard red winter wheat was unknown in America. In the course of two decades the new variety spread all over the Southwest, and now almost two-thirds of the nation's wheat crop consists of hard red winter.

The Kansas milling industry was long characterized by a large number of merchant mills of moderate size. At the end of the first World War the state had 82 mills with capacities of 1000 cwt. or more, but fewer than a dozen of them exceeded 3000 cwt. The great output of the present era comes from 30 mills of commercial size. In 1900 there were 307 mills in Kansas that ground wheat, and in 1958 there were but 37 in the state.

Abilene

Abilene Flour Mills Co. operates a flour mill of 3900 cwt. and 3,700,000 bushels of grain storage. It is located in Abilene, 25 miles east of Salina. The company's flour business is divided between the family and the bakery trade in the Southeast and Midwest.

Abilene Flour Mills Co. is descended from City Mills, built in 1879 by Peter Marx. This mill was sold in 1882 to Park J. Stoddard and Edwin D. Humphrey, and they operated as Stoddard & Humphrey and then as Abilene Mill & Elevator Co. Later P. J. Flenner became the owner. After the mill was destroyed by fire in 1901, it was rebuilt with 800 cwt. capacity by Flenner and Henry Glade and was known as Abilene Milling Co. Engle Bros. acquired the company in 1907, but they went out of business seven years later.

John L. Rodney and Randall W. Arndt formed Abilene Flour Mills Co. in 1915 and bought the idle mill, Rodney being president and Arndt manager. The plant was increased to 1800 cwt., and mills in Warrensburg, Mo., and Kansas City were purchased. Arndt sold his interest in 1918, and T. Lester Welsh (b. 1886 Mo.) became manager. After Rodney's death, the Abilene company was separated from the other enterprises.

Welsh was elected president in 1922 and has held the office more than 40 years, also owning the controlling interest. The mill was expanded by stages to its present size. The plant of Security Flour Mills Co. was leased in 1944 and later purchased by the principals of Abilene Flour Mills Co., and operated as Security Milling Co., Inc. until 1953. Ronald B. (Chick) Laing (b. 1895 Okla.) who joined the company in 1925, has been general manager since 1953.

Mid West Milling Co.—Randall W. Arndt (b. 1856 Wis., d. 1922), who had managed Southwestern Milling Co. and then was associated briefly with Abilene Flour Mills Co., built a 1200-cwt. mill in Abilene in 1917. He formed R. W. Arndt & Co., which was renamed Mid West Milling Co. The mill was later owned by G. A. Rogers, and L. L. Peters was the last manager before it was destroyed by fire in 1927.

Security Flour Mills Co.—In 1884 Alfred W. Rice and John Johntz set up Johntz & Rice Mill Co., and built a 200-cwt. flour mill in Abilene. The plant was sold in 1901 to Henry K. Humphrey, who formed Security Milling Co. In 1907 the property was sold to William H. Kinney, Thomas J. Holdridge and Jed W. Burns, who organized Security Flour Mills Co. and increased the plant to 1800 cwt., with Kinney as president. The company became a unit in the Moore-Lowry chain after Kinney's time, with George M. Lowry as president in 1917-44. W. Alfred Chain (b. 1889 Kan., d. 1954) was general manager in 1909-44.

The mill was leased in 1944 to T. Lester Welsh and associates, and they formed Security Milling Co., Inc. Although a separate corporation, it was operated virtually as a division of Abilene Flour Mills Co. Welsh and associates acquired title to the mill in 1947. Flour milling was discontinued in 1953.

Arkansas City

Arkansas City Flour Mills Co.—Second largest flour mill in Kansas is in Arkansas City, within four miles of the Oklahoma border. Its ancestry goes back to 1879, when a small mill was established on Walnut River. Within a few years three mills were operating on the present mill site.

Arkansas City Milling Co. was organized in 1883, when the three mills were consolidated. The resulting plant had about 200-cwt. capacity. It grew considerably in size, was destroyed by fire in 1903 and rebuilt larger, and it attained 3500 cwt. by World War I. The central figure in early history of the company was Charles H. Searing (b. 1851 N. Y., d. 1924), one of the founders, general manager in 1888-1916 and president in 1905-24. Henry Hill was president in 1888-1905. Fred E. Goodrich (b. 1881 Kan.) came in as general manager in 1916, also becoming president in 1925.

The business drifted considerably after Major Searing's death, the company was acquired briefly by Ferdinand C. Kaths and Louis A. Arneson after they left Larabee, and in 1927 ownership passed to Frank Kell and associates. They organized Kansas Mill & Elevator Co., with Kell as president. James E. Haviland, Andrew Smith and Kent C. Barber each served short terms as manager. In 1931 Morris A. Wilkins (b. 1894 Mo.) began a managership of more than 30 years. The company was reorganized in 1934 as Arkansas City Flour Mills Co., following a receivership, and Wilkins became president.

Dixie-Portland interests purchased control in 1940 from the Kell group. The mill was increased by stages until it has reached 10,000 cwt. Grain storage is 2,500,000 bushels.

New Era Milling Co. has a 5000-cwt. pneumatic mill in Arkansas City and almost a million bushels of grain storage. It is largely but not wholly a bakery flour mill, with its trade in the eastern half of the country. Its head is A. James Sowden (b. 1914 Kan.), whose grandfather was plant superintendent for a quarter of a century.

Andrew J. Hunt (b. 1861 Neb., d. 1918) founded New Era Milling Co. The original mill had 700 cwt. capacity, and was enlarged from time to time. In 1902 Nehemiah Sowden (b. 1854 England, d. 1933), who had been an operative miller in Minnesota and Wisconsin for 22 years and whose father and grandfather had been millers, joined Hunt; and the association of Hunt heirs and Sowdens has continued to the present day.

Ralph C. Sowden (b. 1883 Wis., d. 1960), son of Nehemiah, entered the business in 1906 and became manager ten years later and president in 1918. He was president of Millers' National Federation in 1952-54, an office which Hunt had held 40 years previously, in 1912-14.

New Era was a charter affiliate of Kansas Flour Mills Corp., in 1912, but after two years the Hunt-Sowden interests repurchased their mill. Except for that period, they have owned the predominant share of the company since it was organized. Company presidents: A. J. Hunt in 1899-1918; R. C. Sowden in 1918-56; A. J. Sowden since 1956.

Andrew J. Hunt Trinity Memorial Church in Arkansas City preserves the memory of a miller who rendered distinguished service to the industry during the first World War. It was built in part by the contributions from 113 milling companies.

Atchison

Blair Milling Co.—Atchison was the location chosen by Edward K. Blair (b. 1832 Pa., d. 1897) in 1868 for his flour mill. The 100-cwt. mill grew to 500 cwt. by 1883, and a large corn mill was added in 1910. The latter was partially converted to a flour mill in 1920 but was destroyed by fire the next year, leaving only the original plant. A 2000-cwt. unit was built in 1922 and some years later the capacity was increased to 5000 cwt.

The business was operated as a series of partnerships prior to the incorporation of Blair Milling Co. in 1898. William A. Blair (b. 1862 Kan., d. 1922), son of the founder, was company president in 1898-1922, followed by his brother, J. Wesley (b. 1868 Kan., d. 1929) in 1922-29. Head of the company in 1929-52 was E. Blair Hackney (b. 1893 Kan.), grandson of E. K. Blair. William W. Blair (b. 1907 Kan.), son of W. A. Blair, has held the office from 1952.

The mill was sold to Rodney Milling Co. in 1955, and was dismantled. The Blair company has continued in the elevator business.

Cain Mill Co.—The mill built in 1871 in Atchison by William Bowman and Thomas Murphy became the property of Alford D. Cain (b. 1845 Isle of Man, d. 1898) in 1888, and in the course of time it reached 1600 cwt. capacity. Four of Cain's five sons achieved prominence in Kansas milling circles.

Douglas M. Cain (b. 1872 Kan., d. 1921) managed Cain Mill Co. in 1898-1914. The company then failed. It was reorganized in 1916 as Cain Milling Co., and in 1918 as McDonald Milling Co. The plant was closed in 1920.

John W. Cain, youngest of the brothers, was in Midland Flour Milling Co. and its successor for 35 years and was president of Midland. Victor A. (b. 1879 Kan., d. 1940) headed Leavenworth Milling Co. for 20 years, and Arthur S. (b. 1883 Kan., d. 1952) was associated with William Kelly Milling Co. The latter two were also engaged in the flour business for a long time.

Lukens Milling Co.—David Lukens became sole owner in 1894 of the 1200-cwt. mill that he and J. A. North had built 16 years earlier. It was operated by Lukens in a partnership with his sons, Arthur (b. 1873 Kan., d. 1954), Edwin and David, Jr. (b. 1889 Kan., d. 1926), and in later years by the two older sons.

The first mill was replaced in 1924 by a new plant of 2000 cwt., but this mill was badly damaged by fire in 1937 and was never returned to production.

Attica

Attica Mills—An idle mill in Attica, southwest of Wichita, was purchased in 1916 from Hunter Milling Co. by George H. Hunter's two sons—Charles W. and Harry (b. 1883 Kan., d. 1933). About 1925 they increased the capacity to 1000 cwt. Harry Hunter became sole owner in 1930. Attica Mills was destroyed by fire in 1931.

Buhler

Buhler Mills, Inc. is almost exclusively engaged in the family flour trade, largely in the Middle South. It operates mills in Buhler and Inman, small towns near Hutchinson; they have aggregate capacity of 3100 cwt., more than three times the size of the company 25 years ago. It also has 1,200,000 bushels of elevator space.

The first mill at Buhler, that of Welk and Wiens, was acquired in 1892 by John J. Wall and Herman Rogalsky. It was moved, name and all, in 1906 to McPherson where it remains to this day. Wall and his nephew, Jacob C. Regier (b. 1882 Kan., d. 1944), established another which was named Buhler Mill & Elevator Co. Regier managed the business for 38 years. Associated with him was John J. Buhler (b. 1876 Russia, d. 1933), and in time their sons came into ownership and management. Harold M. Regier (b. 1909 Kan.) became executive vice president in 1944 and general manager in 1962, and Milton J. Buhler (b. 1906 Kan., d. 1959) headed the principal sales office in Memphis.

Buhler Mill & Elevator Co. became Buhler Mills, Inc. in 1956. It acquired the Enns mill in Inman in 1946. Company presidents: Wall in 1906-16; J. C. Regier in 1916-44; C. Nicholas Hiebert (b. 1893 Kan.), whose connection with the company began in 1916, since 1944.

Cherryvale

N. Sauer Milling Co.—From a Southern Illinois mill that had been operated by his family, Nicholas Sauer (b. 1841 Ill., d. 1908) went to Southeastern Kansas in 1902 and established a 1200-cwt. mill. The business was headed for about 20 years by his son, John W. (b. 1868 Ill., d. 1925), and then by Charles S. MacGinniss. A group organized by MacGinniss bought N. Sauer Milling Co. in 1927, and he was president and manager. The company went into receivership in 1941, and after the mill was idle for a year it was acquired by Kansas Milling Co. and operated until 1953, when it was dismantled.

Clay Center

Snell Mill & Grain Co.—Clay Center, northwest of Manhattan, was the site of Snell Mill & Grain Co., founded in 1877. Arthur A. Wixon (b. 1872 Ill., d. 1928) was head of the concern in later years, and V. P. Campbell was manager. The property was purchased in 1927 by Shellabarger Mill & Elevator Co., which operated it under the trade name of Mid-Kansas Milling Co. The 1200-cwt. mill was enlarged to 2100 cwt. during this period, Shellabarger was absorbed by International Milling Co. in 1946, and the Clay Center mill was destroyed by fire a few years after.

Clyde

Clyde Milling & Elevator Co.—In 1900 a small mill was built in Clyde, on the Republican River 50 miles southwest of Manhattan. Clyde Milling & Elevator Co. was organized, A. Wangerian serving as president to 1921. James B. Sager (b. 1872 Ont., d. 1942) was manager in 1903-39, president in 1921-39. A new mill of 1350 cwt. was built in 1921, later being enlarged to 1700 cwt. Control was sold to John K. Pickerill (b. 1890 Kan.) in 1939, and he became president. His son, Ferris W. (b. 1911 Kan.) was manager from 1941, and part owner and president from 1946. The mill was closed in 1949.

Coffeyville

Rea-Patterson Milling Co.—One of the best-known millers in the Southwest during the first third of this century was Rea-

Patterson Milling Co., in the Southeast Kansas town of Cof-feyville. It was an 800-cwt. mill when built in 1894 by Edward S. Rea (b. 1872 Mo., d. 1923) and J. B. Patterson, but it grew to 4000-cwt. size by 1920. The company acquired the 1600-cwt. plant of Langenberg Milling Co., Republic, Mo., in 1918, but operated it only a couple of years.

Rea, president in 1896-1923, was credited with the com-pany's success, and after his time the business went down hill. He was followed as president by Frank H. Patterson, Hazard W. Read (b. 1850 Ill., d. 1930) and I. V. Sanford, and by Addison T. Ragon and John D. Evans (b. 1893 Ky.) as gen-eral managers. Working capital became depleted and the mill was closed early in 1932. It was managed by D. A. Wilbern for the next two years under a receivership, but the mill oper-ated only intermittently.

The semi-idle plant was sold in 1934 to Moore-Lowry Flour Mills Co., and has since been operated by that company.

Ellinwood

Wolf Milling Co.—Ellinwood, just east of Great Bend, was the site chosen in 1877 by John Wolf (b. 1852 Germany, d. 1915), one of the pioneer millers of Kansas. The original mill continued until 1908, when it was replaced by an 800-cwt. plant that was enlarged to 2000 cwt. in 1921. Wolf Mill-ing Co. was organized in 1908, and the founder's son, Fred (b. 1872 Ohio, d. 1939), succeeded to the business. Fred Jr. and Stone O. Cowley ran the mill in later years. It was closed in 1948.

Great Bend

Barton County Flour Mills Co. is in Great Bend, 50 miles northwest of Hutchinson. It has a flour mill of 1200 cwt. that was originally established in 1898 by Moses interests. Charles L. Gunn (b 1859 Ill., d. 1930) purchased control of Barton County Flour Mills Co. in 1905 and enlarged the mill to its present size in 1920. He was president in 1905-25, his son Leonard (b. 1884 Kan., d. 1951) was president in 1925-51, and since the latter date Herbert A. Harms (b. 1895 Neb.), son-in-law of C. L. Gunn, has headed the company. The mill has operated on a light scale, the Gunn-Harms group being much more active in oil than in milling.

Walnut Creek Milling Co.—Great Bend was not long from frontier days when John V. Brinkman established a grist mill there in 1876. It became Walnut Creek Milling Co., which was enlarged by steps to 1000 cwt. With much of Great Bend, it was destroyed by cyclone in 1915, and the new mill had 2000 capacity.

John Brinkman was succeeded by his son, Charles V. (b. 1869 Ohio, d. 1925), who became company head in 1905. Laurence B. Chapman (b. 1899 Kan.), grandson of the founder, was president in 1925-37. Thurman H. Sherwood (b. 1896 Mo.) was general manager in 1937-51 and was followed by Fred Zutavern. The mill was closed the following year.

Harper

Imperial Flour Mills Co.—A small mill existed in Harper, 45 miles southwest of Wichita, prior to 1916, and the company was successively known, in 1916-19, as E. A. Wales Milling Co., Ball Manufacturing Company, Harper Mill & Elevator Co., and Harper Flour Mills Co. The latter became insolvent, and the assets were purchased by executives of Kansas Milling Co. in 1919. They organized Harper Milling Co., which later became Imperial Flour Mills Co. The mill of 1000 cwt. was operated almost as a part of Kansas Milling Co., although they were separate corporations. The mill was destroyed by fire in 1936.

Hutchinson

William Kelly Milling Co. is owned and operated by heirs of the pioneer miller who founded it. The descendants of William Kelly, last surviving member of the rugged band who built mills almost as soon as the plow broke the prairies, have two mills a mile apart. Their capacity is 5600 cwt., wheat storage 1,600,000 bushels. These mills make flour almost exclusively for commercial bakers in the eastern half of the nation.

William Kelly (b. 1858 Ill., d. 1936) went to Kansas in 1874 and worked in mills in Ellinwood, Wichita and Great Bend. In 1883 he became a partner in Hulme & Kelly in Great Bend. In 1896 he built and had a half interest in Monarch Mills, Hutchinson, which he sold to the Sawyers in 1905. The following year he built the Kelly mill of 1000 cwt. This was enlarged to 2000 cwt. in 1911, and in recent years to 2500 cwt. In 1920 his company bought the 2000-cwt. plant of Reno Flour Mills Co., Hutchinson, which now makes 3100 cwt.

The sons of William Kelly are Charles Clifton (b. 1884 Kan.) and Willis N. (b. 1889 Kan.). They entered the business in 1906 and 1912, respectively. The former is board chairman, the latter vice president in charge of production. William G. (b. 1920 Kan.), son of Willis N., joined the company in 1946 and is president and manager. A long-time associate, P. Hume Baum (b. 1884 Ohio, d. 1960), was in the company from 1917 and was general manager in the 1950's.

William Kelly Milling Co. was incorporated in 1906. Its presidents: William Kelly in 1906-36; C. C. Kelly in 1936-60; W. G. Kelly from 1960.

Reno Flour Mills Co.—Hutchinson grain men, headed by L. H. Pettit, organized Reno Flour Mills Co. and built a flour mill of 2000 cwt. in 1918. J. E. Damon was manager. The business was not successful, and the mill was sold in 1920 to William Kelly Milling Co., and is still operated by that company.

Sawyer Milling Co.—Nathan B. Sawyer (b. 1848 Va., d. 1930) bought a half interest in Monarch mill in 1905 from William Kelly, and later came into full ownership. Sawyer Milling Co. was organized by Sawyer and his sons—Edwin A. (b. 1878 Ill.) and Howard (b. 1881 Ill., d. 1926). Their mill had about 1300 cwt. when it was destroyed by fire in 1922, the Sawyers leased a small plant in Wellington for a few years but closed out their business after Howard's death.

Independence
Bowen Flour Mills Co.—The Bowens were millers almost a century, beginning in Iowa in 1848. George W. Bowen and his son, William P. (b. 1855 Iowa, d. 1928), built Eagle Roller Mills of 600 cwt. in Independence, Southeastern Kansas, in 1883. It was operated until 1913, when it was destroyed by fire.

Louis H. Bowen (b. 1878 Iowa), son of W. P., was a flour distributor in Arkansas, and in 1921 he purchased an interest in the Romer-Cassler mill, then being built in Larned, 70 miles west of Hutchinson. His office was in Independence. The 800-cwt. mill was later increased to 1000 cwt. Bowen Flour Mills Co. operated until 1945, a brief part of the time as Bowen-Oglesby Milling Co. The mill was sold to Flour Mills of America, Inc., and was dismantled in 1949.

Inman
Enns Milling Co.—Cornelius Enns (b. 1839 Russia, d.

1904), who was a miller before he emigrated to a Kansas wheat farm, was urged in the 1890's by a group of Mennonite farmers to manage a small mill they had built. That was how the Enns family entered the milling business in America. Cornelius was succeeded by his son, John F. (b. 1879 Russia, d. 1946), and the latter became president when the company was incorporated in 1908. The mill at Inman, a village near Hutchinson, had 1000 cwt. capacity. It was sold in 1946 to Buhler Mill & Elevator Co., and was subsequently enlarged to 1400 cwt.

Junction City

Hogan Milling Co.—Near Fort Riley is Junction City, where Cornelius Fogarty built a mill in 1874. His nephew, Thomas F. Hogan (b. 1869 Ireland, d. 1937), became manager in 1888. He acquired the property in 1902 and organized Hogan Milling Co. three years later. The mill then had 800 cwt. capacity and it reached 1200 cwt. 20 years later and 1600 cwt. 40 years later. The plant was sold in 1943 to Shellabarger Mill & Elevator Co., and was operated by that company and its successor, International Milling Co., until 1949. It was later destroyed by fire.

Thomas F. Hogan was company president in 1905-29; his son, Theodore T. (b. 1902 Kan.), in 1929-43.

Larned

Keystone Milling Co.—After learning the milling trade in his native state, Henry G. Gabel (b. 1855 Pa., d. 1921) established a mill in 1894 in Larned, 70 miles west of Hutchinson, and incorporated Keystone Milling Co. in 1902. He was its president. The mill reached 1200 cwt. capacity. Three sons, Harry L., Eden L. and S. L., took over the business but encountered heavy losses and the concern was ended by receivership in 1933.

Lawrence

Bowersock Mills & Power Co.—A Kansas miller who attained political fame was Justin D. Bowersock (b. 1842 Ohio, d. 1922), who established a small mill in Lawrence in 1880. Bowersock served as a member of Congress in 1893-1907. The mill was expanded over a period of years to 3000 cwt., and Robert R. Clark rose through the ranks to manager. The mill was rebuilt after destruction in the Kaw River flood of 1903, and Robert C. Jackman (b. 1878 Mo., d. 1956) became manager in 1914 and he purchased the property in 1923.

Jackman was one of the first millers to use radio advertising, his Jenny Wren station becoming famous. After 1932 the mill operated only sporadically for several years. In 1937 Fred E. Goodrich came in as manager. The mill was leased in 1943 to Lawrence Milling Co., which enlarged the capacity to 4000 cwt. and used the plant for the production of alcohol grits. The mill has not operated since 1949.

Leavenworth

Leavenworth Milling Co.—The Rush mill of 1000 cwt. in Leavenworth was purchased in 1904 by Victor A. Cain. He formed Leavenworth Milling Co., of which he was president and manager. Mill capacity was increased to 2500 cwt. The business continued until 1926, when the mill was closed.

J. C. Lysle Milling Co.—The Lysles were millers in Leavenworth, Northeastern Kansas, for 80 years. Their entry was in 1874, when James C. Lysle (b. 1828 Pa., d. 1911), who had been a wagon-wheel maker, joined James Dilworth in starting a grist mill. In 1882 Lysle and John Kelley built a mill of 500 cwt. Six years later Kelley & Lysle Milling Co. was incorporated, and in 1898 Lysle bought Kelley's share and Kelley then established Kelley Milling Co. in Kansas City.

Eugene D. Lysle (b. 1871 Kan., d. 1941), who entered the business in 1890, acquired his father's interest in 1909 and assumed the company presidency. The name was changed to J. C. Lysle Milling Co. at that time. The mill then had 3000 cwt. capacity. In 1922 the company built the 3600-cwt. Monarch Mill in Kansas City. It was sold in 1926 to Commander Larabee Corp., and is now operated by a successor, Archer-Daniels-Midland Co.

James C. Lysle II (b. 1896 Kan.) joined the company in 1917 and became president in 1941. The mill was increased to 4000 cwt. in 1943, was sold in 1954 to Bay State Milling Co. and now has 4700 cwt. capacity. J. C. Lysle Milling Co. has remained as a personal investment company.

Liberal

Light Grain & Milling Co., Inc. is in far Southwestern Kansas, north of the Oklahoma panhandle. The business was established in 1915 by Charles M. Light, and a small flour mill was added in 1919 to the line of country elevators. The mill was enlarged until in recent years it reached 1000 cwt. capacity.

The business was operated as a partnership until 1947, when Light Grain & Milling Co., Inc. was formed. Ira R. Salley (b. 1891 Mo.) was president in 1947-57, and was succeeded by Charles M. Light, Jr. (b. 1909 Okla.). Wilfred E. Bush (b. 1897 Kan.) has been vice president and general manager for many years. The company's flour business is with both the family and the bakery trade, chiefly in the Southwest.

Lindsborg

Lindsborg Milling & Elevator Co.—Lindsborg is 20 miles south of Salina, and is the town with the nationally famous Messiah Chorus. It had a flour mill for 70 years. Lindsborg Milling & Elevator Co. was established in 1883, and was owned in 1892-1912 by Gustav I. Toevs (b. 1864, d. 1932), who was later identified with milling in Washington. When control passed to the Johantgen brothers in 1912, the mill had 1200 cwt. capacity. Hayes W. Johantgen (b. 1877 Ohio, d. 1918) was president and manager for six years, and his brother, Walter C. (b. 1873 Ohio), was president in 1918-39. Arthur C. Falen (b. 1884 Kan.) was manager in 1918-37, being succeeded by John W. Johantgen, son of W. C., in 1937-39.

The mill had 1800 cwt. capacity when it was acquired in 1939 by Rodney Milling Co., and it was subsequently increased to 2400 cwt. It was operated until 1954.

Lyons

Central Kansas Milling Co.—Cooper Milling Co. was formed in 1904 to operate an 800-cwt. mill in Lyons, 25 miles northwest of Hutchinson. Jesse Ainsworth and John W. Long bought the business in 1905 and changed the name to Central Kansas Milling Co. The mill was later enlarged to 1200 cwt. Long was manager in 1905-21, followed by his son Alvin in 1921-32. The mill was closed in 1932, then leased the following year by Lyons Flour Milling Co. and operated until 1935.

Lyons Flour Milling Co.—The first Lyons mill was built in 1874 by Holst & Eisenmayer, the latter being father-in-law of Bernhard Warkentin. On the same site George M. Randall, whose son, Harry G., was to be prominent in Kansas milling, erected a 1000-cwt. plant in 1907 and operated it as Lyons

Milling Co. It was sold during the war period to L. B. Young and Malcolm B. McNair, the latter becoming manager.

Henry S. Cowgill and his nephew, John M. Blair (b. 1891 Mo., d. 1934) bought the property in 1927 and organized Lyons Flour Milling Co., Cowgill being president and Blair manager. The mill was enlarged to 1200 cwt. In 1932 fire destroyed the mill. Blair leased the Central Kansas mill in Lyons in late 1933, and then effected a consolidation with John F. Meyer & Sons Milling Co., as Meyer-Blair Milling Co. Blair was killed in a hunting accident, and the company was liquidated 1935.

McPherson

KBR Milling Co.—Queen Bee Roller Mills was built in McPherson in 1880 by Edward A. Colburn (b. 1849 N. Y., d. 1931) and John Hamilton. In 1901, Harry L. Colburn (b. 1872 N. Y., d. 1934) bought the Hamilton interest, and the business was incorporated as Colburn Bros. Co. The mill was destroyed by fire in 1911 and was rebuilt with 1000 cwt. capacity. After 1930 the plant was operated somewhat casually, and in 1938 it was sold to Emil Teichgraeber (b. 1881 Ill., d. 1941). KBR Milling Co. was then organized, Teichgraeber being president.

The Teichgraebers had been millers in Germany and Illinois, and in Kansas they had small mills in Emporia and Marquette. The McPherson mill was increased to 1450 cwt., and the Teichgraeber estate sold KBR Milling Co. to Rodney Milling Co. in 1941. Rodney enlarged the mill several times, and its present capacity is 7200 cwt.

Wall-Rogalsky Milling Co. is located in McPherson, about midway between Salina and Hutchinson. The company operates a flour mill of 2150 cwt. and 1,250,000 bushels of grain storage. The business is divided between family and bakery flour.

Wall-Rogalsky Milling Co. was organized in 1906 by John J. Wall (b. 1862 Russia, d. 1916) and Herman Rogalsky (b. 1859 Germany, d. 1940). The mill they moved from Buhler after they had operated it for 14 years had a capacity of 750 cwt. It was increased to 1700 cwt. in 1917. Wall was a banker and businessman, Rogalsky a practical miller.

Wall was president in 1906-16, and was succeeded by Cornelius A. Hiebert (b. 1873 Kan., d. 1925) in 1916-25. The co-founder's son, Ernest A. Wall (b. 1896 Kan.), has been president since 1925. A business association of more than a third of a century began in 1928, when John B. Wall (b. 1905 Kan.) joined his brother in the business. He is company vice president.

Moundridge

Moundridge Milling Co.—A small flour mill built in 1886 at Moundridge, northeast of Hutchinson, came into the possession of John W. Krehbiel (b. 1860 Ill., d. 1939) in 1889. It was enlarged at intervals until it reached 1800 cwt. capacity. Krehbiel was president of Moundridge Milling Co. for 50 years, and he managed the business in 1889-1922. He was succeeded in turn by two sons—Carl C. (b. 1892 Kan., d. 1935) in 1922-35, and Nelson W. (b. 1898 Kan.) in 1935-48. Nelson W. was president in 1939-48.

Hunt Bros. mill in Pleasant Hill, Mo., was purchased in 1935, but it was destroyed by fire a few years later. Moundridge Milling Co. was sold in 1948 to Lawrence Milling Co., and later to Kansas Milling Co. The plant is used for the production of malted flour.

Newton

Goerz Flour Mills Co.—After a lengthy association with the Warkentin interests, Rudolph A. Goerz (b. 1876 Ill., d. 1945) organized Goerz Flour Mills Co., which built a 2000-cwt. mill in Newton in 1918. He was president and manager. The company became involved financially in 1932, and the controlling interest was then acquired by John J. Vanier. Goerz continued in charge during Vanier ownership. The company was sold in 1936 to the Ross-Zimmerman interests, and in 1942 the name was changed to American Flours, Inc.

Ross Industries, Inc. has three milling divisions that bear the names of former corporations — American Flours, Inc., Hunter Milling Co., and Kansas Milling Co. The mills have aggregate capacity of 23,400 cwt., and the company is the largest in Kansas and ninth in size in the industry. Flour business is chiefly with the bakery trade. The mills have storage for 13,500,000 bushels of grain, and another division is a large factor in the terminal grain business.

Ross Industries, Inc., was formed in 1959 through a re-alignment of properties owned largely by the Ross family. The parent company was American Flours, Inc. which has a 4000-cwt. mill in Newton, 25 miles north of Wichita. This company, which was known as Goerz Flour Mills Co. until 1942, became a Ross property in 1936. Hunter Milling Co. was acquired in 1946 and Kansas Milling Co. in 1959, and subsequently these concerns and a terminal elevator company were merged into Ross Industries, Inc.

The first Ross venture in milling was Whitewater Flour Mills Co., organized jointly in 1918 with their kinsmen, the Zimmermans. This became exclusively a Zimmerman business in 1959. A subsidiary, Ross Milling Co., organized in 1919, operated a mill in Ottawa until 1950.

G. Murray Ross (b. 1887 Kan.), who had been president of Whitewater in 1918-54 and president of American Flours, Inc., and its predecessor since 1936, has been president of Ross Industries, Inc., since its formation. His father, George B. Ross (b. 1864 Ind., d. 1940), who was a farmer, state legislator, and founder of the Kansas state grain inspection system which he directed for six years, was head of the Ross clan. Although he never actually managed any of their milling enterprises, he was the family's elder statesman.

Ottawa

Ross Milling Co.—Excelsior Mills was established in 1883 in Ottawa, 50 miles southwest of Kansas City, by H. D. Crane & Co. The Crane concern sold the plant to Forest Park Milling Co., which finally went into receivership. Barley flour was produced in the mill in 1918-19 by Ottawa Milling Co. Title passed to the Ross-Zimmerman interests in 1919, and they organized Ross Milling Co., a subsidiary of Whitewater Flour Mills Co. The mill then had 1200 cwt. capacity and was later increased to 1800. It was operated exclusively on family trade.

G. Murray Ross managed Ross Milling Co. in 1919-36, and the mantle then rested upon his brother, Carl B. (b. 1899 Kan.), until the plant was dismantled in 1950 after several disastrous floods.

Russell

Russell Milling Co.—Local investors in Russell, 75 miles west of Salina, led by J. H. Hill, a banker, set up a 1000-cwt. flour mill in 1906. The location proved to be somewhat disadvantageous, especially in later years, and the company went through several reorganizations. The plant was sold in 1943 to Mason B. McVeigh, who operated it a year and then resold to Rodney Milling Co. The mill was closed in 1951.

H. E. Hanna was manager in 1906-15; B. Frank Herren (b. 1886 Kan.) in 1916-34; then H. H. Wentworth, Ferris W. Hamm and Herren again for short periods; Frank M. Ross (b. 1900 Okla.) in 1938-42; and Frank Eberly in 1942-43.

Salina

H. D. Lee Flour Mills Co.—Harry D. Lee (d. 1928), the owner of several other large enterprises including H. D. Lee Mercantile Co., entered flour milling in 1899 through the organization of Lee-Warren Milling Co. George F. Warren (b. 1858, d. 1936), who had been connected with Brand-Dunwoody Milling Co., was manager for the first 14 years. The mill had 2000 cwt. at that time, and it was increased to 3600 cwt. by 1920. In 1919 a 1000-cwt. mill was built in Ellsworth, 35 miles west of Salina, but the plant was never operated to any great extent.

Louis G. Gottschick (b. 1867 Germany, d. 1953), who had milled in Ohio and Kansas City, became Lee vice president in 1903, and in 1913 he and Charles M. Todd (b. 1879 Ill., d. 1925) became co-managers. Gottschick was elected president and general manager in 1928, and he held that post until 1945.

John J. Vanier acquired the Lee property in 1936, and in 1945 the mill was sold to the Vanier-controlled Weber Flour Mills Co. The mill has continued to operate to the present under the Weber name, and H. D. Lee Flour Mills Co. is a trade name used by Weber.

Robinson Milling Co.—Robinson Grain Co. expanded into flour milling in 1918 via a new 2500-cwt. mill in Salina. It was principally owned by Charles E. Robinson (b. 1862 Ohio, d. 1940) and he was company president in 1918-34. His son, Harry L. (b. 1897 Kan., d. 1958), was president in 1934-41, and after the latter date the post was held by Edward Morgenstern (b. 1893 Kan.), son-in-law of C. E. Robinson.

The milling company was managed in 1918-29 by James S. Hargett (b. 1886 Kan., d. 1962) and after 1929 by Richard Morgenstern (b. 1896 Kan.), brother of Edward. Hargett went to General Mills, Inc. in 1929, and served as head of the southwestern division of the company in 1935-51.

The flour mill was closed in 1953.

Shellabarger Mills—The Shellabargers began to mill flour in the year of national independence. Martin Shellabarger built a mill at Newville, Pa. in 1776, and his descendants operated it for three generations. Martin's great-grandson, David Shellabarger (b. 1837 Pa., d. 1913) went to Decatur, Ill., in 1855 and established a mill that remained in operation until 1902.

The first Shellabarger milling venture in Kansas ended in failure, in 1871, but the second one was more fortunate. Salina Mill & Elevator Co., organized in 1883 by David, was a success. It became Shellabarger Mill & Elevator Co. in 1910 and Shellabarger Mills in 1943. The original mill of 600 cwt. was enlarged to 3600 cwt. by 1920, and in the 1940's to 7200 cwt. The Snell mill of 1200 cwt. in Clay Center was purchased in 1927, as was also the Hogan mill of similar size in Junction City in 1943.

Shellabarger Mills became one of the leading units of the Kansas milling industry. It was managed until 1895 by the founder, and then in 1895-1917 by his son, Fred D. (b. 1870 Ill., d. 1917). Jess B. Smith (b. 1879 Kan., d. 1954) was general manager in 1917-35. He was a noted industry leader, serving as president of Millers' National Federation in 1934-37. He was the founder of Wheat Flour Institute and he led the fight for wheat quality as president of Kansas Wheat Improvement Assn. in 1937-54. Smith's successor, Elmer W. Reed, had the helm in 1935-49 and later became president of Kansas Milling Co.

The Shellabarger heirs sold the milling company in 1946 to International Milling Co., and after about three years the operations were fully merged. The two smaller plants were lost to fire, but the Salina mill has continued in use.

Weber Flour Mills Co. operates a mill of 4400 cwt. and 2,000,000 bushels of grain storage. It is chiefly engaged in the bakery flour trade, and is one of the companies that comprise the Vanier chain.

This enterprise had its beginning in 1917, when John Weber built a 3200-cwt. mill in Salina and two years later a plant of similar size in Ellsworth, 35 miles west. Weber had little knowledge of milling, and J. Lynch was the company manager to 1920 and Horatio V. Nye (b. 1884 Vt., d. 1937) then held the post for three years. The company fell into difficulty and the mill ran only part time for several years. Receivership took place in 1926.

John J. Vanier, who had acquired Western Star Mill Co. only two years before, and associates obtained control of Weber Flour Mills Co. in 1926, and it has been operating since under his management. He has been president from that time to the present.

The original Weber mill was burned out in 1945, and the company thereupon purchased the plant of H. D. Lee Flour Mills Co., also a Vanier-controlled concern. The former Lee

mill has since been known as the Weber mill and has continued in operation.

Western Star Mill Co. is the parent of the Vanier chain of
flour mills. The Western Star mill has 3600 cwt. capacity and
2,000,000 bushels of grain storage. Its flour business is largely
with the bakery trade in the eastern half of the United States,
but it also includes a significant amount of export shipments.

The Vanier mills are held by separate corporations, each of
which is owned outright or controlled by John J. Vanier (b.
1897 Neb.). They have a combined capacity of 25,200 cwt.,
making the group the eighth in size among milling aggrega-
tions. In addition to Western Star Mill Co., the companies are
Weber Flour Mills Co., Gooch Milling & Elevator Co., Inland
Mills, Inc., Fuhrer Ford Mill Co., Inc. and Red Wing Milling
Co. The Vanier enterprises also include Econo-Flo Flour Service, Inc., which operates nine bulk flour depots in points eastward from St. Louis and Vicksburg. Vanier is also heavily interested in Kansas cattle ranches and in the grain and soybean
business as well as in several other lines.

The Vanier entry into mill ownership took place in 1924
through the purchase of Western Star. It was one of the first
mills in Kansas, having been built originally in 1861, and
during an Indian uprising the following year a stockade was
built around the mill as a protection against raids. It came into
the possession of H. H. Sudendorf in 1876 and was owned
by his family for almost half a century, but operated by managers in later years. The last two managers were Henry E.
Brooks (d. 1923) and John B. Neuhauser. The business was
going down hill when it was sold to Vanier, who had been a
Rodney employee.

The Western Star purchase was followed in 1926 by a deal

that brought the insolvent Weber company into the Vanier fold. In 1929 Vanier and associates bought Topeka Flour Mills Co., but sold the mill in 1938 to Ismert-Hincke Milling Co. Goerz Flour Mills Co. was acquired in 1932 and sold in 1936 to the Ross-Zimmerman interests. H. D. Lee Flour Mills Co. was purchased in 1936. Gooch Milling & Elevator Co. was obtained in 1939, the Inland company in 1945, Fuhrer-Ford in 1959 and Red Wing in 1962. The Weber mill was destroyed by fire in 1945, and Weber then acquired the Lee plant. The Econo-Flo stations have been established during the past ten years, beginning in Chicago in 1953.

Sterling

Arnold Milling Co.—Sterling's first mill was erected in 1876. One of its successors, an 840-cwt. plant built in 1883, was operated under the ambitious name of International Mills & Elevator by Henry J. Arnold (d. 1922). It was destroyed by fire in 1916, and a new 1200-cwt. plant was opened at war's end by Arnold-Madaus Milling Co., William B. Madaus (b. 1885 Mo.) being president. It went into receivership in 1924 and was reorganized as Arnold Milling Co. The mill was later increased to 2000 cwt.

Albert L. Jacobson (b. 1879 Wis., d. 1957) was general manager of Arnold Milling Co. in 1924-45, and president in 1940-45. Control of the company passed in 1946 to Jack H. Rathbone (b. 1914 Kan.) and others in the Magill-Jackman group. Rathbone was president and manager in 1946-54. At the end of that time the mill was sold and converted into a feed plant.

Topeka

Kaw Milling Co.—Built in the 1880's by a promoter named Taylor and long managed by John B. Nicholson, son-in-law of John D. Mulvane, the principal owner, the 2200-cwt. Kaw Milling Co. encountered hard times after 1921. It was taken over by a bank, for a time was managed by Arthur Dillon and then by J. Fields Baldwin (b. 1879 Va., d. 1926), who also ran the smaller Shawnee Milling Co.

The mill was sold in 1926 to Larabee Flour Mills Co., and was called Interior Flour Mills Co. After a year or two the mill went into irregular operation and was closed permanently in 1930.

Willis Norton Co.—Willis Norton was a banker who joined with Thomas Page, a practical miller, in forming Page, Norton & Co. in 1880. They bought a mill that was built in 1875 in Topeka. Page withdrew in 1892 to launch his own mill, and the business then became Willis Norton Co. It was also called Inter-Ocean Mills. Armin Fassler (b. 1858 Ohio, d. 1945), brother-in-law of Norton, managed the business in 1886-1926.

Wichita Flour Mills Co. bought the property in 1927, the manager being Ellsworth B. (Dick) Sewell (b. 1886 Wis.). The mill operated irregularly after 1931 and was destroyed by lightning in 1934. Willis Norton Co. has continued to the present as a trade name of Wichita Flour Mills Co., with Sewell in charge. Office is in Wichita.

Thomas Page Mill Co.—After 12 years' association with the Nortons, Thomas Page (b. 1843 Scotland, d. 1920) built a 600-cwt. mill in 1892 and established Thomas Page Mill Co. It was also known as Mid-Continent Mills. The mill was enlarged to 1600 cwt. by 1900, and in 1902 the 800-cwt. plant of Manhattan Milling Co., Manhattan, was added. The latter mill was closed in the early 1930's.

Page was president in 1892-1920; his son, David G. (b. 1881 Kan., d. 1949), in 1920-45. Management rested largely in E. Walter Morrison in 1928-35 and in Milton P. Fuller (b. 1879 Minn., d. 1954) in 1935-45.

The mill was sold in 1945 to Ismert-Hincke Milling Co., and was transferred in 1955 to Rodney Milling Co. Present capacity is 4200 cwt.

Topeka Flour Mills Corp.—Largest of the Topeka mills was the plant that bore the city's name. Built about 1882 by Herbert H. Hackney (b. 1850 England, d. 1922), it was first called Topeka Mill & Elevator Co. and then Topeka Milling Co. The company failed in 1913, and was succeeded by Topeka Flour Mills Co., which built a new plant of 2400 cwt. in 1915. Principals were S. Peter Kramer (b. 1858 Ohio, d. 1929) and Henry D. Yoder (b. 1862 Ind., d. 1938). Kramer had owned Aetna Mills, Wellington, for some years and Yoder's association had been with Kemper Mill & Elevator Co. and other concerns.

Topeka Flour Mills Co. was acquired in 1929 by John J. Vanier and associates. They organized Topeka Flour Mills Corp., the manager of which was John K. Landes (b. 1877 Ohio, d. 1948), who had been connected with the Maney mills in Oklahoma.

Ismert-Hincke Milling Co. bought the Topeka mill in 1938, soon after the destruction of its Kansas City mill. It has remained in production to the present. Capacity is 7200 cwt. Topeka Flour Mills Corp. is now a trade name owned by Weber Flour Mills Co.

Wellington

Hunter Milling Co.—The Hunter name has been in Kansas milling annals more than 80 years. It is now a division of

Ross Industries, Inc., and the division operates two mills in Wellington, 30 miles south of Wichita. It is exclusively in the bakery flour business.

George H. Hunter (b. 1849 Ohio, d. 1927) bought into Wellington City Mill two years after it was built in 1877. Hunter Mill Co. was incorporated in 1889, and the original little mill grew to 1000 cwt. by 1904 and 3000 cwt. by 1924. The 1200-cwt. mill of Wellington Milling & Elevator Co. was purchased in 1927, and each of the two plants was later expanded somewhat. The Hunter family sold the company to the Ross group in 1946, and it became a division of Ross Industries, Inc., in 1959.

George H. Hunter managed the business from his first connection with it, and was president in 1889-1927. Charles L. Roos (b. 1861 Minn., d. 1941) was general manager in 1916-24; he had previously run a central sales agency for mills, and in 1922-24 he served as president of Millers' National Federation. During the 19 years following Hunter's death, management devolved upon a triumvirate consisting of his son, Charles W. (b. 1873 Ill., d. 1945), and his sons-in-law—William T. Voils (b. 1873 Neb., d. 1947) and J. Harris Carr (b. 1886 Kan.). Voils and C. W. Hunter alternated as presidents and Carr was secretary-treasurer.

Floyd M. Ross (b. 1899 Kan.), nephew of G. B. Ross, was president after 1946.

Wellington Milling & Elevator Co.—Walter G. Moodie (b. 1874 Ky.) had a line of elevators along the Kansas-Oklahoma border, and in 1903 he and a Mr. Carter organized Wellington Milling & Elevator Co. and built an 880-cwt. mill. It was later enlarged to 1200 cwt. Moodie managed the company until 1927, when the mill was sold to Hunter Milling Co.

Capacity was increased to 2000 cwt., and the mill continues to be part of the Hunter facilities.

Whitewater

Whitewater Flour Mills Co. is in the family flour business only, and operates a mill of 1100 cwt. in a village about 20 miles northeast of Wichita. Grain storage capacity is 1,100,000 bushels. Pneumatic equipment was installed in the mill in 1962.

Ross-Zimmerman interests in 1918 purchased the 250-cwt. mill built in 1898 by R. H. Farr and operated as Whitewater Milling Co. They formed Whitewater Flour Mills Co., which in 1919 also acquired a mill in Ottawa that was operated by a subsidiary. G. Murray Ross was Whitewater president in 1918-54, Levi E. Zimmerman (b. 1890 Kan.) since 1954. The business was managed in 1919-36 by Zimmerman and Paul B. Ross (b. 1893 Kan.), in 1936-54 by Zimmerman, and since 1954 by Theodore T. Zimmerman (b. 1910 Kan.).

The Zimmermans, who are father and son, have been sole owners since 1954.

Wichita

Consolidated Flour Mills Co.—For more than 40 years, Consolidated Flour Mills Co. had a chain of country mills in South Central Kansas. It was chartered in 1918 and ceased to be an entity in 1959.

Founders of Consolidated were L. B. Young and Jed W. Burns (b. 1873 Iowa, d. 1954), whose entry into milling took place in 1900 through purchase of the controlling interest in Hutchinson Mill Co., which they renamed Hutchinson Flour Mills Co. In 1917 they also obtained Winfield Flour Mills Co. and Border Queen Milling Co., Caldwell. Aggregate capacity of these mills was 3300 cwt. The new company was domiciled in Hutchinson until 1928, when it was moved to Wichita.

Empire Milling Co., Newton, and its 1200-cwt. mill were added in 1921, and in 1928 the 1300-cwt. Kingman mill of Kansas Flour Mills Corp. was purchased. The Caldwell mill was closed about 1935, the Hutchinson mill was destroyed by fire in 1947 and the other mills were enlarged so that the capacity was almost 8000 cwt. The Newton mill was burned in 1957, and the remaining mills—Winfield and Kingman—reached total capacity of 9100.

L. B. Young was the company's president in 1918-32, but the driving force was Fred F. Burns (b. 1886 Kan., d. 1958), who became general manager in 1922 and president in 1932 and held these posts until 1950. Stock control passed to Kansas Milling Co. in 1929, when Consolidated took a losing market position, but management remained in Burns' hands.

Otto Bresky and associates purchased Consolidated Flour Mills Co. in 1950, and Cecil A. Jordan (b. 1897 Kan.), who had been treasurer from 1929, became general manager for the next ten years. He was succeeded in 1960 by Henry L. Sumpter (b. 1899 Okla.). In 1959 the company was merged into Seaboard Allied Milling Corp., and became a division of the latter. The office was moved to Kansas City at that time.

Kansas Milling Co.—For two generations, Kansas Milling Co. was one of the prestige units of the industry in the Sunflower State. It ceased to exist as a corporation in 1962, when it became a division of Ross Industries, Inc. The division operates the largest flour mill in Kansas, a smaller plant and 4,500,-000 bushels of elevator space. It is primarily a hard wheat bakery mill, serving trade in the central and eastern half of the United States.

Kansas Milling Co. was founded in 1906 by Henry Lassen (b. 1861 Denmark, d. 1919) and Charles M. Jackman (b.

1862 Ohio, d. 1933), just after selling their Oklahoma mill. The Wichita mill initially had 2400 cwt. capacity; it was enlarged to 7500 cwt. by 1920 and increased subsequently until it reached 12,000 cwt.

The company also had a series of satellite mills. The first was at St. John, where the unique "Mill on the Trail" had been part of the Forsha enterprises. It was purchased in 1913 and enlarged to 1400 cwt., but was lost to fire in 1932. The mill in Marion, Ohio, was purchased in 1935, expanded to 1000 cwt. and operated as Marion Milling Co. until it was sold in 1962. The Sauer mill in Cherryvale was acquired in 1942 and used for eleven years. The mill in Moundridge came in via Lawrence Milling Co. in 1952. The Moundridge and Wichita mills now have 13,800 cwt. capacity.

The mill in Harper was purchased in 1919 by Kansas Milling Co. officials, but the operations of the two were closely tied together; it was destroyed by fire in 1936. They also organized Lawrence Milling Co. in 1942, and it operated four mills for several years. Stock control of Consolidated Flour Mills Co. was obtained in 1930 and retained until 1950, but it was not merged into nor managed by Kansas Milling Co

Lassen was president of Kansas Milling Co. in 1906-19, followed by Jackman in 1919-33. For the next 17 years, R. Ward Magill (b. 1891 Kan., d. 1953), son-in-law of Lassen, was president, and David S. Jackman (b. 1890 Kan.), son of Charles M., was general manager. Magill was one of the noted leaders of the industry and served as president of Millers' National Federation in 1940-42.

Large losses in non-milling activities caused control of Kansas Milling Co. to shift, and Fred F. Burns headed the concern almost a year. Elmer W. Reed (b. 1895 Kan.), whose milling experience in Salina and elsewhere ran back 35 years, was president in 1951-60. He was one of the industry's best-known leaders. Francis McKown (b. 1898 Kan.) became president in 1960, a year after ownership of the company went to the Ross interests.

Lawrence Milling Co.—The rise and fall of Lawrence Milling Co. were somewhat bizarre developments during and immediately after the second World War. The active life of the concern was only a little more than five years, but it operated four flour mills with total capacity of almost 10,000 cwt.

Lawrence Milling Co. was first a partnership of Kansas Milling Co. and its principal executives, and later it was incorporated. It leased and rehabilitated three mills in 1943-44 to produce alcohol grits from wheat and after 1945 to make export flour. These were Bowersock Mills & Power Co., G. H. Dulle Milling Co., and Baur Flour Mills Co. Title was taken to the Baur mill in 1946, and Moundridge Milling Co. was acquired two years later. The company was operated in most respects as a division of Kansas Milling Co.

Heavy losses were incurred in 1947-49 by Lawrence Milling Co. in such remote ventures as making moving pictures and launching a soft drink business in Brazil, and the company was liquidated a year or so later. The Moundridge mill was sold to Kansas Milling Co., the Baur plant was converted to a corn mill and closed soon after, and the Dulle and Bowersock mills were shut down in 1949.

Red Star Milling Co.—The man who made Red Star a great name in milling was Louis R. Hurd (b. 1858 Ohio, d. 1927) Two managements in three years had been able to obtain nothing but losses from an 800-cwt. mill in Wichita, and bankers sent for Hurd. He made such a success of Red Star that it soon became one of the top-ranking southwestern mills. The mill grew tenfold in size in less than a decade, and Hurd became chief owner.

As a young man, Hurd played a large part in equipping mills with steel rolls. The first mills to adopt this innovation usually kept guards at mill doors to prevent any spying. Hurd built the Daisy mill in Milwaukee for the only American manufacturer of rolls, and it was used for demonstration purposes. He later managed this mill, then the Daisy mill in Superior and the Southwestern mill in Kansas City before going to Wichita. He was Red Star president in 1908-27, followed by his son, Roger S. (b. 1890 Wis., d. 1933).

Red Star was the only company outside of the Washburn-Crosby units to join in the formation of General Mills, Inc. in 1928. It was wholly owned for several years and then became a trade name. The plant is still in use.

Wichita Flour Mills, Inc. is the parent Moore-Lowry company. It operates a 6000-cwt. mill that chiefly makes bakery flour and it has 3,500,000 bushels of grain storage. The company is owned in the main by members of the Moore and Lowry families.

The Wichita mill was opened in 1914 with 2000 cwt. capacity. The second unit increased the size to 5000 cwt. in 1918. Present capacity was attained about a decade ago.

Founder of the business that grew into the Moore-Lowry enterprises was William H. Kinney (b. 1841 Ohio, d. 1917), who worked in Illinois grist mills 25 years before locating in Kansas in 1877. He had a community mill at Burrton for six years and one near Larned for five. In 1888 he established Hutchinson Mill Co., which was the nucleus for Consolidated

Flour Mills Co. 30 years later. He owned and managed the Hutchinson mill and eventually he had an interest in six other mills.

Kinney organized Pond Creek Mill & Elevator Co. in 1898, and the 700-cwt. plant in the Oklahoma town of that name was managed after 1905 by his sons-in-law, John H. Moore (b. 1875 Texas, d. 1934) and George M. Lowry (b. 1876 Ind., d. 1958). After the mill was destroyed by fire in 1913, they organized Wichita Flour Mills Co., and built a new plant, meanwhile leasing the small Howard mill in that city.

Kinney's controlling interest in Security Flour Mills Co., Abilene, took that company into the Moore-Lowry orbit in 1917. Kansas City Milling Co. was acquired in 1923 and Moore-Lowry Flour Mills Co. was formed to operate the plant. Willis Norton Co., Topeka, was purchased in 1927 and it became a Wichita subsidiary and trade name. Acme Milling Co., Oklahoma City, was acquired in 1929, becoming Acme Flour Mills Co. At that time the combined capacity of the Moore-Lowry plants was about 14,000 cwt.

The Kansas City mill was sold in 1933 but was replaced the following year by the Rea-Patterson plant in Coffeyville, Kan. The Willis Norton mill was lost through fire in 1934. Security was sold in 1947 and Acme ceased to make flour in 1957. These events reduced the mills owned by the Moore-Lowry interests to two, with total capacity of 11,000 cwt.

The company was renamed Wichita Flour Mills, Inc. in 1957. Kinney was president in 1913-17; J. H. Moore in 1917-34; G. M. Lowry in 1934-58; J. Kinney Moore (b. 1908 Kan.), son of J. H. Moore, from 1958. Elmo F. Merrill has been general manager since 1934.

KENTUCKY

Shakertown, a settlement in the Lexington area, was the site of the first mill in Kentucky, built in 1783. It was followed by many others in the bluegrass country, where wheat has now been grown for almost two centuries. Small mills became common there and in several other parts of the state, 461 being reported in 1900. The number remaining in 1958 was 34.

Hopkinsville

Acme Mills, Inc.—After a mill established about 1900 by Galbreath & DeTreville had failed, Acme Mills, Inc. was organized in 1911 by William B. Anderson, Joseph P. Dunlop and J. M. Neblett. They took over the idle plant and operated it until 1927, when it was destroyed by fire. A new mill of 2000 cwt. was then erected, later being increased to 2700 cwt.

Neblett, the first general manager, sold his interest to the Andersons in 1922. William B. Anderson, Jr. (b. 1892 Tenn.) was president from 1913 and general manager from 1922.

The plant was leased in 1942 to Dixie-Portland Flour Mills and operated until 1944. After being idle for a few months, it was sold in 1945 to General Mills, Inc., and has since been a facility of that company.

Hopkinsville Milling Co. was relatively inconspicuous in the halcyon days of soft wheat milling, nearly half a century ago, but it survived vicissitudes that crumpled larger and better-known concerns. In recent years it has become one of the leaders in the soft wheat family flour and self-rising corn meal trade in the middle South.

The business was founded in 1874 as Rabbeth & Brownell, which in 1886 was incorporated as Crescent Milling Co., when Frederick J. Brownell (b. 1835 N. Y., d. 1908) bought out

John T. Rabbeth. Brownell continued as manager until 1903, when he was succeeded by Frank K. Yost (b. 1871 Ill., d. 1937). Yost also became manager of Hopkinsville Milling Co. when that concern was incorporated in 1908 to merge Crescent Milling Co. and Climax Mills, Inc. The latter was formed in 1906 by Ross Rogers. The old Crescent plant was converted in 1917 to a corn mill that now has 1100 cwt. capacity, and the former Climax plant is a flour mill of 1300 cwt.

Frank A. Yost (b. 1902 Ky.), son of Frank K., succeeded to the company management shortly before his father's death, and under his leadership the business has achieved success unmatched in earlier years. He was president of Millers' National Federation in 1954-56, and is prominent in a wide variety of civic undertakings as well as in industry affairs.

Lexington

Lexington Roller Mills, Inc. is located in the largest city in the famous Kentucky Bluegrass region. The company's facilities comprise a flour mill of 1600 cwt. capacity, corn mill of 900 cwt. and feed plant of 350 tons. Its business is largely with the household trade of the Southeast.

The history of Lexington Roller Mills and the career of Joseph LeCompte (b. 1857 Ky., d. 1937) were closely interwoven. The mill was built in 1884 with 400 cwt. capacity. LeCompte managed the business for 53 years, also serving as president in 1916-37. President in 1884-1916 was Lister Witherspoon, the largest stockholder. Joseph A. Goodwin was president in 1937-44.

Sterling T. Chase (b. 1895 Ky.) who had been associated with the company in 1920-32, became general manager in 1939 and also president in 1944. He has continued to hold these posts.

Louisville

Ballard & Ballard Co., Inc.—Great prestige and trade standing were enjoyed by Ballard & Ballard Co., Inc., which for two generations had the largest flour mill in the South and the largest volume of household flour business in that area.

This enterprise began in 1880 as Jones, Ballard & Ballard, a partnership that operated a small mill in Louisville. After this venture ended in disaster, the Ballard brothers established a mill in 1884 that in the course of time reached 5500 cwt. capacity. They operated as a partnership until 1909, when Ballard & Ballard Co., Inc. was formed. Charles T. Ballard (b. 1850 Ky., d. 1918) was president in 1909-18, his brother, S. Thruston Ballard (b. 1855 Ky., d. 1926), in 1918-26. With them was long associated the former's brother-in-law, Gustave A. Breaux (b. 1870 La., d. 1953). Another officer, William E. Castle (b. 1865 England, d. 1945), was president of Millers' National Federation in 1908-10.

Dr. David C. Morton (b. 1878 Ky., d. 1949), son-in-law of Thruston Ballard, was president in 1926-32 and chairman thereafter. He was followed in 1932-44 by Fred Borries (b. 1885 Ind., d. 1957), an industry leader who was president of Millers' National Federation in 1938-40. Two sons of Dr. Morton successively served as president, Thruston B. (b. 1907 Ky.) in 1944-47, Rogers C. B. (b. 1914 Ky.) in 1947-51. Clark R. Yager (b. 1899 Ky.) was widely known in the industry.

S. Thruston Ballard was Lieutenant Governor of Kentucky in 1919-23. His grandson, Thruston B. Morton, was a Congressman in 1947-53, Assistant Secretary of State in 1953-56 and United States Senator beginning in 1957. Rogers C. B. Morton was elected to Congress in 1962 from Maryland.

Ballard & Ballard Co., Inc. originated the refrigerated biscuit business in 1931, and was the principal factor in that field for the ensuing 20 years.

The company was merged into Pillsbury Mills, Inc. in 1951, and for a few years the business was carried on as Pillsbury-Ballard, but eventually was integrated and lost its identity. The Louisville mill was closed in 1961.

MARYLAND

Maryland was celebrated as a wheat growing and flour milling area from the late colonial period, and in the state is the site that has been occupied by flour mills longer than any other in the nation. Baltimore was the premier milling center for more than three decades early in the nineteenth century, and in 1810 there were 65 mills in Baltimore county and 101 in Frederick county. The area continued to be important until after 1900, at which time Maryland reported 280 mills making flour. Decline thereafter was rapid, the 1958 census showing only twelve such mills.

Ellicott City

Charles A. Gambrill Manufacturing Co.—American history abounds in famous mills, and one of the most famous was Patapsco Mills, in Ellicott City, just outside of Baltimore. It was founded in 1774 by the Ellicott brothers, Jonathan, Andrew and Thomas, and it became the foremost mill of its time. This was due to its size (1050 cwt.), the industry and prestige of its proprietors, and Baltimore became a great milling point in considerable part because of the Ellicotts and their mill on the Patapsco.

The Ellicotts were among the first to adopt Oliver Evans' revolutionary scheme of employing the power that ran the mill to convey product about the plant. In fact, many of the features of the Evans system were worked out in Patapsco Mills before 1790. The Ellicotts were Evans' benefactors, but in 1808 they fought his claim to patent rights and lost the battle.

After the Ellicotts, Patapsco Mills was owned by Charles Carroll of Carrollton for some years, and then went to Charles A. Gambrill who with his heirs operated the mill for more than 80 years. It was known as Charles A. Gambrill & Co. until 1881, when Gambrill's nephews, Richard G. and Patrick Macgill, incorporated Charles A. Gambrill Manufacturing Co. Richard G. was the first president, then Patrick, and in 1898 Charles C. Macgill (b. 1864 Md., d. 1923) succeeded his Uncle Patrick.

The historic old mill was destroyed by fire in 1916, and a new plant of 2400 cwt. was built the following year. By 1921 the company was insolvent, the mill was closed and reopened several times, there was a partial loss by fire, and in 1926 the Gambrill interest and the Patapsco name were extinguished when the property passed to M. G. Belding and Morris Schapiro and their Continental Milling Co.

Continental Milling Co. operated the mill until 1930. It was then leased for 25 years to Doughnut Machine Corp. (later called DCA Food Industries, Inc.). The mill was lost through fire in 1941 and was rebuilt with 3500 cwt. capacity. In 1955 DCA Food Industries, Inc. acquired title to the property.

MICHIGAN

Michigan is the largest producer of white wheat east of the Continental Divide, and for many years the Wolverine mills have specialized in supplying the makers of cookies, donuts and crackers. There were 24 flour mills in Michigan in 1958, but despite the moderate size of these plants their total production was considerably larger than that of the 534 mills operating in 1900. The first flour mill in Michigan was built about 1720 by Antoine Cadillac, founder of the French post of Detroit.

Michigan Millers' Association is the only active survivor of the many organizations of similar nature that once were prominent in milling affairs. Michigan mills had an output of 6,201,000 cwt. in 1961.

Augusta

Knappen Milling Co. specializes in the production of edible bran and cracker flour. It is also heavily engaged in grain storage, with 1,700,000 bushels of elevator space. The company is owned by the Knappen family and was organized in 1929 by Charles B. Knappen (b. 1894 Mich., d. 1962). The 300-cwt. mill he acquired was increased a little at a time until it reached 1000 cwt. It was replaced in 1962 by a new mill of 1500 cwt., which has a pneumatic system.

Knappen was president and general manager for 33 years. He was succeeded by Charles B. Knappen, Jr. (b. 1923 Mich.)

Chelsea

Chelsea Milling Co. is exclusively engaged in the household flour mix business and is one of the prominent factors in that specialty field. Its distribution extends to all 50 states and to England. It is owned by the Holmes family and is managed by twin brothers, Howard S., Jr., and Dudley K. Holmes (b. 1913 Mich.).

The Holmes' milling ancestry goes back five generations on one side and six on the other. George W. Peters, great-great-grandfather of the Holmes brothers, established a grist mill in the Chelsea area in 1844, and he and his son-in-law, Samuel Holmes, operated three such mills for many years.

Samuel's son, Harmon S. (b. 1854 Mich., d. 1922), who was primarily a banker, bought Chelsea Roller Mills in 1908 and it was managed by his son, Howard S. (b. 1886 Mich., d. 1936). The present company name was adopted in 1921. The twin brothers, sons of Howard S., took over the management in 1936.

Thomas White, sixth generation ancestor, had a mill near Dayton, Ohio, as early as 1803. His grandson, another Thomas, milled flour in Kansas around 1880. The latter's son, E. K. White (b. 1852 Ohio, d. 1934), bought the Merchant & Sparks mill in 1900; it had been erected in 1879 on the present site of Chelsea Milling Co. White sold this mill to Harmon S. Holmes in 1908. White's daughter, Mabel, married Howard S. Holmes.

Chelsea Milling Co. began producing biscuit mixes in 1930, and since 1956 has confined itself to mixes. Plant capacity of 750 cwt. was increased in 1955 to 1350 cwt. Company presidents: Harmon S. Holmes in 1908-21; Howard S. in 1921-36; Mabel W. in 1936-40; the younger Howard S. since 1940. Dudley K. is vice president and treasurer.

Coldwater

Wm. A. Coombs Milling Co.—Michigan's largest milling enterprise in the nineteenth century was that of William A. Coombs (b. 1840 Me., d. 1898). It had three plants in Coldwater, a town about 20 miles north of the Indiana border, and they had 2400 cwt. capacity of wheat flour and an equal volume of buckwheat.

Coldwater milling history dates from 1837. The first mill passed through several hands before becoming the property of Coombs. During the 1880's he also acquired the mills of Karr Bros. and Johnson, Starr & Co.

After Coombs' time the business was managed by Robert J. Hamilton (b. 1857, d. 1924). The Amendts of Monroe obtained a large interest during World War I, and when the Coombs company went bankrupt in 1922 the failure almost engulfed the Amendt company as well. The largest Coldwater mill was burned down in 1928 and the others were dismantled.

Detroit

Commercial Milling Co.—Although Detroit had 17 flour mills before the Civil War, there was such a scarcity of flour at times that the wholesale grocery of Peter Henkel (b. 1823 Germany, d. 1905) was unable to obtain a sufficient supply. He therefore went into partnership with Peter Voorhees in Commercial Mills in 1855. Commercial Milling Co. was incorporated in 1887 and Voorhees left the enterprise in 1889. The mill was enlarged in 1892, a mill in Cleveland was purchased in 1902 and operated until 1910 when it was sold, and a new mill of 2400 cwt. was completed in 1913 in Detroit. Small milling plants in Richmond, Pontiac, Durand and Lapeer were acquired between 1917 and 1920, but the first two were lost to fire and the others were sold in 1924-25. The Detroit mill was increased to 4400 cwt. in 1927.

Peter Henkel was president in 1887-1905. His son, Robert (b. 1860 Mich., d. 1930), was president in 1905-28, and was succeeded by his son, Fredrec Y. (b. 1897 Mich.). Arthur B. Marcy was vice president in 1930-43. The company continued until 1943, when the business was sold to International Milling Co.

David Stott Flour Mills, Inc.—David Stott (b. 1851 England, d. 1916) had a small mill on Detroit's west side from 1879, and the profits were used to purchase land on the outskirts of the city. These properties became valuable as the city grew, and the Stott real estate holdings were extensive. The mill was increased to 3000 cwt., and was headed and managed for many years by the founder's son, David E. Stott (b. 1872 Mich, d. 1957). It was closed in 1940 in the course of a receivership that was precipitated by long drawn out litigation within the family.

Dowagiac

Dowagiac Milling Co. is affiliated with Blue Bird Baking Co. The 1200-cwt. plant produces soft wheat flour principally for the parent enterprise.

The roots of milling in Dowagiac go back to 1833, when William Renniston built a grist mill in this Southwest Michigan town. This mill continued in use for 115 years. Horace F. Colby (d. 1915), who became the owner of a second mill built in 1858, also acquired the original mill in 1868. Colby operated both mills; after several partnerships, Colby Milling Co. was incorporated in 1891. The second mill was rebuilt in 1908 after destruction by fire, and it was later enlarged into the present plant. Fred H. Baker (b. 1860 Mich., d. 1924) was manager and part owner in 1900-24, followed by Frank W. Richey (b. 1865 Ohio, d. 1957) in 1924-43.

Dowagiac Milling Co. was formed in 1943, when the present owners took over the mill. Louis D. Preonas (b. 1897 Greece) has been president since its organization, and Clarence L. Athanson (b. 1906 Greece) became manager in 1956, his predecessors having been Pandely Kamtchy and Thomas Randall.

Frankenmuth

Star of the West Milling Co., named for the supply ship fired upon near Charleston before the siege of Fort Sumter, operates a flour mill of 950 cwt. in the Michigan "thumb country" north of Flint. It is largely concerned with the cracker trade in the Middle West. The company is a community enterprise, with most of the stock owned in and near the town.

The original plant built in 1871 by John M. Hubinger was a grist mill. Star of the West Milling Co. was organized in 1903 by farmers and businessmen. The mill was rebuilt and enlarged, the most recent occasion having been in 1952. Jacob C. Rummel (b. 1871 Mich., d. 1947) was manager in 1911-47, followed by his son, Otto (b. 1905 Mich., d. 1950) in 1947-50 and Albert H. List in 1950-53. Richard Krafft, Jr. (b. 1929 Mich.) has been manager since 1953.

Grand Rapids

Voigt Milling Co.—The Voigts were millers in Grand Rapids for three-quarters of a century. Carl G. A. Voigt (b. 1833 Germany, d. 1908) bought the Star Mill in 1875 and the Crescent mill in 1882, merging them in 1896. The 500-cwt. plant was increased in size until it reached 1200 cwt. Flour milling was discontinued in 1954.

Voigt Milling Co. was incorporated in 1908. Frank A. Voigt (b. 1861 Ind., d. 1927) was president and general manager in 1908-27, Ralph A. Voigt (b. 1882 Mich.) from 1927. They were sons of the founder, as was Carl S. Voigt (b. 1874 Ind., d. 1958), who was in the company many years.

Hillsdale

F. W. Stock & Sons, Inc.—After 96 years in the business, the Stocks sold their mill in Hillsdale in 1958. The business was established by Frederick William Stock (b. 1825 Germany, d. 1912), who acquired the grist mill of Cook & Waldron in 1862. Capacity was increased and before the end of the century it reached 2000 cwt. The mill was rebuilt and enlarged in the 1930's and a donut mix plant was added a few years later. Present capacity is 6000 cwt., with a million bushels grain storage.

Incorporation took place in 1907, all shares being owned by the Stock family. Presidents: F. W. Stock in 1907-12, his son, Alexander D. (b. 1860 Ind., d. 1942) in 1912-42, and the latter's son, Harold F. (b. 1890 Va.), in 1942-58. Harold F. was the active manager from 1930 and remained in charge for almost two years after the sale. The business was purchased in 1958 by DCA Food Industries, Inc., New York, and is operated as F. W. Stock Division of that company.

Ionia

Runciman Milling Co., a subsidiary of C. H. Runciman Co., was organized in 1952, when the Hale mill was purchased by interests long engaged in grain and bean handling. The mill was enlarged to 1200 cwt. Elevator storage totals 300,000 bushels. Flour business is with the soft wheat bakery trade. Company president is Carl H. Runciman, Jr. (b. 1914 Mich.).

Jonathan Hale (b. 1827 England, d. 1901) had several small mills in Michigan, beginning in 1853. Hale Bros. was formed in 1865 to operate such a mill near Ionia, 30 miles east of Grand Rapids. In 1896 Elmer B. (d. 1924) and Lewis H. (d. 1940), sons of Jonathan, bought out their uncle John, and the enterprise then became Jonathan Hale & Sons, a partnership. Laurence I. Hale (b. 1888 Mich., d. 1952), son of Lewis H., was owner and manager after 1940.

Jackson

Heywood Milling Co.—Jackson was the site of a small mill, built in the early 1880's, that was used primarily for exhibition purposes by a middlings purifier company headed by George T. Smith. Zenas C. Eldred, a Jackson businessman, had an interest in both concerns, and from 1885 the mill was known as Eldred Milling Co. It became insolvent in 1890, and Eldred acquired the entire property, increased the mill to 1200 cwt., and installed Sidney Heywood as manager.

Heywood managed the mill until 1911, when his son, Stephen, took over. The latter bought the business in 1917, changed the name to Heywood Milling Co., and operated the mill until 1932, when it was closed.

Lowell

King Milling Co. operates a 1200 cwt. soft wheat bakery mill in Lowell, just east of Grand Rapids. It is owned and managed by the Doyle family.

The first mill in Lowell was built in 1847, and was in use until 1958—in late years as a corn mill. Lowell Mills, erected in 1867, was acquired in 1890 by Francis King (b. 1820 N. Y., d. 1900), and he organized King Milling Co. The mill of 400 cwt. was destroyed by fire in 1943, was rebuilt with 600 cwt. capacity and was subsequently increased to the present size.

Company presidents: Francis King in 1890-1900; his son, Frank T. King (b. 1856 Mich., d. 1934) in 1900-34; Charles Doyle (b. 1878 Mich., d. 1943) in 1934-36; the latter's brother, William C. (b. 1890 Ark., d. 1945) in 1936-45; King Doyle (b. 1922 Mich.), son of William C., since 1945. Milton P. Fuller was general manager in 1945-50.

Monroe

Amendt Milling Co. serves the soft wheat bakery trade in the East from its 1000-cwt. mill in Monroe, halfway between

Detroit and Toledo. The plant was built in 1941, when an earlier mill was destroyed by fire.

Ancestry of the mill traces to 1820, when Waterloo Flour Mill was established on the River Raisin, in what is now downtown Monroe. Twenty years later Monroe City Mill was built. These mills were later consolidated into Waldorf Mill, which was acquired about 1895 by Conrad Amendt (b. 1833 Germany, d. 1898), who had been an operative miller in Ohio and Michigan. His oldest son, George A. (b. 1872 Ohio, d. 1929) was the leader of five brothers who took over the father's business. They obtained control of William A. Coombs Milling Co., Coldwater, during World War I, but that concern met with financial disaster a few years later. The Monroe company came to the rescue, but the result was receivership for Coombs and reorganization for Monroe. Ownership passed largely to businessmen in Monroe, and Lee O. Bracy (b. 1894 Ohio) managed the enterprise in 1926-59. John B. Watson (b. 1913 N. Y.) has been manager since 1959.

Amendt Milling Co. was formed in 1906. Its presidents: George A. Amendt in 1906-25; H. Austin Consor in 1925-41; Lee O. Bracy in 1941-60; Harry J. Seitz since 1960.

Owosso

Harris Milling Co. has a 2000-cwt. flour mill and a 900-cwt. buckwheat mill in Owosso, between Lansing and Flint, a feed plant and 2,000,000 bushels of grain storage. It also owns Austin-Heaton Co., Durham, N. C. The Harris flour business is largely with the family trade in North Carolina, but it also has a substantial stake in the soft wheat bakery field.

Founder of the business which eventually grew into Harris Milling Co. was John A. Harris (b. 1842 England, d. 1918), whose forebears had been millers in England. The grist mill he built in 1871 at Mount Pleasant, Mich., continued to operate for 79 years. In its later years it reached 700 cwt. capacity, and the plant was converted to feed production when the Owosso mill was erected in 1950.

The business was run for many years by John Harris, his brothers, sons and nephews. His son, Edward O. (b. 1877 Mich.), joined the family enterprise in 1894, became sole owner in 1916 and president of Harris Milling Co. upon its incorporation in 1940. He has been board chairman since 1953 and is still active in the management, his participation covering 69 years.

Robert V. Harris (b. 1906 Mich.), son of Edward O., succeeded his father as company president in 1953. He was chosen as chairman of Millers' National Federation in 1962.

Portland

Valley City Milling Co.—Grand Rapids was the birthplace of Valley Milling Co., which was formed in 1884 and incorporated in 1894. It had three flour mills, one of which was converted to feed production many years ago. The others, known as the Valley and the Model, with about 1000 cwt. each, were destroyed by fire in 1917 and 1923.

Valley City Milling Co. then purchased a small mill in Portland, 20 miles west of Lansing, and enlarged it to 1200 cwt. Offices were moved to Portland in 1932. The mill was taken by fire in 1948, but the company has continued in business by having flour milled to its specifications. It has been primarily a family flour mill.

Management has been in the hands of the Rowe family throughout company history. Presidents: Conrad Swensburg in 1894-98; William N. Rowe (b. 1853 N. Y., d. 1905) in 1898-1905; Rowe's son, William S. (b. 1880 Mo., d. 1923) in 1905-23; another son, Fred N. (b. 1883 Mich.), in 1923-56; and Fred N., Jr. (b. 1921 Mich.) since 1956. The elder Fred Rowe, now chairman of the board, has been in the business more than 60 years.

Quincy

Williams Milling Co. is a newcomer to the Michigan milling scene, having been formed in 1957 when the 600-cwt. mill of McKenzie Milling Co. was leased and later purchased by D. Warren Williams (b. 1905 Mich.). Capacity was doubled and pneumatic equipment installed in 1959, and the mill was increased to 2100 cwt. in 1961. Williams' son, John R. (b. 1927 Mich.), is manager of the company, which chiefly produces cracker flour.

The first mill in Quincy, 25 miles south of Battle Creek, was erected in 1863. It passed through the hands of twelve owners during the next 24 years. It was purchased in 1887 by Felix A. McKenzie (b. 1860 W. Va., d. 1919) and enlarged. He added a buckwheat mill of 1000 cwt. before 1900, and McKenzie Milling Co. was one of the leaders in that trade for more than half a century. Carlton D. McKenzie (b. 1895 Mich., d. 1960) became manager in 1919 and was prominent in industry affairs, serving as president of Millers' National Federation in 1944-46.

MINNESOTA

The milling revolution of the 1870's centered in Minnesota. Here the middlings purifier and gradual reduction were first used in America, here was the first all-roller mill. Minnesota was the first state in flour production for more than 50 years, Minneapolis the world's greatest milling city. These laurels were retained until 1930, yielding to Kansas in the rising importance of southwestern wheat and flour and to Buffalo in the rapid growth of that milling point.

Minnesota's first mill was built in 1823 by the army at Fort Snelling, in the environs of Minneapolis. First grist mill in the state was that of Benjamin Gervais at Little Canada, just north of St. Paul, built in 1844. First merchant mill was at Afton, on the St. Croix east of St. Paul, built in 1846 by Lemuel Bolles.

Minneapolis' first merchant mill was that of Rollins, Eastman & Upton, built in 1854; and the first on the west side of the river was historic Cataract Mills, established in 1858 by Eastman & Gibson. In 1882 Minneapolis had 26 mills with total capacity of 42,000 cwt.; in 1919 there were 29 mills that could produce 190,000 cwt. The four largest companies in the industry still have headquarters in the city.

The milling industry gave Minnesota one United States senator—William D. Washburn—and two governors, John S. Pillsbury and Gen. Lucius F. Hubbard. The latter, who was chief executive in 1881-86, commanded a brigade in Virginia through several hard battles; his mill was at Mazeppa, midway between Rochester and Red Wing, and was a 1200-cwt. plant some miles from a railroad.

Minnesota had 377 flour mills in 1900, and but 27 in 1958. The state produced 26,317,000 cwt. of flour in 1961, standing third.

Albert Lea

Mills of Albert Lea—The idle 1000-cwt. mill of Albert Lea Flour Mills Co., in the Southern Minnesota town of that name, was acquired in 1916 by Shane Brothers and several associates and put into operation. It was owned by the group and not by the company and was called Mills of Albert Lea.

Some time after the Shane failure in 1919 the mill became the property of VanDusen & Harrington Co., and was managed by William Fulton. It became part of King Midas Mill Co. in 1924, when that company was also purchased by Van-Dusen & Harrington Co. The following year the plant was sold to F. Samuel Birkenmayer and in 1926 to E. G. Darson, and was called Albert Lea Milling Co. The mill ran very little and the company became bankrupt in 1929.

Austin

Hormel Milling Co.—It was believed by George A. Hormel (b. 1862, d. 1946) that the men who sold his packing house products could double as flour salesmen, and in 1917 he bought Peerless Roller Mills in Austin to prove his point. The venture was not a success. The mill was enlarged to 3200 cwt., and Hormel Milling Co. was formed in 1921 when it was decided to separate the mill from the meat plant. It was managed by Charles J. Marboe (b. 1877, d. 1925) in 1919-24 and then by Edward Selby. The business was discontinued in 1926 and the mill was dismantled a few years later.

Crookston

Crookston Milling Co.—In 1903 Crookston Milling Co. was organized by Marcus A. Johnson (b. 1849 Sweden, d. 1928) and S. M. Sivertson (b. 1860 Norway, d. 1946), and a small mill was built in Crookston, Northwestern Minnesota. It reached 2400 cwt. capacity in the 1920's and 3600 cwt. by 1945. It had both flour and durum units, but in later years it was exclusively a durum mill. The mill was closed in 1952. Johnson was president, then Sivertson and later John J. Padden.

Duluth

Duluth-Superior Milling Co.—In 1893 Daisy Roller Mill

Co. of Milwaukee, which was controlled by E. P. Allis Co., the great mill builders, opened a 6000-cwt. mill in Superior, Wis., at the head of the lakes. William D. Gray (b. 1843 Scotland, d. 1920), milling engineer who was long associated with Allis, was president. Louis R. Hurd was manager.

Along with many other mills, the Daisy company was absorbed in 1899 by United States Flour Milling Co. Upon the collapse of that venture the next year, Daisy Roller Mill Co. and Listman Mill Co., also in Superior, were incorporated into Duluth-Superior Milling Co., a wholly owned subsidiary of Standard Milling Co., and continued as such until 1932. It then became a division of the parent company. The Listman mill became a durum mill of 4000 cwt.; it was closed in 1936. Meanwhile the Daisy mill had reached 7800 cwt. capacity.

Hurd managed the company in 1893-1904. Joseph A. Walter followed him in 1904-11, and Benjamin J. Stockman (b. 1863 Scotland, d. 1940) held sway in 1912-32. Company offices, which had been in Duluth from the beginning, were moved to Minneapolis in 1932, and for the next four years management was combined with that of Northwestern Consolidated Milling Co. in the hands of Jens Juul. The divisions were merged in 1936 into their parent, Standard Milling Co.

The Superior plant was sold in 1939 to King Midas Flour Mills and has since been used as a durum mill. Present capacity is 8200 cwt.

Duluth Universal Milling Co.—At the end of the nineteenth century, when the twin ports at the head of the Great Lakes were the nation's second largest milling center, Duluth Universal Mill Co. was established by A. D. Goodman (d. 1915). The Gregory-Jennison interests obtained control in 1906, and the concern then became Duluth Universal Milling Co. The original mill was increased over the years to 1500 cwt.

Goodman managed the business in 1900-15, and was succeeded by his son, A. Laird Goodman, in 1915-26 and then by William P. Majo in 1926-40. At the end of that period, William J. Russell (b. 1876 Vt.) bought out his associates and his son, Dudley J. (b. 1913 Minn.) served as president and manager for the ensuing 18 years.

The company went out of business in 1958.

Fairfax

Crescent Milling Co.—In 1905 a flour mill of 1100 cwt. was built in Fairfax, about a hundred miles southwest of the Twin Cities. Fairfax Milling Co. was managed in 1916-21 by Herman F. Wright (b. 1882 Ill.). After receivership, the mill was idle until 1924, when it was purchased by Harold M. Meech and associates. They organized Crescent Milling Co. and operated the mill in conjunction with Red Wing Milling Co. W. A. Chambliss (b. 1888 Okla., d. 1944) was the last manager. The mill closed in 1930.

Fergus Falls

Red River Milling Co.—Fergus Falls, almost 200 miles northwest of the Twin Cities, had seven flour mills late in the nineteenth century. The plant that became Red River Milling Co. was built in 1872 and enlarged in 1895. It was established by Page and Scott, was subsequently owned by David A. Tennant and Walter B. Windsor, and finally by Elmer E. Adams (b. 1862, d. 1950) and Charles Kaddatz. The mill was destroyed by fire in 1916 and rebuilt with 1200 cwt. Charles R. Anderson (b. 1870, d. 1943) managed the business for 40 years. Adams and Kaddatz sold in 1944 to Fred P. Wheeler (b. 1892 Minn., d. 1948) and associates, and Albert W. Hockenberger was manager in 1943-49.

After being idle seven years, the plant was purchased and rebuilt in 1956 by Montana Flour Mills Co. Present capacity is 2200 cwt.

Lake City

Tennant & Hoyt Co. is in Lake City, 80 miles southeast of the Twin Cities, on the Mississippi. The company operates a pneumatic flour mill of 6000 cwt. and 550,000 bushels of grain storage. It is exclusively a miller of bakery flour, with its trade in the Middle West and East.

Robert C. Tennant (b. 1860 N. Y., d. 1927) and Charles G. Hoyt (b. 1847 Me., d. 1912) formed the company in 1901 and built a flour mill of 800 cwt. Tennant had been associated with his brother, David, in a mill in Northfield, and Hoyt had been Pillsbury head miller for 20 years. The Lake City mill was destroyed by fire in 1906 and was rebuilt with 1400 cwt. It grew steadily—to 1600 cwt. in 1916, to 2400 cwt. in 1920, to 2800 cwt. in 1934, to 4000 cwt. in 1941, to 5000 cwt. in 1950 and to 6000 cwt. in 1961.

Tennant served as company president in 1901-27. Richard A. Hoyt (b. 1877 Minn., d. 1947), son of the founder, became president in 1927, and in 1942 he was succeeded by his son, Charles R. (b. 1910 Minn.), the present company head.

Mankato

Hubbard Milling Co. was a pioneer in developing the concentrate concept of livestock feeding, and it operates feed plants with daily capacity of 1300 tons. The Hubbard flour mill is of 3400-cwt. size, and the company's flour business is chiefly with the bakery trade in the East and Middle West. Headquarters is in Mankato, 80 miles southwest of the Twin Cities.

This business was started in 1879 by R. D. Hubbard (b. 1837 N. Y., d. 1905), proprietor of a linseed oil plant. Spurred by a bookkeeper's repeated suggestion, Hubbard built a mill of 600 cwt. It was increased from time to time, and before the end of the century it was a well established spring wheat mill. The original plant was replaced in 1919, the feed concentrate business was begun in 1928 and that activity soon dwarfed the flour mill in size and importance. Pneumatic conveying equipment was installed in the flour mill in 1961.

The bookkeeper who inspired Hubbard's entry into flour milling was George M. Palmer (b. 1853 Wis., d. 1939). Palmer was identified with the enterprise almost 60 years, serving as president more than half that time. He ultimately bought control from the Hubbard estate, and his grandson is now president. Long associated with him was Frank E. Browder (b. 1867 Tenn., d. 1939), vice president.

The company which bears the founder's name has had five presidents: Hubbard in 1879-1905; Palmer in 1905-39; Hosea R. Harmer (b. 1884 Minn.) in 1939-45; Charles B. MacLeod (b. 1897 Mich.) in 1945-58 and subsequently board chairman; Ogden P. Confer (b. 1921 Minn.) from 1958.

Marshall

Marshall Milling Co.—Marshall is in Southwestern Minnesota, not far from the South Dakota border. William Giesecke, who had operated the Sleepy Eye mill for some years, bought a small mill in Marshall in 1893 and enlarged it to 1600 cwt. Control of Marshall Milling Co. was obtained in 1914 by officials of Eagle Roller Mill Co., and Charles Vogtel of the Eagle group became president and Franklin Edwards (b. 1879 N. Y.) general manager. The mill was increased to 6000 cwt. early in the Eagle era.

Control of Marshall Milling Co. passed to Guy A. Thomas and associates about 1922, and disclosure of that fact a few years later led to his resignation from Washburn Crosby Co. The mill operated sparingly and was closed in 1926.

Minneapolis

Archer-Daniels-Midland Co., largest marketer of oilseed products in the United States, ranks sixth in flour milling capacity. It operates flour mills in Minneapolis, Kansas City and St. Joseph, and a durum mill in Minneapolis, with aggregate capacity of 46,800 cwt. The company's flour business is almost exclusively with the bakery trade in the eastern half of the nation. Mill elevator space totals 5,400,000 bushels. In addition to its primary business in linseed and soybean manufacture, the company is extensively engaged in grain storage and marketing, alfalfa dehydrating and the production of industrial chemicals, the latter alone numbering a thousand items.

Archer-Daniels-Midland Co. entered flour milling in 1930 through the purchase of control of Commander Larabee Corp., which was floundering at the time. The latter became a wholly-owned subsidiary and this relationship continued for 29 years. During that time the milling activities of the company were conducted as Commander Larabee Milling Co., and that was the name chiefly known to the trade. In 1959 Commander Larabee was merged into the parent company, becoming part of the agricultural group of Archer-Daniels-Midland Co., this division being headed by Erwin A. Olson (b. 1900 Minn.).

A merger of Archer-Daniels Linseed Co., formed in 1905 by George A. Archer and John W. Daniels, and Midland Linseed Products Co., brought Archer-Daniels-Midland Co. into existence in 1923. The Archers had been in the linseed business since the 1830's in Dayton, and Daniels began there in 1879.

Presidents: John W. Daniels in 1905-24; Shreve M. Archer (b. 1888 S. D., d. 1947), son of the co-founder, in 1924-47; Thomas L. Daniels (b. 1892 Ohio), son of the other co-founder, in 1947-58; John H. Daniels (b. 1921 Minn.), son of Thomas L., since 1958.

Atkinson Milling Co.—The Atkinson brothers worked for Washburn Crosby Co., beginning in the 1880's, and held executive posts for many years. William M. (b. 1868 Ill., d. 1929) ended this association in 1916, when he built a 2000-cwt. mill in Minneapolis and organized a company to which he gave the family name.

In the course of time the Atkinsons had the largest single-plant company in the Mill City. The mill had 7300 cwt. capacity and grain storage of 825,000 bushels. The company was a pioneer in bulk storage of flour through a facility of 80,000 cwt. erected in 1941, and in 1953 it made the first commercial delivery of flour in a bulk truck. Atkinson Bulk Transport Co. patented the system and equipment that made bulk shipment of flour by truck possible.

The founder was president in 1916-29. His brother, Frederick G. (b. 1864 Ill., d. 1940), whose service with Washburn Crosby covered 49 years, headed Atkinson Milling Co. in 1929-36. He was followed by Lawrence B. Lund in 1936-41. Frederick M. Atkinson (b. 1914 Minn., d. 1961), son of Frederick G., was president in 1941-54 and 1959-61, being board chairman in the intervening years. Martin W. Nelson (b. 1897 Minn.) was president in 1954-59, and Dudley J. Russell in 1961-62.

Atkinson Milling Co. was merged with Archer-Daniels-Midland Co. early in 1962, and the Atkinson plant is operated by the latter company.

Baldwin Flour Mills Co.—Dwight M. Baldwin (b. 1867 Minn., d. 1942) entered flour milling in 1889 in association with his father-in-law, M. Sheehan, who had a small mill at Graceville, Minn., not far from the junction of Minnesota and the two Dakotas. Three years later he bought the business. Baldwin Flour Mills Co. was incorporated in 1901, with offices in Minneapolis. In 1918 a second mill was added—an idle plant in Oakes, Southeastern North Dakota, that had been the first durum mill in the nation. Baldwin served as president of Millers' National Federation in 1910-11.

The company was overtaken by receivership in 1930. The Oakes mill was closed, and the Graceville mill continued to operate under the receivership until it was destroyed by windstorm in 1933.

Barber Milling Co.—Cataract Mills was the first mill of importance at the Falls of St. Anthony. It was built in 1858 by Paris Gibson (b. 1830 Me., d. 1920), who became a United States Senator from Montana (1901-05), and William Eastman. The 600-cwt. mill was acquired in 1871 by Gardner & Barber; in 1876 the firm became Daniel R. Barber & Son, and in 1896 Barber Milling Co. was incorporated. The mill had 2400-cwt. capacity in later years. Edwin R. Barber (b. 1850 Vt., d. 1920) was president in 1896-1919, followed by his son and namesake who had been vice president and manager. Barber Milling Co. became insolvent in 1923, the mill was closed and was finally torn down in 1928.

Cannon Valley Milling Co.—Goodhue Mill Co. and its 500-cwt. plant at the falls of the Cannon River were established in 1873 by Charles Moore and Stephen Gardner. Otto Doebler bought the property in 1892 and increased the mill to

1000 cwt. Goodhue Mill Co. became Cannon Valley Milling Co. in 1908, when control went to H. H. Thayer and Jacob O. Ewing (b. 1872 Minn., d. 1947). Thayer was president in 1908-24, Ewing in 1924-30. The mill was lost to fire in 1914, was rebuilt with 3000 cwt. and increased in 1946 to 4000 cwt.

After William H. Bovey (b. 1871 Minn., d. 1943) retired from Washburn Crosby Co. in 1928, he purchased control of Cannon Valley Milling Co., and his son, W. Howard (b. 1897 Minn., d. 1959) was president in 1930-49. Managers in this period were Ewing, Clement H. Cochran and Carl V. Anderson. The mill was closed in 1949.

The mill was in Cannon Falls, 35 miles south of St. Paul. Office was in Minneapolis after 1908.

Capital Flour Mills, Inc.—From the time that the two plants of Capital Flour Mills, Inc., in St. Paul went into production they were used only for grinding durum wheat, and the company was the largest exclusive durum miller.

The company was organized in 1916 by William E. Coles, a mill promoter who was connected for brief periods with half-a-dozen milling concerns. Capital City Milling & Grain Co. was launched with a 600-cwt. plant. The second mill of 1800 cwt. was opened in 1918. The mills were later enlarged to a total of 4300 cwt. The company did well for a few years, but sustained heavy losses later and reorganization was imperative.

Capital City Milling & Grain Co. thus became Capital Flour Mills, Inc., in 1924. The owners brought in Charles P. Walton (b. 1872 Wis., d. 1945) as president and manager. He had operated a small durum mill in North Dakota some years earlier and then was associated with Russell-Miller Milling Co. The company made a complete turnaround and it became one of the leading durum mills. Company office was moved to Minneapolis in 1925.

International Milling Co. bought Capital Flour Mills, Inc., in 1946. Paul M. Petersen (b. 1903 Minn.), who succeeded Walton as president, became an International executive during the period before his retirement in 1958. The former Capital mills are used for durum production by International, and have 5000 cwt. capacity.

Century Milling Co.—The Christian interests' strong opposition to Northwestern Consolidated Milling Co. being merged into United States Flour Milling Co. in 1899 forced them out of Northwestern Consolidated. Under the leadership of George C. Christian (b. 1870 Minn., d. 1919), whose father, George H., had been one of the leading pioneer millers in Minneapolis, they formed Century Milling Co. in 1900 and built a flour mill of 4000 cwt. in Minneapolis. Later they acquired small mills in Aston and Redfield. With Christian as head, the company continued until 1917, and then the business was sold to B. B. Sheffield. It was soon resold to Eagle Roller Mill Co. interests, and the Minneapolis mill was operated until 1921 with Charles Vogtel as president. The mill remained idle for three years and then was reopened briefly before it became permanently idle.

Commander Larabee Milling Co.—Third largest company in the industry for a number of years, Commander Larabee Corp. was an amalgam in 1927 of the Sheffield-controlled companies in Minnesota and Larabee Flour Mills Co., which had mills in Missouri, Kansas and Buffalo. Total capacity of active mills at the time of merger was about 40,000 cwt., of which more than half was in the Southwest. Headquarters was in Minneapolis.

Benjamin B. Sheffield (b. 1860 N. S., d. 1936) was president of Commander Larabee Corp. in 1927-30, as he had been after 1920 of the Commander companies. For about five years, Continental Baking Co. had a large interest in the merged company, but took no part in its management. In 1928 the company acquired the plant of Thornton & Chester Milling Co., Buffalo, to replace the mill in that city that was lost through fire the same year.

Commander Larabee Corp. was reorganized in 1930, following extensive inventory losses the preceding year. At that time control passed to Archer-Daniels-Midland Co., and later it became a wholly-owned subsidiary. Name was changed in 1935 to Commander Larabee Milling Co.

G. B. R. Smith Milling Co. was acquired in 1933 and operated until 1941, when the plant was sold to Quaker Oats Co. The Buffalo mill was enlarged in 1936 and in the war period to 10,000 cwt., but it was closed in 1950. The Wellington mill was destroyed by fire in 1931, and the idle Hutchinson mill was then returned to production until 1959. The Clinton mill was closed in 1952. The Morristown, Stillwater and Janesville mills were closed during the early 1930's. The Montgomery mill was operated somewhat irregularly for several years, but was enlarged to 7000 cwt. during the war period and finally closed in 1952. Result of these changes and substantial enlargement of Kansas City and Minneapolis was an increase to 33,800 cwt. in the late 1950's.

Sheffield's successors as president: William H. Sudduth (b. 1875 Wis., d. 1953), Sheffield's longtime associate, in 1930; Guy A. Thomas (b. 1874 N. Y., d. 1946) in 1930-43; Romaine W. Goodell (b. 1882 Iowa, d. 1951), executive vice president from 1930 and actual manager through the Thomas era, in 1943-47; Clarence M. Hardenbergh (b. 1881 Minn.) in 1947-50; Ellis D. English (b. 1904 Mo.) in 1950-59.

Goodell, Hardenbergh and English were active in industry affairs, English serving as president of Millers' National Federation in 1960-62. Joshua M. Chilton (b. 1888 Mo., d. 1947) was widely known in the grain trade, and was general manager of Grain Stabilization Corp. in the early 1930's.

Commander Larabee was merged into the agricultural division of Archer-Daniels-Midland Co. in 1959.

Commander Mill Co.—The Commander group of companies was controlled until 1920 by the Gregory-Jennison interests. Largest among them was Commander Mill Co., organized in 1909 as successor to James Quirk Milling Co., which built a mill in Montgomery in 1889 and in which the Gregory-Jennison partners had been interested from the beginning. The others were Jennison Bros. Co., established in 1886 and incorporated in 1915 as Empire Milling Co.; Big Diamond Mill Co., bought in 1911 from Sheffield Mill & Elevator Co., which had a mill in Morristown that dated from 1876; W. J. Jennison Co., acquired in 1894; Duluth Universal Milling Co., purchased in 1906; Stillwater Milling Co., obtained in 1909 and converted soon after to durum production and then merged into Commander Mill Co.; and smaller properties in Mapleton and Elysian, which were closed many years ago. Mills in Rush City and Madelia were leased for several years.

After 1908 William G. Gooding (b. 1863 Minn., d. 1939) was president of all the Commander companies except Duluth Universal. Headquarters of all companies except Duluth Universal was in Minneapolis.

The Gooding interest in Commander, Big Diamond and Empire was purchased in 1920 by Benjamin B. Sheffield, one of the partners. Control of the companies then passed to Sheffield, although a large interest was retained until 1928 by the others. Sheffield became president of each company at that time, and his companies then had aggregate capacity of about 11,000 cwt. In 1922 the durum mill of Yerxa, Andrews & Thurston passed into his hands. The plant was enlarged to 4000 cwt., and in 1928 a spring wheat mill of equal size was added. This enterprise was operated as Minneapolis Milling Co. In 1924 the Madelia mill of C. S. Christensen Co. was purchased but was closed soon afterward.

Commander and its associated companies merged in 1927 with Larabee Flour Mills Co. The resulting company, Commander Larabee Corp., was third largest in the industry and had active mills of more than 40,000 cwt. capacity. The Commander, Empire, Big Diamond and Minneapolis companies retained their identities for a few years, but by the middle 1930's they had become trade names only.

General Mills, Inc. is the largest milling company in the world as well as in the nation. It has 17 flour mills in the United States, with 129,900 cwt. capacity, including 4200 cwt. durum and 2400 cwt. rye, and more than 48,000,000 bushels of grain storage. The company participates in every phase of milling, doing business in all states as well as abroad. It is one of the chief producers of breakfast cereals, flour mixes and refrigerated doughs. It is also an important manufacturer of certain industrial chemicals, electronic products and substances derived from oilseeds. Total annual business amounts to $550,-000,000.

General Mills, Inc., was formed in 1928, primarily as an expansion of the business that had evolved from General Washburn's first milling venture more than 60 years before. The

1928 move consisted of establishing a holding company that took over the ownership of Washburn Crosby Co., Inc., Royal Milling Co., and Red Star Milling Co. Within a year the Sperry chain, six of the Kell companies, El Reno Mill & Elevator Co., and a formula feed company had been added.

Each of the milling subsidiaries continued to do business in large measure as before, competing with each other as well as with other mills. Only general policies were determined by the parent company. This procedure changed gradually, the subsidiary corporations were merged into General Mills, Inc., in 1937 and the latter then became an operating company. Five milling divisions were set up, but after a few years they declined in importance and by war's end the business was largely centralized.

Total milling capacity of General Mills, Inc., has changed but little since the company was fully organized. Two mills have been purchased—Red Band Co., Inc. in 1933, and Acme Mills, Inc., in 1945, with capacities of 3000 cwt. and 2000 cwt., respectively. Two new mills have been constructed—3300 cwt. in Los Angeles in 1948 and 6000 cwt. in Des Moines in 1960. Seven of the original plants have been closed—Waco in 1932, Perry in 1936, Vernon in 1937, Portland in 1948, Kalispell in 1948, Oklahoma City in 1953 and Louisville in 1954. Capacity in Minneapolis has been scaled down from 34,600 cwt. to 13,800, in Buffalo from 39,200 cwt. to 30,900, in Wichita from 7200 cwt. to 5200, and in Tacoma from 9300 cwt. to 8400. Other plants have been increased—Chicago from 6000 cwt. to 8200, Kansas City from 12,500 to 14,200, Wichita Falls from 5400 cwt. to 6200, El Reno from 2000 cwt. to 2700, Amarillo from 2100 cwt. to 2500, Great Falls from 2500 cwt. to 3200, Spokane from 3750 to 4900, Ogden from 4400 cwt., to 6300, and Vallejo from 6600 cwt. to 7800.

The great growth of General Mills, Inc., during the past third of a century has largely come through diversification. The main avenues have been breakfast cereals, flour mixes, electronic and mechanical devices, soybean processing and several special lines. One major venture, formula feed, was discontinued in 1962 although the company was one of the principal factors in that business.

Extensive technological research has marked the history of General Mills, Inc. In addition to many lesser developments, this resulted in the Bellera milling process, announced in 1959; it utilizes a short, simple flow and provides high extraction of flour in the first reduction steps. It is a considerably simplified process in which pneumatic conveying is used. This process has been installed in the Des Moines, Minneapolis and Buffalo mills. The Los Angeles, Ogden and Kansas City plants have pneumatic installations, Los Angeles being the first American pneumatic mill.

James Ford Bell (b. 1879 Pa., d. 1961), who had been president of Washburn Crosby Co., Inc., was the founder of General Mills, Inc., its president in 1928-34 and board chairman in 1934-47. He was a man of great vision and ability and largely responsible for the company's research program. He was head of the millers' committee that formulated the wartime industry control program in 1917 and became chairman of the milling division of United States Food Administration. Closely associated with Bell in forming General Mills, Inc., were two men who later became company presidents—Donald D. Davis (b. 1888 Ill., d. 1950), who served in 1934-42, and Harry A. Bullis (b. 1890 Neb.), president in 1942-48 and board chairman in 1948-58. Bullis had a leading part in a wide variety of public activities both before and after retirement. Leslie N. Perrin (b. 1886 Ill.) was president in 1948-52.

Charles H. Bell (b. 1907 Minn.), son of J. F. Bell, was president in 1952-61 and then became chairman. General Edwin W. Rawlings (b. 1904 Minn.) was elected president in 1961.

General Mills' men have long been active in industry affairs. Gerald S. (Spike) Kennedy (b. 1894 Minn.), whose service in the company began in 1914 and who was board chairman in 1958-61, was president of Millers' National Federation in 1956-58. Sydney Anderson (b. 1881 Minn., d. 1948), who was a member of Congress in 1911-25 and then was full-time president of the Federation for four years, was also a noted leader of the industry. Others who were widely known, all vice presidents of General Mills, Inc., were Walter R. Barry (b. 1896 Ill., d. 1963), grocery products head; Walter H. Mills (b. 1890 Mass.), authority on wheat grades; G. Cullen Thomas (b. 1890 Ind.), leader in enrichment; Samuel C. Gale (b. 1895 Minn., d. 1961), advertising genius; and Don A. Stevens (b. 1903 N. D.), general manager of the milling division.

International Milling Co. is second largest milling company in the world and third largest in plant capacity in the United States. In this country the company operates 16 mills having 81,000 cwt. capacity (including 9000 durum and 1600 rye), more than 20,000,000 bushels of grain storage and 1700 tons of formula feed capacity. Through its affiliates, Robin Hood Flour Mills, Ltd., and Molinos Nacionales C. A., the company runs five mills in Canada and three in Venezuela, with total capacity of 45,400 cwt. Its aggregate capacity is thus 126,400 cwt.

International Milling Co. is heavily concentrated in the domestic bakery trade, in which it is in first place east of the Rockies; and in flour exports, shipping to about 70 world markets. It also has a large semolina business throughout the nation and a family flour trade in the eastern half of the country.

Founder of what became International Milling Co. was Francis A. Bean (b. 1840 Mass., d. 1930), whose milling career had three parts of about 20 years each. First of these periods was in a small mill in Faribault, Minn. of which he was proprietor after being an employee of his father, Samuel; this experience ended in bankruptcy in 1891. Second period began the next year in a rented mill of 400 cwt. in New Prague, 35 miles southwest of Minneapolis, progressed through a mill of his own there and a degree of growth that included other mills as well as an enlargement of New Prague. The third period began in 1910, when the company name was changed to International Milling Co. and when his son, Francis A. (Frank) (b. 1878 Minn., d. 1955), and William L. Harvey (b. 1871 Ill., d. 1938) took the foundation laid by the elder Bean and built it into an enterprise that moved up to its present high position in the industry.

New Prague Flouring Mill Co. had 1000 cwt. capacity when its plant was built in 1896. Within the next decade Bean acquired mills in Blue Earth and Wells, both of which were operated until 1937. In 1904 he bought the 1200-cwt. mill of Western Flour Mills Co. in Davenport, Iowa, which had been built in 1892 by Riverside Milling Co. During the next eight years the Canadian field was entered via mills in Moose Jaw and Calgary. At that time, also, the founder paid off the debts that had accrued from the Faribault failure, even though they had long been legally outlawed. He was largely retired after 1910, although he continued as company president.

Headquarters was moved to Minneapolis in 1923. The Mystic mill in Sioux City had been acquired in 1920, and the American capacity of the company was 15,600 cwt. when it went to Minneapolis. A flour mill of 5000 cwt. was built in Buffalo in 1927 and was soon enlarged. Seven years later Greenville Milling & Elevator Co. was purchased.

During the second World War, International was a leader in converting surplus wheat into alcohol grits for use in making synthetic rubber, and the company was one of several that took part in producing the grits. Then followed a series of plant purchases that carried the company into third place in the industry—Commercial Milling Co. in 1942, Wabasha Roller Mill Co. and Eastern Semolina Mills in 1943, Ponca City Milling Co. and Shellabarger Mills in 1946, Capital Flour Mills, Inc. in 1946, Midland Flour Milling Co. in 1948, Federal Mill, Inc., in 1950 and Eagle Roller Mill Co. in 1951. A subsequent purchase was the Cleveland plant of Montana Flour Mills Co. in 1954. Meanwhile, other mills had been erected in Canada—in Saskatoon in 1927 and Humberstone in 1940 and St. Lawrence Flour Mills Co., Ltd., was acquired in 1952.

Present capacities of the company's American mills: Baldwinsville 4000 cwt. (durum), Blackwell 3700 cwt., Buffalo 17,500 cwt., Cleveland 4000 cwt., Davenport 5400 cwt., Detroit 7500 cwt., Greenville 4600 cwt., Kansas City 5300 cwt., Lockport 2400 cwt., New Prague 5800 cwt., Newton 2900 cwt., New Ulm 1600 cwt. (rye), Salina 7500 cwt., St. Paul 5000 cwt. (durum), and Wabasha 3800 cwt.

Harvey and Frank A. Bean divided management responsibilities in the two decades after 1910, and Harvey served as president in 1930-38. He was succeeded by Bean in 1948-43, and he by Charles Ritz (b. 1891 Ont.) in 1943-55. Ritz had previously been Canadian general manager and then Robin Hood president. He has been board chairman since 1955, and a leader in the industry as well as in the company.

Atherton Bean (b. 1910 Minn.), son of Frank A. Bean, has been company president since 1955. During the war years he was an official of the Office of Price Administration and presided over, with great distinction, the formulation of price ceilings on mill products. The ceiling program was regarded both in the government and in the industry as one of the most carefully prepared and workable orders issued in the control period.

Other International officers who have been active in industry affairs are Harry F. Marsh (b. 1874 Iowa, d. 1941), Percy B. Hicks (b. 1894 Manitoba, d. 1955), Malcolm B. McDonald (b. 1905 Minn.), P. Norman Ness (b. 1905 N. D.) and John Tatam (b. 1911 Minn.).

W. J. Jennison Co.—The Gregory-Jennison interests centered in a grain commission and private banking firm that was established in 1886, incorporated in 1927 and renamed Gregory Co. in 1944. Founder was Willis J. Jennison (b. 1852 Vt., d. 1908), and his chief partners were William D. Gregory (b. 1854 Ohio, d. 1929), William G. Gooding and William H. Sudduth. William J. Russell, a nephew, succeeded to the Jennison interest, and Lawrence S. Gregory and Benjamin B. Sheffield were leading later partners.

Jennison entered the milling business in 1882 in Watertown, S. D., and with his brother, John W., established a mill in Janesville in 1886. After the firm was organized, the partners acquired seven mills over a period of time and operated them through separate corporations. One of these was the 400-cwt. mill of A. W. Lathrop & Bros. in Appleton, 150 miles west of Minneapolis. Title to this mill was secured in 1894, and W. J. Jennison Co. was organized in 1896. Gooding became manager at that time and was president in 1908-1932. Jennison was president during the first 12 years.

The original mill was enlarged by stages to 1800 cwt. in 1920, and in much later years it was increased to 3000 cwt. Offices were in Minneapolis throughout company history. L. S. Gregory was president in 1932-60, Stanley A. Dillon since 1960. Gustave Mehlin (b. 1892 Minn.) and Malcolm D. Smith were co-managers in 1920-27 and Mehlin was general manager in 1927-61.

W. J. Jennison Co. bought Zenith Milling Co., Kansas City, in 1927, but dismantled the mill after about two years.

Although the Appleton mill was closed in 1961, the company has continued in other lines of business.

H. H. King Flour Mills Co.—Faribault, on the Cannon River 50 miles south of the Twin Cities, was named for Alexander Faribault, a French-Canadian fur trader who became a pioneer miller. His mill became the property of B. B. Sheffield in the 1880's. After the plant was destroyed by fire in 1896 it was rebuilt with 2000 cwt. capacity. Henry H. King (b. 1862 Me., d. 1948), who had a mill in nearby Jordan, bought a half-interest at about that time, and Sheffield-King Milling Co. was chartered in 1902. King bought out Sheffield some time later, and the company name was changed in 1923 to H. H. King Flour Mills Co. A durum unit was added in 1929, bringing capacity up to 4000 cwt. The flour mill was closed in 1948 and the durum mill in 1956, but the company continues in other activities. King was president until 1942, his son-in-law, L. George Truesdell, Jr. (b. 1903 Minn.), thereafter. James M. Quilty was manager in 1930-41, Arthur W. Quiggle (b. 1890 Minn.) in 1941-56.

King Midas Flour Mills—King Midas was the principal flour brand of Shane Bros. & Wilson Co., Philadelphia flour distributors who became millers in 1912. When their enterprises in the East failed soon after the end of the war, the subsidiary that operated the mills in Hastings and Shakopee, Minn., was taken over by Philadelphia banks and run by them until 1924. The Shane name was discarded in the process, and the company adopted the brand as its name.

The banks sold King Midas Milling Co. to VanDusen & Harrington Co., a Minneapolis grain house that also was the owners of Mills of Albert Lea and of Dakota Mill, an idle plant in Minneapolis once operated by National Milling Co. (a local concern, not to be confused with the Toledo company of the same name). King Midas Mill Co. became a wholly-owned subsidiary of the grain company, and it operated Dakota Mill and the plants in Hastings and Shakopee. The Albert Lea mill was soon sold. The Shakopee mill of 1400 cwt. was lost to fire in 1925, and the other mills had total capacity of 8500 cwt.

VanDusen and Harrington both passed away in 1928 and their company was purchased soon after by F. H. Peavey & Co. King Midas continued as a subsidiary and a few years later became a division as King Midas Flour Mills. By the 1930's King Midas was in first place in durum milling, in addition to doing a substantial business with bakers and the home trade. In 1939 its facilities were increased through the purchase from Standard Milling Co. of the Daisy mill in Superior. This plant was largely rebuilt and in recent years the capacity has been 8200 cwt., Hastings being 9500 cwt., including 1000 cwt. rye flour. Dakota Mill was closed in 1961.

King Midas has continued as a Peavey enterprise for 35 years. The parent company purchased Russell-Miller Milling Co. in 1954, and the two milling divisions were consolidated six years later as Russell Miller-King Midas Mills, which in 1963 was renamed Peavey Co. Flour Mills.

William Fulton (b. 1869 Scotland, d. 1942), who had

been manager of the Shane mills, was president of King Midas or manager of King Midas division in 1924-41. Romaine W. Goodell was general manager in 1924-30. William M. Steinke and Henry E. Kuehn, who had been associated with Fulton for 27 years, became co-managers of King Midas in 1941-54. Kuehn was general manager in 1954-60.

King Midas' Hastings mill was a historic establishment. It was founded in 1863 by Stephen Gardner, who pioneered in New Process milling. Charles Espenschied (b. 1849 Mo., d. 1926), son-in-law of Gardner, became manager in 1878 and later the owner until 1897. Gardner Mills was then sold to Seymour Carter (b. 1862 Ill., d. 1923), but the company became insolvent and the mill was sold to the Shanes in 1912. Although Espenschied was retired from milling, he was the second president of Millers' National Federation, serving in 1904-06.

Northwestern Consolidated Milling Co.—Disturbed over the Pillsbury-Washburn merger in 1889 and attempting to oppose bigness with another large company, six of the smaller Minneapolis mills joined in 1891 as Northwestern Consolidated Milling Co. These mills were the Galaxy, Columbia, Crown, Zenith, Pettit and Northwestern. They had been established between 1871 and 1883, and they had aggregate capacity of about 22,500 cwt., larger than Washburn Crosby and four-fifths the size of Pillsbury-Washburn. The company was operated for several years by a committee representing the various interests, but it was obliged to reorganize in 1895 and for the next 13 years it was headed by Albert C. Loring as general manager.

Minneapolis Flour Manufacturing Co. was formed in 1892 as a combination of Excelsior, Standard and St. Anthony mills, with total capacity of 7000 cwt. It was established for the same reason.

The owners of both Northwestern Consolidated and Minneapolis, tired of sharp competitive conditions that prevailed in the 1890's, joined in the United States Flour Milling Co. in 1899, and when that enterprise failed the next year the two companies became part of the properties that the bankers put into Standard Milling Co., a holding company. At that time Minneapolis Flour Manufacturing Co. was merged into Northwestern Consolidated.

Northwestern Consolidated was a wholly-owned subsidiary of Standard Milling Co. until 1932. It was then merged into the parent company and became an autonomous division until 1938, when the divisions were abolished. After Loring's time, the general manager in 1908-28 was Harry P. Gallaher (b. 1859 Mo., d. 1938), who became president in 1928-32. His son, Robert H. (b. 1892 Minn., d. 1962) was general manager in 1928-32, Jens Juul in 1932-36.

Crown was the last surviving unit of the famous old company, being operated until 1952. The other mills had been closed one at a time during the preceding half century, but only three of them were in use after the late 1920's.

Northwestern Milling Co.—The 1200-cwt. mill in Little Falls, a hundred miles northwest of Minneapolis, was built in 1901. It was owned by Pennsylvania people, and when the business failed to prosper John W. Stephenson went to Little Falls to run the mill. In 1919 a half-interest was acquired by William H. Bovey and Morris L. Hallowell (b. 1888 Minn.), and the office was then moved to Minneapolis. Stephenson was president and Hallowell general manager. The company went out of business in 1934.

Peavey Co., long one of the largest grain companies in the nation, is fourth in size among American milling companies. It operates nine flour mills in seven states, with aggregate capacity of 59,800 cwt. (including 8200 durum and 1000 rye) and more than 10,000,000 bushels of mill and terminal storage. Its milling activities are carried on under the name of Peavey Co. Flour Mills, doing business almost on a nation-wide basis in bakery flour and it is also prominent in the household trade in certain areas.

F. H. Peavey & Co. was founded in 1874 and incorporated in 1906. It entered flour milling in 1928 through the purchase of VanDusen & Harrington Co., a grain concern that owned King Midas Mill Co. The latter became a Peavey division in the middle 1930's. In 1954 the company acquired Russell-Miller Milling Co. The two milling divisions operated separately until 1960, and at that time they were merged as Russell Miller-King Midas Mills. Company name was changed to the present style in 1963, and the milling business then received the name of Peavey Co. Flour Mills.

The flour mills of Peavey Co., and their capacities, are as follows: Buffalo 13,000 cwt., Alton 12,900 cwt., Dallas 8500 cwt., Billings 2900 cwt., Grand Forks 2400 cwt., Hastings 8500 cwt., and Minot 2400 cwt. The rye mill of 1000 cwt. is in Hastings, and an 8200-cwt. durum mill is in Superior.

Totton P. Heffelfinger (b. 1899 Minn.) has been Peavey president since 1959. His brother, F. Peavey Heffelfinger (b. 1897 Minn.), was president in 1945-59 and is now chairman. They are grandsons of Frank H. Peavey, who established the business in Sioux City and moved to Minneapolis in 1884. Head of Peavey Co. Flour Mills is William M. Steinke, executive vice president.

(The) *Pillsbury Co.* is second largest among flour millers in the United States, having eight plants with total capacity of 92,500 cwt., and doing business throughout the nation and participating in a large way in the overseas trade. Mill elevator space is more than 20,000,000 bushels. The company has two flour mills in Canada, total capacity 15,000 cwt.; a mill in Venezuela and an interest in mills in Guatemala, Salvador and the Philippines. It is also a major factor in the formula feed industry, operating ten plants that have 2490 tons capacity, and it has two poultry processing plants.

Pillsbury is the largest producer of refrigerated doughs and of prepared flour mixes for both bakery and household use. In each of these new and rapidly growing fields, there are five Pillsbury plants in the United States and one in Canada. The company has facilities in France for specialty bakery goods, candy and macaroni and in 1962 it purchased control of a food company in West Germany. It also has a soybean plant, a paper mill and bag factory, it is a producer of certain household chemicals and several minor food items. Annual sales approximate $400,000,000.

Founder was Charles A. Pillsbury (b. 1842 N. H., d. 1899), who went to Minneapolis in 1869 and leased the 400-cwt. mill of Frazee & Murphy. He had the backing of his uncle, John Sargent Pillsbury (b. 1828 N. H., d. 1902), a hardware merchant who became perhaps the most famous Governor of Minnesota, serving in 1875-81, and his father, George A. (b. 1818 N. H., d. 1898), a street railway operator. The elder Pillsburys were partners but not managers.

The Pillsbury enterprise grew rapidly. The original mill was remodeled and enlarged in 1870 to 2500 cwt., and C. A. Pillsbury & Co. was established in 1871. Seven years later the celebrated "A" mill was built, with 5000 cwt. initial capacity, then the largest mill in the world. The firm had almost 20,000 cwt. capacity by 1886, in and near Minneapolis. This period of sensational growth coincided with the beginning of a tremendous demand for spring wheat flour from home and abroad.

A British syndicate purchased control of C. A. Pillsbury & Co. in 1889, and with it they consolidated Washburn Mill Co., which had been owned by Senator William D. Washburn (b. 1831 Me., d. 1912). The merged company was called Pillsbury-Washburn Flour Mills, Ltd., and its aggregate capacity of 29,000 cwt. made it the largest concern of its kind. Headquarters was in Minneapolis, and C. A. Pillsbury was managing director in 1889-99. He was succeeded in 1899-1908 by Henry L. Little (b. 1857 N. H., d. 1921).

The British company was overcapitalized and was able to pay dividends in only a few years, and after 1900 it suffered substantial losses. In 1908 it went into receivership when unauthorized speculation in wheat created a large deficit. The result was that Pillsbury lost its foremost position among milling companies.

Pillsbury Flour Mills Co. was organized in 1909 to operate the mills owned by the British company. Albert C. Loring (b. 1858 Minn., d. 1932), who had managed Northwestern Consolidated Milling Co. until he became chief of the Pillsbury receivers, served as president for the next 23 years. He was one of the great men of the milling industry. His chief lieutenant was John S. Pillsbury II (b. 1878 Minn.), son of the founder; he was vice president in 1909-32 and board chairman in 1932-52. His twin brother, Charles S. (b. 1878 Minn., d. 1939), and their cousin, Alfred F. (b. 1869 Minn., d. 1950), son of the Governor, were officers.

Pillsbury Flour Mills Co. became a publicly-owned company in 1924, soon after it absorbed its British predecessor by buying the Minneapolis mills. An unfinished mill in Atchison, Kan., was purchased in 1922 and completed with 5000 cwt. capacity. At the same time a mill of 20,000 cwt. was built in Buffalo. The company established a plant of 7000 cwt. in Enid, Okla., in 1926, and three years later a mill of the same size was built in Springfield, Ill.

Then came a series of plant purchases. Control of Astoria Flouring Mills Co. was acquired in 1929, sole ownership coming three years later. In 1941 Pillsbury bought Globe Grain & Milling Co., which had six plants with total capacity of 10,000 cwt. Ten years thereafter, Ballard & Ballard Co., Inc., entered the Pillsbury fold. The Ballard purchase precipitated a monopoly charge by the Federal Trade Commission, leading to more than a decade of litigation. The properties that were acquired were operated as semi-autonomous units for a time, but ultimately each was absorbed. Company name was changed in 1944 to Pillsbury Mills, Inc., and in 1958 to The Pillsbury Co.

Copeland Flour Mills, Ltd., and Renown Flour Mills, Ltd., with mills in Calgary, Alta., and Midland, Ont., were merged into Pillsbury in 1952, and are operated as Pillsbury Canada Ltd.

Pillsbury plant capacity in and near Minneapolis in 1922 was 57,600 cwt. Present capacity in that area is 9500 cwt., the reductions having taken place in the middle 1930's and the early 1950's. The Atchison mill was increased over a period of time to its present 9000 cwt., Buffalo to 28,000, Enid to 9500, Springfield to 22,000. The San Francisco and Los Angeles mills of the former Globe chain were closed in 1946 and 1948, the Ogden mill was increased to 7000 cwt. from 5000, the old Sacramento mill was replaced by a new plant of 3000 cwt. in 1947 and a new pneumatic mill of 4500 cwt. was opened in Los Angeles in 1961. The Astoria and Louisville mills were closed in 1961.

Pillsbury entered a period of vigorous growth in the post-war era. To some degree, this was manifested in its milling activities, as already noted, but it was especially evident in diversification of an important nature. The flour mix business became significant by 1946; the refrigerated dough field was entered in 1951; the company became a sizable factor in formula feed, and various specialties were added to its product line. The foreign enterprises were also added in that period.

National attention has been commanded by the annual bake-off contest, which was initiated by Pillsbury in 1949.

The company also launched a major new development in milling processes through air classification of flour, which was announced in 1957.

Loring's successors as president: Harrison H. Whiting (b. 1877 Minn., d. 1936) in 1932-36; Clark Hempstead (b. 1874 Ill., d. 1952) in 1936-40; Philip W. Pillsbury (b. 1903 Minn.), son of Charles S., in 1940-52; Paul S. Gerot (b. 1902 Iowa) since 1952. Philip succeeded his uncle, John S., II, in 1952 as board chairman. Since 1956 the president has been flanked by three executive vice presidents: Benjamin J. Greer (b. 1905 Minn.), Dean McNeal (b. 1912 Kan.) and Robert J. Keith (b. 1914 Wis.). Terrance Hanold (b. 1912 Minn.) became executive vice president in 1963.

Pillsbury vice presidents who have attained prominence in the industry are Max A. Lehman (b. 1876 Germany, d. 1950), production head; Alfred E. Mallon (b. 1892 Minn., d. 1947) and Anthony B. Sparboe (b. 1898 Iowa), export leaders; and Howard W. Files (b. 1893 S. D., d. 1957), general officer who served as president of Millers' National Federation in 1950-52.

Bradshaw Mintener (b. 1902 Wis.) resigned as a Pillsbury officer to become Assistant Secretary of Health, Education and Welfare in 1954-56.

Russell-Miller Milling Co.—Great prestige among spring wheat mills was enjoyed by Russell-Miller Milling Co., which evolved from several small mills in North Dakota and grew into one of the larger companies in the industry after it expanded also into the hard winter and soft winter wheat areas.

John Russell, a banker, and his son-in-law, Arthur Miller (b. 1852 England, d. 1933), a practical miller, formed a partnership in 1882, during the first Dakota boom. They bought a small mill that had been built by Hiram Walker in 1879 in Valley City, in what is now North Dakota. It was enlarged to 350 cwt., and a mill in Jamestown was added four years later. The proprietors then incorporated Russell & Miller Milling Co., and it acquired Grand Republic Mill, 4600 cwt., in Superior, at the head of the lakes. This move proved to be disastrous, as the company became insolvent during the financial panic of 1893 and it lost Grand Republic.

Russell-Miller Milling Co. of North Dakota was formed in 1897, largely by Edward P. Wells (b. 1848, d. 1936), Jamestown banker. Harry S. Helm (b. 1867 Ill., d. 1947) became general manager of the reorganized company and principal architect of its success. In 1902 North Dakota Milling Co., Grand Forks, was purchased and the mill enlarged; Jamestown, lost by lightning, was replaced; Valley City was rebuilt, making total capacity 3600 cwt. The Valley City mill was lost to fire in 1903 and rebuilt with 2400 cwt. In 1906 a 1600-cwt. mill was built in Minot, and with enlargements of other mills the company capacity was then 8000 cwt.

Russell-Miller Milling Co. moved to Minneapolis in 1907 and opened a 5000-cwt. mill there the following year. Soon afterward 1000-cwt. mills were built in the Montana towns of Billings and Sidney. Missouri Valley Milling Co., with plants in Bismarck, Mandan and Dickinson, was purchased. In 1919 the Minneapolis mill was increased to 11,000 cwt., the Sidney mill was rebuilt after destruction by fire, and a 3600-cwt. mill was built in Buffalo in 1924. The older half of the Minneapolis mill was then closed, as were the mills in Jamestown, Bismarck and Dickinson, as the remaining mills were enlarged.

The company was exclusively in spring wheat until 1941, when Stanard-Tilton Milling Co., with mills in Dallas and Alton, was acquired. The Alton mill was lost to fire in 1946 and rebuilt with 11,000 cwt. capacity. The Sidney and Mandan mills were closed a few years later, Valley City early in 1963. Everett, Aughenbaugh & Co. was acquired in 1926 and Minot Flour Mill Co. in 1951, but their mills were not operated by Russell-Miller.

Russell-Miller Milling Co. was reincorporated in 1935, with North Dakota left out of the name. Control of the company was acquired in 1954 by the Peavey interests and in 1960 it became a Peavey division under the name of Russell Miller-King Midas Mills. In 1963 the division name was changed to Peavey Co. Flour Mills.

Wells was president in 1897-1918; H. S. Helm in 1918-39; Charles G. Ireys (b. 1878 Mass., d. 1943), son-in-law of Wells, in 1939-42; Leslie F. Miller (b. 1883 N. D., d. 1958), son of Arthur Miller, in 1942-53; Michael F. Mulroy (b. 1886 N. D.), who began with the company in 1902 and was general manager from 1939, in 1953-54; George W. P. Heffelfinger (b. 1901 Minn.) in 1954-58; William M. Steinke (b. 1892 Minn.) in 1958-61. Others in the company who attained industry prominence were Harry Snyder (b. 1867 N. Y., d. 1927), the first great mill chemist; Willis C. Helm (b. 1870

Wis., d. 1949)), general manager in 1918-39 and president of Millers' National Federation in 1942-44; William R. Heegaard (b. 1902 N. D.), vice president; Henry E. Kuehn (b. 1896 Minn.), executive vice president; and Dr. Betty J. Sullivan (b. 1902 Minn.), renowned cereal chemist.

Springfield Milling Corp. is named for the Minnesota town, 125 miles southwest of the Twin Cities, in which its flour mill of 2200 cwt. is located. The company has grain storage for 600,000 bushels. Its flour business is almost wholly with the bakery trade in the Middle West and East.

The company's predecessor was Springfield Milling Co., organized in 1891 by Peter Ruenitz and Henry Bendixen (b. 1854 Germany, d. 1932) to acquire the mill built in 1885 by Anton Schneider. Ruenitz was president and was followed in 1917 by his son, F. Albert (b. 1883 Minn., d. 1933). Julius A. Rieck (b. 1873, d. 1939), who had been manager from 1909, became president in 1932.

After milling operations were suspended in 1936, the idle plant was purchased by the Gregory interests, which formed Springfield Milling Corp. and moved the office to Minneapolis. The mill, which had 1200 cwt. capacity prior to the first World War, was increased to its present size. Lawrence S. Gregory (b. 1893 Minn., d. 1960) was president in 1936-60, and Stanley A. Dillon (b. 1903 Minn.,), who had been general manager from 1936, also became president in 1960.

A. L. Stanchfield, Inc.—For about 15 years the State of Minnesota operated a testing mill in Minneapolis, but after this activity ceased the mill was purchased by Archie L. Stanchfield (b. 1890 Minn.), feed jobber and feed manufacturer, and it was enlarged until it finally attained 3000 cwt. capacity. It was put into operation in 1943 on alcohol grits, and two years later it was converted to a durum mill and run until 1950 as A. L. Stanchfield, Inc.

Washburn Crosby Co., Inc.—Cadwallader C. Washburn (b. 1818 Me., d. 1882) had the "vision of an inspired pioneer." As a young man he emigrated to Wisconsin, became a lawyer and leading lumberman, held two high offices, commanded a brigade in Grant's army, attained success in business and finance, and his milling ventures in time generated the largest enterprise of their kind in the world.

The seven Washburn brothers all became famous. Cadwallader, Israel and Elihu served together in Congress from three states, Cadwallader and Israel were governors, Elihu was Secretary of State and Minister to France, William became a Congressman and United States Senator, Sidney was head of a great banking house, Samuel a sea captain, Charles an editor and author and Minister to Paraguay. Both Cadwallader and William were mill owners, Cadwallader was a member of Congress in 1855-61 and 1867-71 and Governor of Wisconsin in 1872-74. William was a Congressman in 1877-81 and United States Senator from Minnesota in 1885-91.

As early as 1856, C. C. Washburn believed that the rapid gain in population in what was then called the Northwest, the increasing wheat production in that area and the power of the Falls of St. Anthony would create a flour milling center. However, his first mill (1650 cwt.) was not built until 1866, and the lessees, Judd & Brackett, failed two years later. George H. Christian (b. 1839 Ala., d. 1918) then became Washburn's partner and milling manager, and the firm of George H. Christian & Co. was so successful that Christian retired in 1875 reputedly worth a million dollars. More importantly, he had been the power and inspiration behind Edmund LeCroix as that genius built a middlings purifier, which catapulted spring wheat flour to world-wide fame and demand. Washburn's second mill, built in 1873, was managed by John A. and Llewellyn Christian, brothers of George H., and operated as John A. Christian & Co., the non-resident owner and major partner seeming to prefer relative anonymity.

John Crosby (b. 1829 Me., d. 1887) and William H. Dunwoody (b. 1841 Pa., d. 1914), both destined to become milling greats, joined Washburn in 1877, Crosby as manager, and in 1879 the operating partnership became Washburn, Crosby & Co. Dunwoody's initial great feat was breaking down the walls of prejudice that had prevented the British market from accepting spring wheat flour, and in a few years a great flood of this product was moving across the Atlantic.

After the great explosion of May 2, 1878, in which the second Washburn mill was blown up and several other mills wrecked, Washburn built an all-roller mill of 5000 cwt. capacity, the first west of Philadelphia to be so equipped. Thus the two most significant events in the milling revolution of the 1870's—perfection of the purifier and introduction of the roller mill—took place in large measure under Washburn auspices.

The Washburn heirs became the owners of the mills, the operating company having only a series of leases. On two notable occasions the company narrowly missed losing the mills to outside interests, a hazard that did not end until Dunwoody purchased the major part of the Washburn shares in 1899.

James S. Bell (b. 1847 Pa., d. 1915), who had headed a leading flour firm in Philadelphia, became manager in 1888 and president when Washburn Crosby Co., Inc., was incorporated the following year. Bell was known in the industry as the great merchant. During his regime there took place the first company expansion outside of Minneapolis. In 1892 company executives established Royal Milling Co. in Great Falls, Mont., a 600-cwt. mill that was operated along with Washburn Crosby although they were separate corporations. In 1903 the Buffalo mill of 7000 cwt. was built, and that same year John T. Rabbeth Mill & Elevator Co. in Louisville was purchased. Meanwhile Washburn milling capacity in Minneapolis was increased until it reached a high point of 54,000 cwt., and the Buffalo mill became the world's largest when it attained 37,000 cwt. The company went into first place in size in the industry in 1909.

Bell was succeeded in 1915-19 by John Washburn (b. 1858 Me., d. 1919), son of the founder's brother, Sidney, and he in 1919-25 by John Crosby, Jr. (b. 1867 Me., d. 1962), who served 61 years as a director of Washburn Crosby Co. and its successor. James Ford Bell, son of the great merchant, was president in 1925-28. During this era, the unfinished Liberty Milling Co. in Kansas City was acquired, as was Star & Crescent Milling Co. in Chicago, both purchases taking place in 1922.

The postwar period brought extensive diversification, a far-reaching research program, and the breakfast cereal business. It attained a climax in 1928 through the formation of General Mills, Inc., Washburn Crosby being split into four companies each bearing the famous name. They became wholly-owned subsidiaries. In 1937 the parent became an operating company, the former subsidiaries then being divisions and used as trade names. Before a decade had passed, Washburn Crosby had become little more than a memory.

Among those in the company who attained great prominence were Frank F. Henry (b. 1870 Indian Ocean, d. 1961), who headed the Buffalo mill for 30 years; Charles C. Bovey (b. 1864 N. B., d. 1955), who succeeded J. F. Bell as president; William G. Crocker (b. 1864 Minn., d. 1922); Benjamin S. Bull (b. 1869 Minn., d. 1920); and Franklin M. Crosby (b. 1875 Me., d. 1947), son of John Crosby, and the company's wheat trader. Hugh R. McLaughlin (b. 1878 Minn., d. 1962) and William R. Morris (b. 1880 Wis.) became presidents of the two largest Washburn Crosby companies in 1930 and were division presidents after these companies were absorbed in 1937.

Yerxa, Andrews & Thurston—Three Pillsbury executives left the company in 1914 to build a 2500-cwt. durum mill. Dwight K. Yerxa (b. 1881 Minn.) became president and James C. Andrews (b. 1867 N. H., d. 1924) vice president. The mill operated eight years and then was sold to Benjamin B. Sheffield, who organized Minneapolis Durum Products Co., which was absorbed shortly after by Commander Milling Co. The plant, now 4200 cwt., and known as the Nokomis mill, is the durum unit of Archer-Daniels-Midland Co.

Montevideo

Chippewa Milling Co.—The first Chippewa mill was managed by H. C. Stebbins, but when it was burned down in 1909 he transferred his activities to Red Wing. The second mill in Montevideo, which is about 125 miles west of Minneapolis, was built in 1912. It was a child of ill fortune. The 1100-cwt. mill was closed and reopened several times, under a succession of managers and various owners. The mill last produced flour in 1928.

New Ulm

Eagle Roller Mill Co.—For 97 years there were flour mills in New Ulm that bore the name of Eagle; and for more than 60 years of that period Eagle was one of the great names among spring wheat mills.

The first Eagle mill was built by F. Rehfeld and Frederick Beinhorn in 1856 in New Ulm, a hundred miles southwest of the Twin Cities. It was burned down in 1860, and the rebuilt mill was destroyed in the Sioux Indian War three years later. In 1865 another Eagle mill was built by J. Pfenninger and Werner Boesch, but was replaced in 1877 by the fourth plant to bear the Eagle name. It had about 400 cwt. capacity.

William and Charles Silverson, flour merchants and bakers in Cincinnati, built a mill at Nicollet in 1885, and upon its loss to fire the following year they went to nearby New Ulm and bought the Eagle plant. It expanded rapidly—to 1000 cwt. in 1889, to 2000 cwt. in 1891 and to 7000 cwt. a decade later. A rye and corn mill was added in 1911, a feed mill in 1924. New Ulm Roller Mill Co. was purchased in 1943. Eagle capacity reached 7400 cwt. wheat flour, 2700 cwt. rye and 1400 cwt. corn meal.

Eagle Roller Mill Co. was incorporated in 1892. Charles Silverson (b. 1850 Germany, d. 1912) was president in 1892-1912, followed by his brother, William (b. 1852 Germany, d. 1924), who was largely inactive. Charles Vogtel (b. 1867 Germany, d. 1920) was general manager for many years, and was president of Eagle's affiliates, Century Milling Co. and Marshall Milling Co. Henry L. Beecher (b. 1870 Iowa, d. 1933) became general manager in 1920 and president in 1924; he was also chairman of Millers' National Federation in 1927-29. President in 1933-51 was Edgar C. Veeck (b. 1883 Ind.), a widely-known operative miller, whose uncle, John H. Siegel, had been vice president in 1896-1919. A. Floyd (Casey) Anglemyer (b. 1891 Ind.) was a long-time officer.

International Milling Co. purchased Eagle Roller Mill Co. in 1951, but closed the Eagle plant two years later.

New Ulm Roller Mill Co.—Two small mills in New Ulm were merged in 1895 to form New Ulm Roller Mill Co. They were City Mills, built in 1874, and Empire Mills, dating from 1880. The Empire plant was destroyed by fire in 1910 and rebuilt with 1280 cwt. capacity. The 600-cwt. City mill, which was making rye flour, was burned in 1933 and not replaced. The Empire unit was enlarged to 1800 cwt. The company was absorbed by Eagle Roller Mill Co. in 1943; since 1951 the plant has been used as a rye mill by International Milling Co.

Charles L. Roos, who had been manager of City Mills from 1885, was general manager of New Ulm Roller Mill Co. in 1895-1901 before going on to a notable milling career in the Southwest. His successors were Benjamin J. Stockman in 1901-12; August C. Dahl (b. 1877 Minn., d. 1955) in 1912-21; and Richard Swartz (b. 1887 Kan.) in 1921-43.

Perham

Globe Flour Mill Co.—Perham is in the lake country east of Fargo. A small mill there was purchased in 1912 by David A. Tennant (b. 1856 N. Y., d. 1926) and Walter B. Windsor (b. 1860, d. 1930), who also had interests in several other mills. They enlarged the Globe mill to 1300 cwt., and in 1924 they sold it to William G. McLaughlin, son-in-law of Tennant. The mill was closed in 1935.

Red Wing

LaGrange Mills—A milling company that continued for 84 years was established in Red Wing in 1877. It was obliged to go through receivership in 1885 and was reorganized under the leadership of Fred Busch, a banker, who continued as head of the business. The company was locally owned and the 2500-cwt. plant was largely devoted to the production of spring wheat bakery flour, although in the distant past it also enjoyed an export business of consequence. Bay State Milling Co. bought the plant in 1961.

Roll of company presidents: E. W. Brooks in 1877-80, Armand Seeback in 1880-85, Fred Busch in 1885-1908, Bernard Gerlach (b. 1857 Minn., d. 1941) in 1908-33, William S. Weiss (b. 1869 Minn., d. 1959) in 1933-52, Louis W. Back (b. 1887 Ill.) in 1952-61. Gerlach was manager in 1899-1922, Weiss in 1922-46 and Back in 1946-61.

Weiss' tenure with the company began in 1889 and continued for 62 years, and Back's covered 52 years.

Red Wing Milling Co. has a spring wheat bakery flour mill in the town for which the company was named. Its outlets are scattered over the eastern half of the nation. Located on the river, it was one of the first mills to utilize barge shipment in the renaissance of water transportation in recent years.

The milling history of Red Wing goes back to 1873, when the 800-cwt. Bluff Mill was erected. Four years later the Diamond Mill of 1200 cwt. started up. In 1878 they were combined under the Diamond name. T. B. Sheldon was president, and later E. L. Baker held the office. These mills were destroyed by fire in 1891.

Simmons Milling Co. was organized in 1901, with N. K. Simmons (d. 1929) as manager. It built a 2000-cwt. mill on the site of Diamond Mill. The name was changed to Red Wing Milling Co. in 1907. The controlling interest was purchased in 1909 by H. C. Stebbins (b. 1864 Conn., d. 1921). After his death the property was acquired by the Meech group, and they held it until 1962 when Vanier interests purchased control.

Red Wing Milling Co. presidents: Stebbins in 1909-21; Harold M. Meech (b. 1882 Conn., d. 1949) in 1921-49; Meech's widow, Lucy H., in 1949-62. John Dengler (b. 1891

Minn., d. 1957) was general manager in 1949-56, and that position has been held since 1956 by Jefferson D. Sogard (b. 1921 Mo.), son-in-law of Meech. Sogard also became president in 1962.

St. Cloud

Great Northern Flour Mills Co.—George Tileston built his mill in St. Cloud, 70 miles northwest of the Twin Cities, in 1889, and it reached 2000 cwt. capacity. George Tileston Milling Co. was sold in 1914 to William E. Coles and associates, and they formed Great Northern Flour Mills Co. After the war the mill ran indifferently and was finally closed in the early 1930's.

St. Paul

Amber Milling Division of Farmers' Union Grain Terminal Assn. operates a durum mill of 3300 cwt. in Rush City, 50 miles north of St. Paul. Its business is with macaroni manufacturers over most of the nation. Headquarters is in St. Paul, in conjunction with the parent organization, which is the largest grain cooperative in the United States. The latter was established in 1938, under the sponsorship of the Farmers' Union state organizations of Minnesota, the Dakotas and Montana.

Local capital in Rush City built the mill in 1910. It then had 500 cwt. capacity. About a decade later the mill became idle when the company encountered financial trouble. It was reopened in 1924 as Diefenbach-Prina Milling Co., but this venture ran into difficulty and in 1926 the plant was converted to durum milling, and was operated for two years as Durum Milling Co. John F. Diefenbach (b. 1875 Minn., d. 1952) was president and manager of both, as he was also of Amber Milling Co., formed in 1928 by four macaroni manufacturers.

The mill was increased to 2000 cwt., and Patrick H. Hoy (b. 1914 Minn.), now a top official of General Dynamics Corp., became general manager in 1939-42.

Control of the mill passed to Farmers' Union Grain Terminal Assn. in 1940, and it acquired title in 1944. The mill was then enlarged and modernized. Julius M. Waber (b. 1906 Minn.) was general manager of the milling division in 1942-54, Eugene W. Kuhn (b. 1910 Minn.) since 1954.

Old-Fashioned Millers, Inc. operates one of only two mills of substantial size in the United States that are employed solely in producing stone-ground flour. The mill has 2000 cwt. capacity, and is located in downtown St. Paul. Its product is limited to whole wheat and whole rye flours, and its market is both with the small package trade and with commercial bakers.

The present company was organized in 1919 by James C. Enright (b. 1862 Ont., d. 1940), who began producing stoneground flour in 1910, first in St. Paul and then in Blooming Grove, Minn. He returned to St. Paul in 1922 and purchased the idle plant of William Lindeke Roller Mills the following year. The Lindeke mill was built in 1885 and operated until 1919. The 500-cwt. mill was later enlarged to its present size.

Adelaide M. Enright, the founder's daughter, has been company president and manager since 1941.

St. Paul Milling Co.—An 1800-cwt. flour mill was established in St. Paul in 1915 by the Fleming family, which formed St. Paul Milling Co. The mill was closed about 1934.

Sleepy Eye

Sleepy Eye Milling Co.—Ish-Tak-Ha-Ba, meaning drooping eyelids, was a Sioux Indian chief who befriended the white settlers in Southern Minnesota in the 1860's when they were in desperate need of friends. A town named in his honor became the site of a famous mill.

Sleepy Eye Milling Co. was organized in 1883 by William Gieseke. When he sold a decade later, the mill had 1400 cwt. capacity. In another ten years it had been expanded to 11,000 cwt. The company enjoyed a tremendous business. The author of its good fortune was Arnold C. Von Hagen (b. 1868 Wis., d. 1938), president and manager. Unfortunately, the company was wrecked by wheat speculation and went into receivership in 1909. It was operated by the bondholders, who attempted to reorganize it as United Mills Corp., but in 1917 the plant was sold to Kansas Flour Mills Corp. Capacity was reduced to 4000 cwt., and the mill ran until 1921 and then was closed.

Wabasha

Wabasha Roller Mill Co.—James G. Lawrence (b. 1836 N. Y., d. 1928) arrived in Wabasha, a Mississippi River town 90 miles southeast of the Twin Cities, in 1862 and went to work in a newly-established flour mill. He became the owner in 1878, and Wabasha Roller Mill Co. was organized four years later. The mill reached 1800 cwt. capacity in the Lawrence days, and the company attained distinction and prestige as one of the most successful spring wheat mills of moderate size.

William B. Webb (b. 1882 Me., d. 1947), son-in-law of Lawrence, purchased control of Wabasha Roller Mill Co. in 1919. The business continued in Webb's hands until 1943, when it was sold to International Milling Co. The mill now has 3800 cwt. capacity.

Lawrence was company president for 46 years, beginning in 1882. Webb became general manager in 1913 and was president after 1928.

Waseca

Everett, Aughenbaugh & Co.—Eaco, the diminutive by which Everett, Aughenbaugh & Co. was known, was formed in 1877 by William Everett (b. 1828 N. J., d. 1892), who managed the business, and John W. Aughenbaugh (b. 1846 Ohio, d. 1923), who ran the mill. Everett's sons, Edward A. (b. 1867 Wis., d. 1928), and Guy W. (b. 1875 Minn., d. 1957), later succeeded to his interest. Eaco was a partnership for 48 years, not being incorporated until 1925. It had a mill of 2800 cwt. in the Southern Minnesota town of Waseca. It also owned the trade name of Claro Milling Co., which had had mills in Lakeville and New Richland. The Everetts obtained a large interest in Hubbard Milling Co. in 1905 and held it until 1918.

The company was merged with Russell-Miller Milling Co. in 1926. The Waseca mill was not operated thereafter, but a separate sales organization was maintained until 1934. Eaco has continued as a trade name to the present.

Winona

Bay State Milling Co., for half a century a top-ranking spring wheat mill, broadened its operations in 1954 by acquiring a Kansas plant. It bought a second Minnesota mill in 1961. These moves put it in fourteenth place in size in the industry. All its facilities are employed in milling hard wheat flour for bakers. The company has total capacity of 16,800 cwt., as well as 3,000,000 bushels of elevator space.

Bay State Milling Co. was founded in 1899 by Bernard J. Rothwell (b. 1859 Ireland, d. 1948), Boston flour merchant, and associates. They purchased the 3200-cwt. plant of L. C. Porter Milling Co., built in 1890. The mill was enlarged to 5000 cwt., it was destroyed by fire in 1911 and rebuilt, and it was later enlarged to its present size of 8700 cwt. wheat and 1100 cwt. rye.

The southwestern acquisition was the idle Lysle mill in Leavenworth, Kan., and it was also increased, to 4700 cwt. The plant of LaGrange Mills was purchased in 1961.

Herbert C. Garvin (b. 1862 Wis., d. 1942) was the first general manager, serving in 1899-1921. Frank J. Allen (b. 1882 Minn.), who began with the company the year the Bostonians bought the mill, managed the business in 1921-52; he was chairman of Millers' National Federation in 1935-37. His successors have been George E. Kelley (b. 1895 N. D.) in 1951-59 and Paul B. Miner (b. 1909 Ind.) since 1959.

All Bay State presidents have been Rothwells—Bernard J. in 1899-1940; his son, Paul T. (b. 1892 Mass.) in 1940-59; and the latter's son, Bernard J. II (b. 1922 Mass.) since 1959. Paul T. became board chairman in 1959.

MISSOURI

Milling of flour in St. Louis began in 1766, when one Tailion brought millstones from France. His mill was acquired in 1778 by the famous August Choteau and it was operated by Choteau and his heirs for about 75 years. St. Louis was a flour market and wheat market of consequence early in the 1800's, being one of the chief suppliers of the South, and in 1858-79 it was the nation's foremost milling center. It was the chief soft wheat milling point until after the first World War, since which it has milled as much or more hard wheat as soft.

Kansas City's first flour mill was established in 1870, but the city did not become important as a milling center until after 1900. This was coincident with the rise to importance of hard winter wheat, for which it has been the leading market from the early days. Kansas City flour production doubled in the 1920's, as it had in the preceding decade, and in 1937 it surpassed Minneapolis and went into second place nationally. It has retained that position to the present except for 1943-47 and 1953.

Missouri had 740 flour mills in 1900 and but 18 in 1958. The state was fourth in flour production in 1961, the year's production being 20,245,000 cwt.

Aurora

Majestic Milling Co.—Thirty miles southwest of Springfield is Aurora, where the Davis and Woodfill families built a mill of 2000 cwt. in 1906 and established Majestic Milling Co. It was managed through most of its existence by J. S. Flautt. The mill was sold in 1932 to Dixie-Portland interests and enlarged to 3000 cwt. It was destroyed by fire in 1939.

Boonville

Boonville Mills Co.—Three generations of the Sombart family ran Sombart Milling & Mercantile Co. in Boonville, river town in mid-Missouri. Charles Sombart (b. 1856 Mo., d. 1925) was the last. He sold the flour mill in 1918 to O. Fletcher Kelley (b. 1892 Mo.) and associates. Kelley was manager of Boonville Mills Co. the next 25 years and president from 1928. The company was one of the first to specialize in bakery cake flour. The mill of 1000 cwt. was lost to fire in 1943 and Kelley went into the grain business in Kansas City.

California

Kuhlmann-Meyer Milling Co.—Twenty miles west of Jefferson City is California, where the Holbrecht mill was purchased in 1895 by Henry E. Kuhlmann and Martin Meyer. Their mill gradually grew to 750 cwt. capacity, and in 1925 the Kuhlmann family became sole owners. The business was managed for many years by Henry W. (b. 1880, d. 1959) and Walter Kuhlmann. The company was purchased in 1946 by Mason B. McVeigh, who increased the mill to 1000 cwt. It was closed in 1948.

Carthage

Cowgill Flour Mills, Inc.—Carthage, near Joplin in Southwest Missouri, was the mill site chosen in 1873 by Henry C. Cowgill (b. 1846 Ohio, d. 1914) and A. M. Hill, who formed Cowgill & Hill Milling Co. Their mill was burned out in 1903 but was rebuilt with 1000 cwt. capacity. Cowgill then became sole owner.

Cowgill headed the company until 1909. He was followed in 1909-12 by his son-in-law, C. A. Blair, and in 1912-42 by his son, Henry S. (b. 1878 Mo., d. 1946). The company became Cowgill Flour Mills, Inc., in 1927, and at that time Henry S. purchased the interest of his brother, Lloyd, who then acquired Brand-Dunwoody Milling Co. Henry S. also became president of Lyons Flour Milling Co. in 1927.

The company went out of business in 1942.

McDaniel Milling Co.—The original flour mill on the site now occupied by Morrow Milling Co., feed manufacturers, was built in 1848. From 1884 to 1900 it was operated by McDaniel & Morrow, and at the end of that period the McDaniel brothers established McDaniel Milling Co. and built a 1200-cwt. mill. It was managed for about 15 years by Horace Staley, then by William McDaniel and a succession of others. The last manager was Walter Evans.

The mill was sold in 1941 to National Biscuit Co. It has remained in production and the present capacity is 3300 cwt.

Glasgow

Glasgow Milling Co.—Almost a hundred miles east of Kansas City, on a great bend of the Missouri River, is Glasgow where Harrison Marr Milling Co. was established in the early 1870's. Oliver Harrison bought the mill about 1900 and renamed in Glasgow Milling Co. He sold the 1200-cwt. plant in 1920 to Don S. Price, his son-in-law. The mill was destroyed by fire in 1924.

Hannibal

Carter-Shepherd Milling Co.—Spencer M. Carter (b. 1825 Ky., d. 1922) had a milling career of 78 years. After working in Illinois and Missouri mills for 18 years, he built Eagle Mills in 1862 in the Mississippi River town made famous by Mark Twain. It was rebuilt in 1882 with 1000 cwt. capacity. John B. Shepherd (b. 1840 Ohio, d. 1916) joined Carter in ownership and management in 1896. The mill operated until 1925.

Hannibal Milling Co.—Empire Mills was established in 1875 by David Dubach (b. 1826 Ind., d. 1897), who had operated Magnolia Flour Mills from 1866. The business was later incorporated as Hannibal Milling Co., which became well known in the southern trade. The 1000-cwt. mill was closed for several years, but was reopened by Dubach in 1891 and it remained in operation until 1929. O. M. Friend (b. 1854, d. 1932) was president and manager in later years.

Higginsville

Higginsville Milling Co.—Forty miles east of Kansas City is Higginsville, where a flour mill was built in 1881 by Lyman Lamb. It was acquired from him about 1900 by Edgar Asbury. The original mill was destroyed by fire in 1911 and a 1200-cwt. plant was then built by Asbury and his son, Edgar,

Jr. The business was reorganized in 1927 as Higginsville Milling Co., and was managed by R. Samuel Hayes.

The mill was purchased in 1930 by Dixie Portland interests and was known thereafter as Higginsville Flour Mill. Robert M. Pease was manager in 1930-38. It was increased to 4000 cwt. during the 1940's under the management of Hubert C. Edwards. The mill ceased to make flour in 1952.

Independence

Waggoner-Gates Milling Co.—Independence, marshalling point for many of the wagon trains that carried the pioneers westward in the middle years of the nineteenth century, was the place where William H. Waggoner (b. 1839 Pa., d. 1921) established a grist mill in 1866. The enterprise grew, the original mill was replaced by a larger plant, the mill reached 1000 cwt. capacity before 1900 and later was enlarged to 2600 cwt. The company became a leading factor in the soft wheat trade.

Waggoner-Gates Milling Co. was incorporated in 1883. George P. Gates (b. Vt. 1833, d. 1905), a lumber dealer, became a partner at that time; he was the grandfather of Bess Wallace, who became Mrs. Harry S. Truman. Waggoner was company president in 1883-1921, he was followed in 1921-39 by Thomas O. Cunningham (b. 1861 Ind., d. 1939) and in 1939-55 by Waggoner's son, Arch B. (b. 1895 Mo., d. 1955). Others active in the management in later years were Frank G. Wallace (b. 1887 Mo., d. 1960), brother of Mrs. Truman, and Robert H. Montgomery (b. 1890 Mo.).

The mill was closed in 1953, but the company's leading brand is still distributed.

Jackson

Cape County Milling Co.—Southeast Missouri was the locale for a milling company that was managed by one man for

56 years—the entire history of the company except for two years. Cape County Milling Co. and Ruddell M. McCombs (b. 1870 Mo., d. 1953) were practically synonymous terms for two generations.

Cape County Milling Co. came into being in 1895 through a consolidation of three small mills—two in Jackson, one at nearby Burfordville. The latter was a historic old mill, established in 1799 and operated under both French and Spanish rule in its early years. It is now owned by Cape Girardeau County Historical Society. One of the Jackson mills was owned by F. Tiedeman, the other by Harrell-Buehler Milling Co.

A. R. Byrd, manager and part owner of Harrell-Buehler Milling Co., was Cape County president in 1895-1911. McCombs, his nephew, was an officer from the start; in 1897 he became manager and in 1911 president. He retained these posts the remainder of his life.

The three plants, which had total capacity of about 2600 cwt., were closed and sold in 1953.

The Alsop flour bleaching process was perfected in 1903 in the Cape County mill by James N. Alsop.

Jefferson City

G. H. Dulle Milling Co.—Missouri's capital city had a Dulle mill more than a century. The business began in 1846 when Gerhard H. Dulle (b. 1817 Germany, d. 1884) took charge of Casey & Hardin's mill. In 1854 he built his own mill and it was replaced in 1870 by an 800-cwt. plant known as Capital Star Mill. The latter was destroyed by fire in 1897 and a new mill of 1000 cwt. was built. It was later enlarged to 1200 cwt.

The founder operated as a sole proprietorship. His sons,

Henry J. (b. 1848 Mo., d. 1921) and Bernard (b. 1851 Mo., d. 1906) incorporated as G. H. Dulle Milling Co. in 1886, and Henry J. managed the company until 1914. Joseph H. Dulle (b. 1873 Mo.), son of Bernard, was general manager in 1914-35. Henry J. Dulle, Jr. (b. 1887 Mo.) was general manager in 1935-50. The plant was leased in 1944 to Lawrence Milling Co., and was sold in 1950 to become a feed mill.

Joplin

Brand-Dunwoody Milling Co. — President Truman was born at Lamar, Mo., in 1884, and in that same year the Brands and Dunwoodys built a mill there. They moved to Joplin in 1898 and acquired the Sargent mill, which they gradually enlarged to 1600 cwt. John F. Dunwoody (b. 1847 Pa., d. 1918) headed the enterprise and was succeeded by his son, William B. (b. 1874 Mo., d. 1937). The latter sold the business in 1927 to Lloyd Cowgill (b. 1880 Mo., d. 1930).

After standing idle for eight years, the mill was reopened in 1938 by W. Wood Marshall. His Marco Mills, Inc. operated the plant almost five years. It was then leased to Standard Milling Co. for the production of alcohol grits and became dormant in 1946.

Kansas City

Flour Mills of America, Inc. until recent years the largest milling company in the Southwest, is now principally engaged in the storage of grain. Its milling operations are limited to a 2600-cwt. plant in New Braunfels, Texas, and to a 14,000-cwt. mill in Kansas City that has been employed irregularly in late years. Elevator space totals 10,800,000 bushels.

Flour Mills of America, Inc. was created in 1926 as a publicly-owned holding company, with Kansas Flour Mills Corp.

and Valier & Spies Milling Co. as subsidiaries. Aggregate active milling capacity then controlled was about 20,000 cwt. Its affairs were dominated by Thad L. Hoffman (b. 1881 Kan., d. 1933), its first president, just as Kansas Flour Mills Corp. had been.

In 1934 Flour Mills of America, Inc. became an operating company, its subsidiaries being converted into divisions. Ralph W. Hoffman (b. 1874 Kan., d. 1949) succeeded his brother as president, serving in 1934-41.

Heavy losses in grain speculation sent Flour Mills of America, Inc. into a trusteeship in 1938. Reorganization brought in Eugene P. Mitchell (b. 1886 Mo., d. 1955), who had been sales manager for General Mills and Larabee, as president in 1941-46. Texas capitalists then gained control, and Henry H. Cate (b. 1897 N. C.) was president in 1946-53. During this period the Fort Scott and Great Bend mills were reopened for several years and the Kansas City and St. Louis mills were considerably enlarged.

Another grain market episode resulted in a second trusteeship in 1953 and another reorganization brought in Michael F. Mulroy, who had just retired from Russell-Miller Milling Co. as president. The Texas group returned to control in 1955, Cate becoming board chairman. During this time Bewley Mills and H. Dittlinger Roller Mills Co. were merged into Flour Mills of America, Inc., but the Bewley plant was closed within a year.

Ill-fated market ventures produced another crisis in 1957 and control passed to an insurance company. The Alva and Kansas City mills were closed, and the St. Louis mill was sold to Colorado Milling & Elevator Co. After a period of idleness, Kansas City was reopened in 1961 and has been operating sporadically.

John M. Ferguson (b. 1907 Texas), who is also president of Houston Fire & Casualty Co., has been president of Flour Mills of America, Inc., since 1957.

Ismert-Hincke Milling Co.—Ismerts were millers in Lorraine for six generations, and they remained in the business after John Ismert (b. 1841 France, d. 1915) emigrated to America. He was employed in or managed mills in Illinois, Missouri and Kansas before Ismert-Hincke Milling Co. was established in Kansas City in 1905. The mill had 3000 cwt. capacity, but in much later years it was enlarged by stages to 7200 cwt.

The company achieved greatness under the founder's son, Theodore F. Ismert (b. 1866 Ill., d. 1924), who managed the business from 1910. He was a homespun merchandising genius, the company was a large factor in the export trade and it had the first mill laboratory in the Southwest. He was so well known in the trade that his bulletins were signed only as "Theodore" without any further identification.

Ismert-Hincke acquired the Crosby mill in Topeka in 1916. It had been established in 1883 by Daniel Crosby (b. 1835 Me., d. 1928) and managed in later years by his nephews, Theodore D. and Daniel Hammatt. Ismert-Hincke officials bought the 1000-cwt. Tiblow mill in Bonner Springs, Kan., in 1925 and made flour there for about two years.

John Ismert was president in 1905-15, followed by Theodore F. in 1915-24 and George E. Hincke (b. 1881 Ill., d. 1959), the latter's brother-in-law, in 1924-37. During the Hincke regime, Jay B. M. Wilcox was general manager.

The company was sold in 1937 to Otto Bresky and associates, and Bresky became president. The Kansas City mill was destroyed by fire in 1938 and the company continued in business by buying the plant of Topeka Flour Mills Corp. In 1945 it bought the mill of Thomas Page Milling Co., but this mill was sold to Rodney Milling Co. in 1955. John A. Willis, Jr. (b. 1892 Minn., d. 1958) was general manager of Ismert-Hincke in 1937-54, and Lin M. Lundgaard has held the post since 1954.

Along with the other Bresky properties, Ismert-Hincke was merged into Seaboard Allied Milling Corp. in 1959 and it became a division.

Kansas City Milling Co.—On the site where R. E. Kidder Flour Mills was destroyed by fire in 1918, William J. and Harry J. Kaull built a 2400-cwt. plant the following year. They were from Glen Elder, Kan., where their father, F. M. Kaull, ran a small mill in 1881-1911, and the sons continued the business. Their Kaull Milling Co. in Kansas City was soon in financial straits; it was reorganized in 1920 and again in 1921 and then was sold at receiver's sale. It had three managements in less than a year.

DeForrest Piazzek (b. 1868 Kan., d. 1933), head of a grain company, acquired the property in 1922 and organized Kansas City Milling Co. About a year later he sold the plant to Moore-Lowry interests, who operated it as Moore-Lowry Flour Mills Co. until it was sold to Loose-Wiles Biscuit Co. in 1933.

Kansas Flour Mills Corp.—First mill consolidation of consequence in the Southwest took place in 1912 in the formation of Kansas Flour Mills Corp. The charter affiliates were C. Hoffman Milling Co., Enterprise; Pratt Mill & Elevator Co., Pratt; Kingman Milling Co., Kingman; Anthony Milling Co., Anthony; Moses Bros. Mill & Elevator Co., Great Bend; and New Era Milling Co., Arkansas City. These mills ranged from 800 to 1800 cwt. in size at that time, and they had aggregate capacity of about 8000 cwt. Wichita was headquarters until 1916, Kansas City thereafter.

Bulte Mills in Kansas City was purchased in 1914, and a little later Goodlander Mills of Fort Scott, and the Alva and Cherokee mills in Oklahoma came in. However, New Era returned to individual ownership after two years. When the new Kansas City mill of 6000 cwt. was completed in 1923, the company had 24,400 cwt. capacity in the Southwest. It had invaded spring wheat territory in 1917 and 1918 by purchasing Sleepy Eye Milling Co. and Listman Mills, but these deals proved not to be advantageous and the northern mills were operated only for short periods.

The theory behind the merger of small milling companies into Kansas Flour Mills Corp. was that centralized selling would prevent the recurrent periods of demoralized flour prices. It did not work out that way, as the predominant skills in the company were in grain marketing rather than in flour merchandising. A subsidiary, Kansas Grain Co., grew until it handled half the Kansas wheat crop for a number of years. However, the flour business diminished to the point that less than half the capacity was in use by the early 1930's. The Kingman mill had been sold, Fort Scott leased, Cherokee and Anthony destroyed by fire, Enterprise and Great Bend became idle, and only Alva and Pratt of the country plants operated after 1931.

The men who put Kansas Flour Mills Corp. together were, in the main, Lincoln E. Moses (b. 1860 Pa., d. 1928), Thomas J. Holdridge (b. 1844, d. 1918), and the Hoffman brothers —Ralph W., Emmet V. (b. 1876 Kan., d. 1924) and Thad L., along with Frank D. Stevens, a mill association official. Holdridge owned the Kingman and Anthony mills and an interest in several others; he was a mill owner rather than an operator, a man who bought and sold mills rather freely.

Moses was the first president, serving in 1912-23. He and his brothers, Edward L., Seward and C. L., had made quite a success in their Great Bend mill, and he enjoyed great prestige in the industry. When Moses retired, control passed to the Hoffmans. Thad L. was president in 1923-33. General managers, responsible for sales and operations, were John B. Hupp (b. 1872 Ind., d. 1920) in 1912-20; Emmet V. Hoffman in 1920-24; and William R. Duerr (b. 1885 Mo., d. 1958) in 1924-34.

Although several companies which formed Kansas Flour Mills Corp. had distinctions of their own, most famous was the Enterprise mill. Founded in 1869 by Christian Hoffman (b. 1826 Switzerland, d. 1921), it was the first Kansas mill to ship flour out of the state (1873) and the first to make an export shipment (1882). The company enjoyed a large domestic business as well. The founder's son, Christian B. (b. 1853 Switzerland, d. 1915) left the company in middle age to become a lecturer for socialism and edit a socialist daily. Three grandsons reached top positions in the company.

Kansas Flour Mills Corp. and Valier & Spies Milling Co. joined in 1926 in forming Flour Mills of America, Inc. The latter was a holding company for eight years, after which the operating companies were merged into the parent. Thus the life of the first large Kansas milling company was only a little more than 20 years.

Kelley Milling Co.—After disposing of his interest in the mill which he had helped found in Leavenworth in 1882, John Kelley (b. 1844 England, d. 1918) built a mill in Kansas City in 1899 and gave his name to the company. It reached

3600 cwt. capacity. Arthur Kelley succeeded his father as president. The mill was destroyed by lightning in 1921.

Larabee Flour Mills Co.—Foreclosure of a mortgage opened the way to the formation of one of the large milling companies of two generations ago. Three deaths among its principal officers in little more than a year served to bring the dream of empire to an end.

The Larabees entered milling in 1898, when the banker in Stafford, 45 miles west of Hutchinson, was obliged to take over a 600-cwt. mill there. His sons operated the property as Stafford Mill & Elevator Co., and when the mill was destroyed by fire in 1900 it was rebuilt twice as large.

Larabee Flour Mills Co. was organized in 1913. Frederic D. Larabee (b. 1868 N. Y., d. 1920) was its directing genius; his brother, Frank S. (b. 1864 N. Y., d. 1921), was the balance wheel. Their associate, August J. Bulte (b. 1863 Mo., d. 1922), ran the mills and sold the flour. Bulte was a miller by inheritance and experience; he had been a partner in Meyer & Bulte, with mills in St. Louis, Rolla and Clinton, and then had founded August J. Bulte Milling Co. in Kansas City in 1905. The failure of that concern six years later seems to have affected his standing only slightly.

The Larabee company expanded rapidly, beginning in 1916. A mill of 3000 cwt. was built in Hutchinson, and within a year or so the company bought the mill in Clinton, the Aetna mill in Wellington, the famous Excelsior mill in Marysville, the Queen Bee mill in Sioux Falls (which was operated only a year), and finally built a 12,000-cwt. mill in St. Joseph in 1918. Offices, which had been in Hutchinson for 15 years, were moved to Kansas City in 1919. At that time, the company's active milling capacity was almost 20,000 cwt., a close second in size in the Southwest.

Disaster came when the Larabee brothers died within a few months, and a year later Bulte was lost in a plane wreck off the Florida coast. Ferdinand C. Kaths (b. 1872, d. 1960), Topeka banker, became president, and Louis A. Arneson general manager. The company drifted, although it acquired the J. A. Walter mill in Buffalo and the Monarch mill of J. C. Lysle in Kansas City in 1926. Early in 1927 the company joined with the Sheffield interests in Minnesota to form Commander Larabee Corp., headed by Sheffield. The Larabee unit was managed successively by Harry G. Randall (b. 1882 Kan., d. 1936), Walter C. Smith, Robert H. Montgomery, John A. Willis, Jr., Timothy C. McGrath (b. 1883 Ill.) and Glenn F. Hilts.

The Stafford mill was sold in 1918 after being leased, the Marysville mill was closed about 1926, the Kaw mill in Topeka was acquired in 1926 but closed within a few years, the Wellington mill was destroyed by fire in 1931, Clinton was closed in 1952, and Hutchinson in 1959. Half of the St. Joseph mill was removed to Buffalo in 1936, but 15 years later it was enlarged to 10,000 cwt. The Kansas City mill was enlarged by stages to 15,000 cwt.

Midland Flour Milling Co. — The name of Bernhard Warkentin (b. 1847 Russia, d. 1908) is indelibly associated with the introduction of hard winter wheat in Kansas. He was a miller in the Crimea before emigrating to America in 1870. He was one of the advance scouts sent by the Mennonites to find suitable land in America when they determined to leave Russia. Most of them were farmers and when they came to Kansas many brought along Turkey Red seed wheat. It was the first hard winter wheat grown in this country. Later—in 1882 —Warkentin imported 10,000 bushels of Turkey Red seed from his native country.

Warkentin's first American mill was in Halstead, north west of Wichita, famed also for being the locale of *The Horse and Buggy Doctor,* a best-selling book in the 1930's. Halstead Milling & Elevator Co., built before 1875, was operated until 1930, and it reached 1000 cwt. capacity. He added Newton Milling & Elevator Co. in 1886 and Blackwell Milling & Elevator Co. in 1899, in the Kansas and Oklahoma towns of these names. The companies were controlled by Warkentin, and his long-time partner, John H. McNair (b. 1853 Pa., d. 1924) became head of the milling chain at the founder's death.

Carl B. Warkentin (b. 1880 Kan., d. 1942), son of Bernhard, succeeded McNair in 1915. He bought the Midland mill in Kansas City from Shane Bros. & Wilson Co. in 1919 and organized Midland Flour Milling Co. In 1924 the three smaller companies were merged into Midland, and headquarters was in Kansas City from that time.

Midland Flour Milling Co. was one of the leaders of the southwestern milling industry throughout the second quarter of the century. C. B. Warkentin was chairman of Millers' National Federation in 1929-31. Company managership was held in 1924-26 by Harry G. Randall and in 1926-42 by John W. Cain (b. 1888 Kan., d. 1954). Cain became company president in 1942-48.

The Warkentin heirs sold Midland in 1943 to a group headed by Paul Uhlmann of the grain company bearing his name. Uhlmann became board chairman. In 1945 the plant of Slater Mill & Elevator Co. was purchased, but it was closed in 1949.

International Milling Co. bought Midland Flour Milling Co. from the Uhlmanns in 1948 and the latter company was absorbed. Cain had charge of International's southwestern plants for the next six years. Three of the former Midland mills —in Kansas City, Newton and Blackwell—are now operated by International, their present capacity being 11,900 cwt.

Moore-Lowry Flour Mills, Inc. has a 5000-cwt. mill and 700,000 bushels of grain storage in Coffeyville, in Southeastern Kansas on the Oklahoma border. Company office is in Kansas City, and its flour business is largely with the bakery trade. The company is owned by the same people as Wichita Flour Mills, Inc., but the two are separate corporations.

Moore-Lowry Flour Mills Co. was formed in 1923 by John H. Moore and George M. Lowry, who were the principals in Wichita Flour Mills Co. and other milling enterprises. They purchased the 2000-cwt. plant of Kansas City Milling Co., and organized a new company to operate it. Elmo F. Merrill (b. 1897 Mo.) became general manager a few months later and has continued to hold this position more than 39 years.

The Kansas City mill was sold in 1933 to Loose-Wiles Biscuit Co., and Moore-Lowry Flour Mills Co. purchased the idle Willis Norton plant in Topeka from Wichita Flour Mills Co. and put it into operation. It was destroyed by lightning within a month, and the company had no mill for a year. It then purchased the 3600-cwt. Coffeyville plant of Rea-Patterson Milling Co., which had operated somewhat irregularly for a couple of years. This mill was subsequently enlarged to its present size, and has been the Moore-Lowry mill since 1934.

The company name was changed in 1957 to its present style. J. H. Moore was president in 1923-34; his son, J. Kinney Moore in 1934-58; Merrill from 1958.

Rodney Milling Co.—A newly-organized company that began doing business early in 1921 struggled through a long series of crises. Its plant was a rebuilt brewery in Kansas City, in which the machinery from a defunct mill in Atchison was installed. It had a minimum of capital and literally had to pull itself up by its bootstraps. Its founder, John L. Rodney (b. 1868 Iowa, d. 1922), who had a fabulous reputation as a flour salesman, passed away during its second year. Somehow it survived these troubles and it became the nucleus of the largest milling company in the Southwest.

Otto Bresky (b. 1889 Minn.) was interested in the company from the beginning and he acquired control in 1928. Meanwhile, Harry A. Sterling (b. 1886 Minn.) was president and manager in 1922-28. Bresky, who was also head of Seaboard Flour Co., became president and Louis S. Myers (b. 1896 Russia, d. 1951) general manager in 1928. After a few years the company got on its feet and began to expand. The Kansas City mill was increased in size several times, ultimately attaining 8300 cwt. Lindsborg Milling & Elevator Co. was purchased in 1939, KBR Milling Co. in 1941, Russell Milling Co. in 1944, the former Thomas Page mill in 1955 and Blair Milling Co. the same year, although the Blair plant was not operated by Rodney. Russell and Lindsborg mills were closed in 1951 and 1954. KBR was enlarged by stages from 1450 cwt. to 7200, Thomas Page from 1600 cwt. to 4200. Richard G. Myers succeeded his father as manager in 1951.

The Bresky group purchased Ismert-Hincke Milling Co. in 1937 and Consolidated Flour Mills Co. in 1950. These companies, along with Rodney, were merged into Seaboard Allied Milling Corp. in 1959, and have been Seaboard Allied divisions since the merger.

Seaboard Allied Milling Corp. is the largest milling company in the Southwest and seventh in size in the industry. It has six mills in the Kansas area and early in 1963 it opened a pneumatic plant in Chattanooga. Total capacity of these mills is 40,000 cwt. and elevator space operated is 31,000,000 bushels. The company is predominantly in the bakery flour business and is a large factor in the trade throughout the eastern half of the nation.

Seaboard Allied Milling Corp. was established by Otto Bresky (b. 1889 Minn.) and associates, who were also the principals in Seaboard Flour Co. Their first milling interest was in Rodney Milling Co. in 1921. They acquired Ismert-Hincke Milling Co. in 1937 and Consolidated Flour Mills Co. in 1950. The three companies had separate managements but overall policies were centrally controlled. In 1959 the three were merged into Seaboard Allied, which then became an operating company for the first time, and the former milling companies thereupon became divisions of the parent concern.

The Seaboard Allied mills comprise the Rodney plants of 8300 cwt. in Kansas City, 4200 cwt. in Topeka and 7200 cwt. in McPherson; the Ismert-Hincke mill of 7200 cwt. in Topeka; and the Consolidated plants of 5000 cwt. in Kingman and 4100 cwt. in Winfield. The new mill in Chattanooga has 4000 cwt. capacity.

Otto Bresky is president of Seaboard Allied Milling Corp. His Seaboard Flour Co. does a large flour distributing business in New England and New York. Richard G. Myers (b. 1921 Mass.), who had been general manager of Rodney Milling Co., has held the same post in Seaboard Allied Milling Corp. since the latter became an operating company.

Rosedale Milling Co.—Kimball Milling Co., owned by George I. Kimball, had a mill of 600 cwt. that was built in 1901. It was sold by Kimball's estate to W. Wood Marshall in 1917 and enlarged to 1000 cwt. This mill was destroyed by fire in 1924. Oscar L. Bauer (b. 1889 Kan.) then organized Rosedale Milling Co., and built a new mill of 2000 cwt. on the site, Bauer being president. In a reorganization in 1927, Marshall again became owner. The mill was largely idle through the 1930's and was purchased in 1940 by Continental Baking Co., which converted it to a whole wheat plant and increased it to 3100 cwt. It was sold in 1951 to Flour Mills of America, Inc., and was operated for two years before it was closed.

Southwestern Milling Co.—For many years the largest flour mill in the Southwest was the plant of Southwestern Milling Co., on the Kansas side of Kansas City.

The first Southwestern mill was built in 1906, and was a plant of 3000 cwt. It was destroyed by fire in 1914 and was replaced by a mill of 6000 cwt. By 1920 the mill attained 12,000 cwt., and in 1942 it was enlarged to 15,600 cwt.

Southwestern Milling Co. was a wholly-owned subsidiary of Standard Milling Co., and its plant was the only one ever built by that company. During its first five years its managers were Louis R. Hurd and then Randall W. Arndt. In 1911 Clarence M. Hardenbergh began an 18-year tenure as general manager. He was followed by Jens Juul (b. 1888 Denmark) in 1929-32 and by Charles W. Sherman (b. 1884 Kan., d. 1950) in 1932-38.

Southwestern Milling Co. became a division of Standard Milling Co. in 1932, but with a managerial set-up that was independent of the other divisions. The divisions were abolished in 1938. The Kansas City mill was operated until 1952 when it was dismantled.

Standard Milling Co., the headquarters of which is in Kansas City, operates a mill in Buffalo that has 7000 cwt. wheat flour and 800 cwt. rye flour capacity. It is largely engaged in the bakery trade in northeastern metropolitan areas, but it also has household flour business. The company is controlled and managed by the Uhlmann family, which is also a large participant in the grain business.

After the United States Flour Milling Co. went into receivership in 1900, New York financial houses set up Standard Milling Co. as a holding company for several of the better properties. Hecker-Jones-Jewell Milling Co., Northwestern Consolidated Milling Co., and Duluth-Superior Milling Co. became wholly-owned subsidiaries, and combined they had about 60,000 cwt. capacity and thus comprised the largest aggregation in the industry. Southwestern Milling Co. became the fourth unit when its mill was built in 1906.

Control of Standard Milling Co. rested with financial interests for the next 29 years. Gold Dust Corp. obtained a majority interest in 1929, and it remained in that diversified group of concerns until 1946, the name of the parent changing meanwhile to Hecker Products Co. and then to Best Foods, Inc.

Standard's first two presidents were generals — Samuel Thomas in 1900-03 and Brayton Ives (b. 1840 Conn., d. 1914) in 1903-14. They were followed by Alfred P. Walker (b. 1864 Ont., d. 1934) in 1914-29, and in 1929-32 by George K. Morrow (b. 1873 Ont., d. 1941). The first miller to head Standard was John A. Sim (b. 1877 Ont.), long a Hecker-Jones-Jewell official. He converted the four subsidiary companies into autonomous divisions in 1932, and in 1936 merged the divisions into Standard Milling Co., which then became an operating company for the first time. He was president in 1932-40.

Best Foods, Inc., sold the mills in 1946 to a new Standard Milling Co. that was formed by Joseph C. Beaven (b. 1896 Wash., d. 1951) and William C. Engel (b. 1897 Mo.). Beaven, who had been president of the old company from 1940, continued in that post in the new organization, Engel being executive vice president. The Uhlmann group secured control in 1951, Paul Uhlmann (b. 1884 Germany) being elected president after Beaven's death. His son, R. Hugh (b. 1916 Mo.), became president in 1961, and Paul Jr. (b. 1920 Mo.) executive vice president.

Company offices were in New York until 1938, in Chicago in 1938-52, and since that time in Kansas City.

The Superior mill was sold in 1939 to King Midas Flour Mills, the mill in Loudonville, Ohio, that was acquired in 1947 went to Sunshine Biscuits, Inc. in 1953, and the Kansas City and Minneapolis mills were closed in 1952.

Zenith Milling Co.—One of the first mills in Kansas City was that of Zenith Milling Co., built in 1871. It was purchased in 1882 by Louis S. Mohr (b. 1846 Pa., d. 1932) and associates. The mill reached 2000 cwt. capacity. Mohr was president for 45 years. The company was sold in 1927 to W. J. Jennison Co., and was managed first by Albert L. Goetzmann and then by Malcolm D. Smith. The plant was dismantled in 1929.

New Haven

Wolff Milling Co.—On the Missouri River 60 miles west of St. Louis, George Wolff (b. 1842 France, d. 1917) established New Haven Roller Mills in 1876. Incorporation as

Wolff Milling Co. took place in 1888. The mill had 800 cwt. capacity until 1930, when it was increased to 2000 cwt. The founder's sons, George, Jr. (b. 1878 Mo., d. 1962) and Emil (b. 1881 Mo., d. 1950) succeeded to the business, George, Jr. becoming manager in 1913 and president five years later. The enterprise continued until 1950, when the mill was closed.

St. Joseph

Aunt Jemima Mills—National advertising established Aunt Jemima as the symbol for pancakes, and the mill which made her famous changed its name in her honor. This event took place in 1914, when Davis Milling Co. became Aunt Jemima Mills.

Davis Milling Co. was founded by R. M. Davis, and was managed by him for many years. The concern was in moribund condition in 1903, when a St. Joseph bank brought in a new manager—Robert R. Clark (b. 1861 Kan., d. 1945). Clark made a great success of pancake flour under the Aunt Jemima name.

Aunt Jemima mills, which then had a plant of 3200 cwt., was merged with Quaker Oats Co. in 1925, and Clark remained as St. Joseph division manager until 1938. The mill continues in use.

St. Louis

Baur Flour Mills Co.—Herman Baur (b. 1848 Germany, d. 1934) entered the flour business in St. Louis in 1870. His son, Andrew (b. 1877 Mo., d. 1951), joined the family firm about 1895. They moved from flour distribution to flour milling in 1925, when they bought an idle 800-cwt. plant in the south part of the city. It was then known as Ziebold Milling Co., but earlier it had been called Des Peres Milling Co., and still earlier had been Carondelet Milling Co.

Baur Flour Mills Co. increased the mill to 1500 cwt. capacity. Andrew Baur was president in 1925-41, his son, Andrew H. (b. 1915 Mo.), in 1941-42. The mill was leased in 1944 to Lawrence Milling Co., which exercised a purchase option two years later. The mill was closed in 1948.

Bernet, Craft & Kauffman Milling Co.—Two St. Louis flour men joined forces in 1887 and formed Bernet & Craft Flour Co. They were Christian Bernet (b. 1850 Switzerland, d. 1929) and Henry G. (Pop) Craft (b. 1845 N. Y., d. 1925). The latter was part owner of a small mill in nearby Troy, Ill., and the firm acted as agents for many other small mills in the area. The third partner, Frank E. Kauffman (b. 1852 Ohio, d. 1933) joined in 1903 when the firm built a 4200-cwt. mill in Mount Carmel, Ill., in the lower Wabash Valley. The company was incorporated at that time. Craft was president in 1903-25 and Bernet in 1925-29, succeeded by the latter's son, Albert E. A big southern business was built up. The company was merged in 1930 with Hall Milling Co., through Commonwealth Flour Mills, Inc. Fire destroyed the mill in 1931 and the business came to an end in 1938.

Hall Milling Co.—Largest hard winter wheat millers during the last quarter of the nineteenth century were Kehlor Bros., a firm which had mills with aggregate capacity of 18,000 cwt. The business began in 1869 when James B. M. Kehlor (b. 1841 Scotland, d. 1903) bought famous Laclede Flouring Mills Co. in St. Louis. Two years later he added the Pacific mill. These mills were closed when he built a 3000-cwt. mill in East St. Louis in 1882. It was increased to 5400 cwt. in 1891. Kehlor also bought the 4400-cwt. Litchfield Flouring Mills Co., Litchfield, Ill., in 1885 and built the Rex mill of 8000 cwt. in 1892 in Kansas City. The Litchfield mill was lost to fire and the Rex Mill was dismantled in 1906.

Kehlor Flour Mills Co. was incorporated in 1903, with George F. Tower (d. 1924) as president in 1903-07. Edward C. Andrews (b. 1862 Tenn., d. 1929) began a 13-year managership in 1910, and Kehlor's son-in-law, Peyton C. Carr (b. 1864 Mo., d. 1947), was president in 1907-25. In the latter year the company was sold to a grain man, Marshall Hall (b. 1875 Ky., d. 1925), but he died soon after taking possession. The enterprise was renamed Hall Milling Co. soon afterward.

Paul M. Marshall (b. 1890 Pa., d. 1957) and associates bought Hall Milling Co. in 1927, Marshall becoming president. It was combined with Bernet, Craft & Kauffman Milling Co. in 1930 under a holding company called Commonwealth Flour Mills, Inc., which Marshall also headed. The business was liquidated in 1938 and the Hall mill dismantled.

Marshall's early milling experience was with Shane Bros. & Wilson and King Midas. After the Hall company was dissolved, he became a leading figure in the soft wheat milling industry as the excutive officer of National Soft Wheat Millers' Association.

J. F. Imbs Milling Co. is on the threshold of its centennial. The output of its 4200-cwt. mill in nearby Belleville, Ill., goes both to the household and the bakery trade. The company has 550,000 bushels of grain storage.

Joseph F. Imbs (b. 1844 France, d. 1926) entered the flour commission business in St. Louis in 1863, and the following year he also acquired Crown Mills in Belleville. He operated Crown until 1889, when he bought the historic Harrison Mills, likewise in Belleville. It dated back to 1818 and has been rebuilt several times. The firm of Imbs, Meyer & Fusz became J. F. Imbs & Co., and in 1907 incorporation took place under the present name. Throughout its history, the office has been in St. Louis.

Imbs was company president in 1907-26, and the office was held in 1926-62 by his son, Al V. (b. 1878 Mo.), who entered the business in 1898. Al V. and his brother, Robert F. (b. 1886 Mo.), secretary-treasurer, have been associated in business since 1907. Joseph F. Imbs II (b. 1922 Mo.), son of Al V., joined the family enterprise in 1950 and was elected president in 1962.

Plant Flour Mills Co.—For almost a century there was a Plant mill in St. Louis. The business was launched in 1840 by George P. Plant (d. 1873) with whom his brother, Samuel (d. 1866), became associated. The former's son, George H. (b. 1847, d. 1929), became head of the concern in the early 1870's. At about that time George P. Plant & Sons Milling Co. was incorporated, and George H. Plant was president more than 50 years.

Samuel Plant II (b. 1872 Mo., d. 1953), son of George H., was general manager in 1908-24. He became president of Millers' National Federation in 1916-18. The original mill had been destroyed by fire in 1891 and was rebuilt with 5000 cwt. capacity. This mill was replaced in 1920 by a new mill of 6000 cwt. Evert L. Stancliffe was general manager in 1924-27.

Frank Kell and associates bought the Plant mill in 1926 and organized Plant Flour Mills Co. The following year Morris A. Wilkins became general manager, Kell's son, Joseph A. (b. 1895 Texas, d. 1939), being president. The company went out of business in 1931.

Ralston Purina Co.—Whole wheat flour as a by-product

in the manufacture of a breakfast cereal was made by Ralston Purina Co., beginning in 1903 in St. Louis and in 1927 in Davenport, Iowa. The flour capacity of these plants was about 1000 cwt. each. The company discontinued flour production in 1946.

Regina Flour Mills Co.—After 20 years as a flour merchant in St. Louis, first with Imbs, Meyer & Fusz, then as Fusz & Backer, and also acquiring a lead-mining fortune, Louis A. Fusz (b. 1839 France, d. 1924) entered milling in 1885 through the purchase of Atlantic Mills. He named it Regina Flour Mills Co. in honor of his mother. It was managed for a time by George W. Bain (b. 1836 Scotland, d. 1891) and then by Fusz' son, Firman D. (b. 1870 Mo., d. 1945). Bain was a national figure in the industry, having been president of Millers' National Association in 1875-83, when that organization was most active.

The St. Louis mill continued to operate until about 1910. Some years earlier a small mill was purchased in Washington, 50 miles west of St. Louis, and it was enlarged to 1000 cwt. The Washington mill was operated until 1926, when it was sold to Dixie-Portland interests and used by them until 1932.

Saxony Mills—A flour mill that was built in 1849 by Ernst W. Leonhardt (b. 1820 Germany, d. 1896) and John Shuricht was named in honor of their native land. Saxony Mills was incorporated in 1852. The original 1200-cwt. mill was rebuilt in 1897 just in time to be partially destroyed by a great tornado and was subsequently restored and increased to 2500 cwt. capacity.

Saxony Mills ran for a century, the site being taken in 1949 for a superhighway. The company was liquidated in 1953. Its presidents: Ernst W. Leonhardt in 1852-96; his son, Robert H.

(b. 1864 Mo., d. 1936) in 1896-1936; the latter's son, Roger A. (b. 1897 Mo.), in 1936-53.

Valier & Spies Milling Co.—What grew into the largest mill in soft wheat territory originated in 1868, when Charles Valier (b. 1843 Germany, d. 1913) and his father-in-law, Jacob Spies (b. 1814 Germany, d. 1906) built a small mill at Marine, an Illinois village 35 miles northeast of St. Louis. In 1889 a second mill was built, in neighboring St. Jacob. These mills reached a total capacity of about 1600 cwt., and were operated until 1924.

Valier's sons—Louis A. (b. 1876 Ill., d. 1952) and Charles E. (b. 1882 Ill.)—established a 1600-cwt. mill in St. Louis in 1913 and a second unit two years later. It was enlarged to 5000 cwt. in 1919 and became a large factor in the southern trade. The mill had 7000 cwt. by 1929 and was increased to 11,000 cwt. in 1942. Still later it reached 13,000 cwt.

Valier & Spies Milling Co. joined Kansas Flour Mills Corp. in forming Flour Mills of America, Inc., in 1926, and about a decade later it was merged into the parent company. Thereafter it was known as Valier & Spies Division, but a separate identity was maintained until the early 1950's. The Valier plant was purchased in 1957 by Colorado Milling & Elevator Co., and is known as St. Louis Flour Mills.

Valier & Spies Milling Co. was incorporated in 1903. The Spies interest was acquired at about that time by the Valiers. The founder was president in 1903-13, Charles E. Valier in 1913-28, and Louis C. Chase (b. 1882 Ohio) in 1928-51.

St. Marys

St. Marys Mill Co.—The Mississippi River town of St. Marys, 70 miles below St. Louis, was a mill site from 1858.

The mill was purchased in 1864 by Louis Schaaf (b. 1839, d. 1922) and operated by him until 1902. The business was conducted in 1902-39 by Schaaf's sons, Edward (b. 1864 Mo., d. 1944) and Walter. The original mill was replaced about 1900 by a 1600-cwt. plant.

The company was acquired in 1939 by C. B. Ragland Co., wholesale grocers, and Clyde B. Smith (b. 1895 Ky.), who had been associated with Acme Mills, Inc. Smith became president. In 1946 the mill was sold to Lathrop Grain Corp., which became Interstate Grain Corp. Mill capacity was increased to 2300 cwt. The mill was dismantled in 1950.

Sikeston

Scott County Milling Co. is located in Sikeston, in South-eastern Missouri. It has a line of country elevators, 2,500,000 bushels of storage facilities, a feed plant and 800-cwt. corn mill in addition to a flour mill of 1100 cwt. Its flour business is largely with the soft wheat bakery trade.

Scott County Milling Co. was organized in 1905, through a consolidation of four small companies—two in Sikeston, the others at nearby Oran and Dexter. One of the Sikeston mills had been built in 1892 by William C. Bowman (b. 1859 Mo., d. 1950) and G. B. Greer (b. 1862, d. 1937). Bowman sold out in 1900 and bought Dexter Milling Co. A year later, with Charles D. Matthews (b. 1842 Mo., d. 1917), Bowman built another mill in Sikeston. These mills and the Greer-Ebert mill in Oran were joined in the merger that produced Scott County Milling Co.

The Dexter mill of 700 cwt. was closed in 1941, as was the original Sikeston mill of 600 cwt. in 1950. The Oran mill was idled in 1961.

W. C. Bowman was president of Scott County Milling Co. in 1905-50. He was succeeded by his son, Lyman R. (b. 1883 Mo.), who joined the company in 1905 and became general manager in 1915 and president in 1950-62. Another son, Lee (b. 1891 Mo.), entered the company in 1911 and was elected president in 1962.

Slater

Slater Mill & Elevator Co.—Built in 1900, the Slater mill was increased to 600 cwt. before the first World War, to 1600 cwt. in the 1920's and to 2500 cwt. in 1945. John Reiderer (b. 1870, d. 1946) was company president until 1931. Charles Bolte (b. 1870 Germany, d. 1949), who had been manager, then became owner and president. Bolte sold the company in 1945 to Midland Flour Milling Co., Midland was merged into International Milling Co. in 1948, and the Slater mill was closed the next year.

Springfield

Eisenmayer Milling Co.—After their father had operated a grist mill in Southern Illinois for 41 years, Andrew J. Eisenmayer (b. 1861 Ill., d. 1935) and his brother Julius (b. 1864 Ill., d. 1925) established a 400-cwt. mill in Springfield, the queen city of the Ozarks, in 1884. Eisenmayer Milling Co. was incorporated in 1895 and the mill was later increased to 1600 cwt. capacity.

A. J. Eisenmayer was company president for 40 years. His son, Walter C. (b. 1891 Mo., d. 1936) became manager in 1927 and president in 1935. Lin M. Lundgaard began a three-year general managership in 1936. The mill was purchased in 1939 by Dixie-Portland interests and was operated by them until 1942, when it was dismantled.

John F. Meyer & Sons Milling Co.—John F. Meyer (b. 1830 Germany, d. 1920) was a leading flour merchant in St. Louis for many years. He was a partner in Imbs, Meyer & Fusz, all of whom ultimately operated their own flour mills, and after 1872 he was head of Meyer & Bulte.

Meyer became a miller in 1894 through the purchase of Queen City and Model Mills, both in Springfield. John F. Meyer & Sons Milling Co. was incorporated in 1900, Meyer serving as president the remainder of his life. The Springfield mill capacity was 1600 cwt. Camp Spring Milling Co., Nashville, Ill., with 1200 cwt., was acquired in 1912, but was not operated after 1927. Ferdinand F. Meyer (b. 1871 Mo., d. 1929) succeeded his father as president, followed by his brother, Louis S. (b. 1873 Mo., d. 1935). Company office was in St. Louis until 1915, and thereafter was in Springfield.

Meyer-Blair Milling Co. was a short-lived merger of the Meyer company and Lyons Flour Milling Co. It was formed in 1934 with L. S. Meyer as president and John M. Blair as general manager. The Springfield mill was sold in 1935 to Colorado Milling & Elevator Co., which operated it until 1951 under the trade name of Springfield Flour Mills.

Sweet Springs

Sweet Springs Milling Co.—Samuel Hayes was the last manager of the 1000-cwt. flour mill in Sweet Springs, which is about 60 miles east of Kansas City. The mill went out of business in 1922.

MONTANA

Wheat production in Montana was quite limited until 1910, but thereafter it increased rapidly, and its commercial milling industry largely dates from that era. However, there has been a flour mill in Great Falls from 1893. A few very small mills had existed as early as the 1870's to supply the mining camps.

Montana produced 2,826,000 cwt. of flour in 1961.

Cascade

Cascade Milling Co.—Two small mills were consolidated in 1921 to form Cascade Milling Co., in the town of that name south of Great Falls. The mill was enlarged to 1200 cwt. August Schwachheim, the founder, was president to 1931. William C. Boeke (b. 1873 Germany, d. 1931) was manager, and was succeeded by W. A. Flood. The mill was closed in 1936.

Great Falls

Montana Flour Mills Co. has two flour mills in Montana and one in Minnesota, with aggregate capacity of 7350 cwt. It has feed mills of 400 tons, a large line of country elevators and 3,100,000 bushels of mill storage. It is the largest factor in the milling and grain business in the state. The major part of its flour production goes to West Coast bakers, a lesser volume to bakers in the Middle West and East.

This company was organized in 1911. It was then located in Lewistown, in almost the exact center of Montana. Its first mill was in Harlowton, a 1300-cwt. plant built by Grafton (N.D.) Roller Mill Co. In the company's second year, it purchased the Judith Basin Milling Co., Lewistown, and its 700-cwt. mill. The latter mill was sold in 1928 to Judith Milling Co., but repossessed in 1931 after Judith's bankruptcy and then operated until 1955. The Harlowton mill became inactive in 1957.

Montana Flour Mills Co. moved from Lewistown to Great Falls in 1917 and built a 2100-cwt. mill there. Two years later the 1600-cwt. plant of Bozeman Milling Co. in the town of that name was acquired from the Story family. The 600-cwt. mill in Missoula of the former Northern Flour Mills Co. was purchased in 1934; it was sold to Continental Baking Co. in 1941, but repurchased in 1945. It was destroyed by fire in 1949.

Short wheat crops in Montana in the drouth years caused the company to buy the 3000-cwt. mill of Fairchild Milling Co. in Cleveland, Ohio, in 1936. This mill was operated for eighteen years and then was sold in 1954 to International Milling Co. As a partial replacement, the company acquired an idle mill in Fergus Falls, Minn., which now has 2200 cwt. capacity.

Mills presently in use are in Great Falls, 3150 cwt., and in Bozeman, 1650 cwt., in addition to the Minnesota facility.

Montana Flour Mills Co. has been largely owned throughout its history by several pioneer Montana families. Four of its present directors are sons of men who founded the business.

The company's first president was Austin W. Warr, a banker who served in 1911-17. Charles R. McClave (b. 1872 N. Y., d. 1956), who learned milling in his home state and was general manager from 1911, was president in 1917-46. He was followed for ten years by Paul R. Trigg (b. 1882 Iowa, d. 1956), and since 1956 the president has been Charles G. McClave (b. 1910 Mont.), whose father was Charles R. The corps of top officials has included William N. Smith (b. 1867 Minn., d. 1957), Rodney J. Anderson (b. 1882 Minn., d. 1962) and Albert F. Strobehn (b. 1886 Iowa).

Royal Milling Co.—Officials of Washburn Crosby Co. established a 600-cwt. flour mill in Great Falls in 1893 and organized Royal Milling Co. William M. Atkinson, who later founded the company that bore his name, was manager in 1893-1904. James W. Sherwood (b. 1868 Minn., d. 1941) managed the company in 1904-28. The Great Falls mill was enlarged to 2500 cwt. in 1916.

Three additional mills were acquired by the company—a 650-cwt. plant in Kalispell, Mont., bought in 1902 and operated until 1948; and mills of about twice that size in Pasco, Wash., and Ogden, Utah, purchased in 1927 but dismantled within a year or so.

Royal Milling Co. became a General Mills subsidiary in 1928 and was merged into the parent company in 1937.

Hobson

Judith Milling Co.—An ill-starred milling venture began in 1917, when Samuel B. Fairbank and Arthur A. Freeseman, Jr., bought a small mill at Hobson, a village west of Lewistown. It was enlarged and the capacity reached 1300 cwt. ten years later. In 1928 the 1000-cwt. Lewistown mill was purchased from Montana Flour Mills. Co. In 1931 the owners were prosecuted for fraud in connection with warehouse receipts, and Judith Milling Co. was liquidated.

NEBRASKA

Perhaps the most significant event in Nebraska milling history was the great improvement that took place in the 1940's in the character of the wheat crop of Nebraska. Before that time Nebraska wheat was the lowest in milling quality of any part of the hard winter wheat area—since then it has usually had superior milling values. The state milled 7,631,000 cwt. of flour in 1961, standing tenth in this respect. There were 258 mills in Nebraska that made flour in 1900, but their number had fallen to 20 in 1958.

Crete

Crete Mills—Nebraska had been a state only two years when a flour mill was built in 1869 in Crete, 25 miles southwest of Lincoln, by G. W. Bridges and O. W. Baltzley. This mill and another near the village were consolidated a decade or so later by Charles C. White (d. 1895) and a new plant of 600 cwt. was erected in 1883.

Albert L. Johnson (b. 1864 Wis., d. 1948), brother-in-law of White, worked in the mill for a time, left, returned in 1885 and became manager in 1895. When Crete Mills was incorporated in 1901, he began a 46-year tenure as president. A new flour mill of 2000 cwt. was built in 1921, a corn mill of 4400 cwt. being added later. A feed mill of 400 tons was built and the flour mill was enlarged to 3000 cwt.

Johnson's son, Ben L. (b. 1899 Neb.) was president in 1947-53, having previously been executive vice president. General managers, beginning about 1910, were Cord L. Aller, Hugh A. Butler (b. 1878 Iowa, d. 1954), Port A. Johnson (b. 1888 Neb.), Evert L. Stancliffe (b. 1888, d. 1956), Earl A. Talhelm (b. 1885 Neb., d. 1947) and Charles H. Johnson (b. 1908 Idaho). Talhelm held this position for 20 years. Port Johnson was a son of Albert L.; Stancliffe, a son-in-law; and Charles Johnson, a grandnephew.

Crete Mills was sold in 1953 to Lauhoff Grain Co., which closed the flour mill in 1955, but has continued to use the other facilities.

Hugh A. Butler was United States Senator in 1941-54.

Lexington

Lexington Mill & Elevator Co. stands within sight of the historic Oregon Trail over which the pioneers traveled westward a century ago. It operates a 1600-cwt. flour mill, a feed plant and 1,300,000 bushels of grain storage in a town two hundred miles west of Omaha. One of the few interior mills in Nebraska, its trade is with family, bakery and export outlets.

Plum Creek, the original name of the town, gave its name to the mill built in 1884 by E. M. Leflang and other Danish immigrants. Five years later, when Plum Creek became Lexington, the mill name changed likewise. The first mill was lost through fire in 1915, and the second mill of 1000 cwt. was increased to its present size in late years. John E. Jacobson (b. 1884 Neb., d. 1930), who began as an office boy in 1901, bought out the original owners in 1924 and succeeded Arthur Leflang as president. His brother, G. Kenneth (b. 1897 Neb., d. 1957), then held the office for 27 years, followed by John E.'s son, Clarence E. (b. 1912 Neb.), in 1957. Lee D. Jacobson (b. 1928 Neb.), son of G. K., is executive vice president.

Lexington Mill & Elevator Co. was the defendant in the famous flour bleaching test case, in which the government contended that the product was deleterious to health. In 1915 the Supreme Court upheld appellate court decisions to the contrary, thus ending a seven-year legal battle.

Lincoln

Gooch Milling & Elevator Co., one of the Vanier properties, has a flour mill of 7000 cwt. in Nebraska's capital city, a feed plant of 800 tons, corn mill of 1000 cwt., and 4,000,000 bushels of elevator storage. Its flour business is with the bakery trade in the Middle West and East and with the household trade in the Middle West.

This enterprise began in 1908, when Herbert E. Gooch (b. 1879 Ill., d. 1938) built a 400-cwt. flour mill. It was enlarged by stages until it reached 4000 cwt. by 1920. Gooch had a newspaper and several other businesses. He failed in 1938, and the flour mill and related lines were acquired the following year by John J. Vanier.

F. Earl Roth (b. 1879 Iowa, d. 1957), who had been general manager under Gooch, served as president of Gooch Milling & Elevator Co. in 1939-49. During this period the mill was increased to its present size. Harry B. Lilly (b. 1898 Ky.) has been president since 1949.

Nebraska City

Schminke Milling Co. — Established in 1876 by Paul Schminke (d. 1892) in the town 40 miles south of Omaha, the Schminke mill was operated by three generations of the family—the founder, his son, D. W., and the latter's son, Karl. On several occasions the mill was closed for lengthy periods. It has not made flour since 1948.

Omaha

Maney Milling Co.—A flour mill of 2800 cwt. capacity that was named for its principal stockholders, who had several mills in Oklahoma, was established in Omaha in 1909. No significant change in size took place for 35 years, and then it was enlarged to 4000 cwt. Control was lost in 1930 by the Maneys and thereafter the company was largely owned by the Schaefers. James W. Maney was president in 1909-30, Herman K. Schaefer (b. 1876 Germany, d. 1956) in 1930-49. Thomas F. Blake was manager the first five years, and thereafter Schaefer managed the business.

The mill was closed in 1949.

Nebraska Consolidated Mills Co. is eleventh in size in the milling industry. It operates three flour mills in Nebraska and three elsewhere—total capacity 19,700 cwt.—two corn mills, three feed plants and 4,750,000 bushels of grain storage. It is prominent in the bakery flour business throughout the eastern half of the country, it has the only flour mill in Puerto Rico and it participates heavily in family flour and feed in Alabama and Georgia.

The company was created in 1919, through the affiliation of four small mills in East Central Nebraska. Total capacity of these mills was about 2000 cwt. Largest was Henry Glade Mills, founded in 1883 in Grand Island, and that town was company headquarters until 1922. The company then doubled its size by purchasing the idle plant of Updike Milling Co. in Omaha, and company offices were moved to the Nebraska metropolis.

Four years later the idle Brown mill in Fremont was acquired, the Omaha mill was lost to fire in 1931 and replaced by a larger plant, the Grand Island mill was replaced in 1938 by a new and larger mill. The other original mills were closed, Hastings being the last, in 1950. The mills now operated in Omaha, Fremont and Grand Island have total capacity of 10,-000 cwt.

The company pioneered in utilizing the transportation economies of the inland waterway system by putting a new mill in Decatur, Ala., in 1941. The 1700-cwt. Decatur mill has grown to 4000 cwt., in addition to a corn mill and feed plant and operates under the trade name of Alabama Flour Mills.

During the first half of the 1950's, Nebraska Consolidated had the Duncan Hines franchise for cake flour, but sold the business in 1956 to Proctor & Gamble Co.

Two soft wheat mills were purchased in 1957—the Lillie and Garland plants. The former was destroyed by fire within a year of purchase.

Entry into Puerto Rico took place in 1959, when a 4200-

cwt. pneumatic flour mill, corn mill and feed plant were opened in a suburb of San Juan. Molinos de Puerto Rico is the only such enterprise in the commonwealth.

Alva R. Kinney (b. 1870 Ohio, d. 1946), who entered the milling business in 1904 in Ravenna, Neb., was the founder of the company and its president in 1919-38. Filbert A. Glade (b. 1880 Neb., d. 1930) was general manager in 1929-30, and Robert S. Dickinson (b. 1889 Neb.) was general manager in 1930-54 and president in 1938-54. Dickinson's son-in-law, J. Allan Mactier (b. 1922 Neb.) succeeded to these posts in 1954. Another leading factor in the company was Joseph H. Weaver (b. 1888 Pa., d. 1954).

Omar, Inc.—An Omaha malt plant was converted into a 3200-cwt. flour mill in 1918 by William J. Coad (b. 1879 Wyo., d. 1961) and associates, and they formed Omaha Flour Mills Co. The Coad interests also went into the baking business, and in 1925 National Baking Co. was incorporated, the milling company becoming a subsidiary. The name of the latter was changed some years after to Omar Mills, Inc. and still later to Omar, Inc. The Omaha mill was enlarged to 4000 cwt., and in 1936 a mill of 1000 cwt. was built in Denver.

Coad was president in 1918-27 and in 1933-40. Chauncy Abbott, Jr. (b. 1883 Neb., d. 1932) was manager the first nine years and president in 1927-32. William J. Coad, Jr. (b. 1910 Neb.) was president from 1940. General managers were Milton P. Fuller in 1934-35, Larry L. Breitenbauch (b. 1893 Minn., d. 1939) in 1935-38, and Harold Roth (b. 1894 Neb.) in 1940-46.

The mills were sold in 1949 to Colorado Milling & Elevator Co., which has continued to operate them. Omar, Inc., retained the bakeries almost a decade before selling to Continental Baking Co.

Updike Milling Co.—Nelson B. Updike (b. 1872 N. J., d. 1948) was a national figure in the grain trade, but his milling ventures were not successful. He formed Updike Milling Co. in 1910 and acquired a 2000-cwt. mill in Omaha. The business was managed after 1914 by William H. Yohe (d. 1937). The 1400-cwt. Phoenix plant in Davenport, Iowa, was purchased in 1920, but in less than a year it was sold to Freihofer Baking Co. The Omaha mill had been idle for a year when it was sold in 1922 to Nebraska Consolidated Mills Co.

Schuyler

Wells-Abbott-Nieman Co.—For many years the largest mill in Nebraska was in Schuyler, 65 miles west of Omaha. It had its beginning in a community mill built in 1870 near the town by Nathan W. Wells and Henry W. Nieman. Twelve years later they joined with Chauncy Abbott (b. 1857 Wis., d. 1918) and built a 600-cwt. mill in Schuyler. Later they organized Wells-Abbott-Nieman Co., in which Abbott acquired the controlling interest in 1895. The mill was increased in size; in 1908 it reached 5000 cwt. and then 6000 cwt. in 1919. Abbott was president and manager in 1895-1918. Gerald Ehernberger (b. 1879 Neb.) was manager most of the next decade; he is now in his 67th year in the grain business.

The company became insolvent in the wheat market debacle in 1921, and thereafter it operated somewhat irregularly. Several attempts were made at reorganization, but the milling of flour came to an end in 1929. The plant burned down in 1933.

Wymore

Black Bros. Flour Mills—An Illinois mill was moved in 1874 on flat cars to Beatrice, 40 miles south of Lincoln, and in much later years it reached 1400 cwt. capacity. The owners built a smaller plant in nearby Blue Springs about 1880; the second mill was moved to Wymore in 1924. The Beatrice mill was destroyed by fire in 1936, and the Wymore mill was then increased from 800 to 1200 cwt. Flour milling was discontinued in 1949, but the company has remained in non-milling activities.

The original owners were William C. Black (b. 1835 Pa., d. 1919) and his brother, Cochrane S. (b. 1837 Pa., d. 1905). The business was operated as a partnership and continued as such until 1921, when Black Bros. Flour Mills was incorporated with William C. Black, Jr. (b. 1878 Ill., d. 1958) as president until 1935. Cord L. Aller (b. 1866 Pa., d. 1937) served as manager for 15 years, beginning in 1922. Wyman B. Kenagy (b. 1906 Neb.) became president in 1947.

NEW HAMPSHIRE
Concord

Stratton & Co.—The only flour mill of commercial size in New England was that of Stratton & Co., at Penacook, a village in the environs of New England's capital. The business had continued for 95 years when it was liquidated in 1953. The mill had 1000 cwt. capacity.

The mill was built in 1858 by John H. Pearson & Co. It was operated until 1913 by a succession of partnerships, the last of which was Stratton & Merrill Co., which began in the early 1870's. Upon the incorporation of Stratton & Co. in 1913, George L. Stratton (b. 1838 Mass., d. 1924), who had been manager for many years, became president. He was succeeded in 1924-41 by Richard P. Johnston (b. 1877 N. H., d. 1941), whose father had acquired part of the Merrill interest; and he in 1941-53 by Gardner Tilton (b. 1898 Mass.), grandson of Stratton.

NEW JERSEY

New Jersey was important in colonial times both as producer of wheat and miller of flour. Its first mill was built in 1670 in Newark by Robert Treat and Richard Harrison. Even as late as 1900 the state had 166 mills that ground wheat. Only one now remains.

Clifton

New Jersey Flour Mills Co. is the only flour milling enterprise in the state. It was established as Clifton Cereal Mills in 1917 in a suburb of Passaic by Lorenzo F. Orbe (b. 1881 Italy, d. 1949). He had been jobbing flour under the name of New Jersey Flour Co., and the two concerns were consolidated in 1920 as New Jersey Flour Mills Co. The original 1000-cwt. mill was increased gradually to the present 2000 cwt. The trade is exclusively with bakers in eastern metropolitan areas. The Orbe family has owned the business from its founding. Company presidents: L. F. Orbe in 1920-49; his son, Lawrence F. Orbe, Jr. (b. 1910 N. J.), since 1949.

The Orbes organized North East Flour Mills, Inc. in 1946, when they acquired the idle 1000-cwt. mill of Blaine-Mackay-Lee Co., North East, Pa. They operated this plant about three years.

NEW YORK

Three cities in the Empire State have been leaders in flour milling in three distinct periods of time. First was New York City, which was the most important milling center in Colonial

America until 1750. Next was Rochester, which held first place among milling cities in 1836-57 and gained such world-wide fame that it was long known as the Flour City. Finally, Buffalo rose to supremacy among milling cities in 1930, a position that it has continued to hold.

New York's dominance of milling was based upon the large amount of wheat grown on Manhattan Island and in adjacent New Jersey; Rochester's upon the power generated by the Genesee River and the use of Erie Canal for transportation; Buffalo's upon the shipping advantages of the Great Lakes and milling Canadian wheat in bond. Buffalo was a milling point as early as 1836, but its main development took place after 1900.

In Buffalo was built the first grain elevator in 1842 by Joseph Dart. This device greatly simplified the handling and marketing of wheat.

The state produced 28,445,000 cwt. of flour in 1961, exceeded only by Kansas. It had 571 mills in 1900, most of them located in the western half of the state, and 30 in 1958.

Baldwinsville

Eastern Semolina Mills, Inc.—Baldwinsville, a few miles out of Syracuse, was the town where James Frazee (b. 1827, d. 1914) began a milling career of 57 years in 1850. He built Union Mills there in 1859, and the business was incorporated as James Frazee Milling Co. in 1892. The company was sold in 1907 to Ralph H. Quackenbush, who then became president. In 1920 a new mill of 1000 cwt. was built, and in 1924 the business was reorganized as Baldwinsville Flour Mills, Inc. The mill operated spasmodically for more than a decade, and in 1938 it was purchased by a syndicate of macaroni manufacturers who organized Eastern Semolina Mills, Inc. Colburn S. Foulds was president.

The mill, which was then about 1500 cwt. capacity, was sold in 1943 to International Milling Co., which subsequently enlarged it to 4000 cwt. It is used as a durum mill.

Binghamton

George Q. Moon & Co., Inc.—On the Chenango River a flour mill was built in 1854 by a young millwright named George Q. Moon (b. 1828 N. Y., d. 1898). Later it was moved a few miles into Binghamton and enlarged to 1000 cwt. The business was operated successively by the founder, his son, Walter J. Moon (b. 1857 N. Y., d. 1937) and by the latter's son, William W. (b. 1885 N. Y.). In 1898 George Q. Moon & Co., Inc. was formed. The flour mill was destroyed by fire in 1938, but the company has continued in the feed business. Clarke C. Davis (b. 1898 Colo.) was elected president in 1950.

Buffalo

Thornton & Chester Milling Co.—Globe Mills, built about 1836 by Stephen W. Howell, was the first merchant mill in Buffalo. It was acquired in 1845 by Thomas Thornton and Thomas Chester and operated under their names for 83 years. The original mill was destroyed by fire in 1878 and was rebuilt alongside the National Mill, which the owners purchased in 1868. They also had a mill in Lockport, and in 1880 total capacity of their plants was 1700 cwt.

Thornton & Chester Milling Co. was incorporated in 1899, and the mill was later increased to 2200 cwt. Benjamin W. Appleton (b. 1864, d. 1928), a relative of Chester, served as president. The business was sold in 1928 to George Urban Milling Co., and the plant went at the same time to Commander

Larabee Milling Co. After being greatly enlarged in 1936, the mill was closed in 1950.

George Urban Milling Co. has been headed by four successive George Urbans. It now operates a flour mill of 6000 cwt. and rye mill of 1000 cwt. in Buffalo. The company has 200,000 bushels of grain storage. It is engaged very largely in the bakery field in the northeastern states.

The first George Urban (b. 1820 Germany, d. 1888) was a flour merchant in Buffalo from 1846, and he and his son, George, Jr. (b. 1850 N. Y., d. 1928), established a mill of 1500 cwt. in 1881. This mill went into the United States Flour Milling Co. in 1899, George, Jr. becoming president of the latter. The mill emerged from the ensuing receivership as part of Standard Milling Co., but the plant ceased to operate in 1903. Meanwhile, George Urban Milling Co. had been formed and it opened a new 3000-cwt. mill. It was later increased in size and rebuilt in 1951.

George Urban, Jr. was company president in 1902-28; his son, George P. (b. 1877 N. Y.), in 1928-52; and George P., Jr. (b. 1914 N.Y.) since 1952. George Urban, Jr. was an intimate of Grover Cleveland, and at his country place the meetings were held that opened the way for Cleveland to become Governor and President.

Joseph A. Walter Milling Co.—After being manager of Duluth-Superior Milling Co., and then of Hecker-Jones-Jewell Milling Co., Joseph A. Walter (b. 1865 Germany, d. 1946) in 1913 formed a company to which he gave his own name. For almost a decade it was a milling company without a mill, but in 1922 the old Banner mill, which was erected in 1879 but idle for some years, was returned to production. The 2000-

cwt. plant was operated until 1926, when it was sold to Commander Larabee Corp. It was destroyed by fire two years later.

Geneva

Finger Lakes and Upper Hudson Flour Mills—Continental Grain Co. acquired two small mills in New York State in 1937-38 and enlarged them. First was C. C. Davidson Milling Co., Geneva, established in 1902 and incorporated in 1926; this plant was rebuilt with 2400 cwt. capacity. The other was Boutwell Milling & Grain Co.'s rye mill in Troy, increased to 800 cwt. These mills were operated as Finger Lakes and Upper Hudson Flour Mills, and were managed by Finis E. Cowan from 1939. They were merged into Arrow Mills, Inc., when that company was chartered in 1945, but continued to use the Finger Lakes name. The mills ceased to produce flour in 1948.

Ithaca

Cooperative GLF Exchange, Inc., one of the largest manufacturers and distributors of formula feeds, has among its minor lines a flour mill of 800 cwt. in Churchville, west of Rochester. The mill is a soft wheat plant and its product goes largely to bakers in New York and New England.

GLF entered the milling business in 1937 with a small mill in Hemlock. The Churchville mill was acquired in 1942 and was rebuilt ten years later. Bayard H. Staplin (b. 1897 N. Y.) was manager of the milling division in 1937-61, John F. Teahan (b. 1923 N. Y.) since 1961.

Lockport

Federal Mills, Inc.—The list of industry services rendered by Fred J. Lingham (b. 1875 Ont., d. 1954) is indeed impressive. He headed the milling division of the U. S. Food Administration in 1918, resigning the Federation presidency to do so; he was president of Millers' National Federation a second time in 1933-34; he served more years (not consecutively) on the Federation board and executive committee than any other man; he played an influential role in the formulation of federal grain grades; and there were few millers' committees of importance during a 35-year period on which he was not a member. He was basically an industry-minded man.

Lingham's heritage was in milling, his father, Thomas, having had a mill in Canada. After twelve years as a broker in Boston, Lingham bought an interest in Federal Milling Co. in Lockport, 25 miles east of Niagara Falls, the majority owner being Howard M. Witbeck (b. 1864 N. Y., d. 1929), who also had other milling properties. Witbeck had acquired the property in 1907.

Federal Milling Co. became Federal Mill & Elevator Co. in 1922, and Federal Mill, Inc. in 1930. The mill had 2000 cwt. capacity. Lingham became company president in 1920, continuing to head and manage the business until the company was sold in 1950 to International Milling Co. The mill has continued in use to the present.

Thompson Milling Co.—Thompson's mill was established in 1890, and it had 1600 cwt. capacity in later years. It was operated first by Thompson, and then by Brewer, and in the 1920's it was idle for several years. The mill was purchased in 1930 by Charles E. Dickinson (b. 1863 Mass., d. 1933), who owned some of the assets of the former Niagara Falls Milling Co., and it was restored to production intermittently for the next three years, using both the Thompson and Niagara Falls names. The mill went out of business in 1933.

New York

DCA Food Industries, Inc. owns and operates two flour mills, in Ellicott City, Md., and Hillsdale, Mich. These are primarily captive mills, as a large part of their output is shipped to the doughnut plants of DCA. The mills have a total capacity of 9100 cwt.—3500 in Ellicott City and 5600 in Hillsdale.

The Ellicott City mill was leased in 1930 from Continental Milling Co., and the plant was purchased in 1955. It was rebuilt following destruction by fire in 1941. This had previously been the mill of C. A. Gambrill Mfg. Co., which succeeded historic Patapsco Mills.

The Hillsdale mill was acquired in 1958 from F. W. Stock & Sons, Inc.

The original corporate name of the present company was Display Doughnut Machine Corp., formed in 1920. There were several changes of name before DCA Food Industries, Inc. was adopted in 1956. David M. Levitt has been president since 1949.

General Foods Corp., the largest factor in the packaged foods industry, is also engaged in flour milling. It has soft wheat mills in Evansville, Ind. and Pendleton, Ore., with total capacity of 7100 cwt., and grain storage of 4,100,000 bushels. The company makes a high percentage of the household cake flour, and is also in the cake mix and bakery cake flour business.

Flour specially designed for making cakes was originated by Igleheart Bros., Inc., and that company was acquired in 1926 by General Foods Corp. Swansdown brand is so widely known that it has long been almost a generic name for cake flour for home use.

The Phoenix mill in Evansville was purchased in 1926

by Igleheart, the Dunlop mill in Clarksville, Tenn., in 1930, and the Collins mill in Pendleton was leased in 1937 and acquired three years later. The first two of these mills were closed, in 1949 and 1956, respectively.

Igleheart Bros., Inc., remained as a corporation until 1935, and the Igleheart division of General Foods continued under Igleheart management until after 1942. In recent years it has been merged into the Jell-O division.

Hecker-Jones-Jewell Milling Co.—Five companies with mills in New York City were consolidated in 1892 by Thomas A. McIntyre. These were George V. Hecker & Co., Jones & Co., Jewell Milling Co., Staten Island Milling Co. and King County Mills, and the product of the merger was called Hecker-Jones-Jewell Milling Co.

Largest and best-known of the group was George V. Hecker & Co., which dated back to 1842, when John and George Hecker built Croton Flour Mill. They were operating mills with total capacity of 4000 cwt. by the Civil War era, and they were the first to put self-rising flour on the market, in 1852. John V. Hecker (b. 1848 Vt., d. 1924) became the first president of Hecker-Jones-Jewell, retiring in 1897. Alfred Reuter was general manager until 1909.

The success of Hecker-Jones-Jewell gave impetus to McIntyre's grand plan to form a milling trust in 1899, but his United States Flour Milling Co. went on the rocks a year later. Standard Milling Co. emerged from the wreckage as owner of several properties, including Hecker-Jones-Jewell Milling Co. General Brayton Ives, a financier, was president of both companies in 1903-15.

The original mills were closed by 1910 and were replaced by a new mill of 20,000 cwt. at Corlears and Water Streets. In

1912 a 4400-cwt. mill was established in Buffalo. Joseph A. Walter was general manager in 1909-13. His successor was John A. Sim, who also became president in 1928-36. The mill in New York City was closed in 1931.

Along with three other milling subsidiaries of Standard Milling Co., Hecker-Jones-Jewell was merged into the parent company in 1932 and it became a division. Joseph C. Beaven managed the division in 1932-36. The Buffalo mill, which now has 7800 cwt. capacity, is the only plant presently operated by Standard Milling Co.

National Biscuit Co., largest cracker and biscuit manufacturer in the nation, is also the seventh miller in size. It operates three flour mills, all of the product of which, except millfeed, is used in the company's bakeries. These mills chiefly produce soft wheat flour.

The company's entry into milling took place in 1926, when it purchased National Milling Co., Toledo, and its plant of 4000 cwt. It leased the Fort Scott mill of Kansas Flour Mills Corp. in 1929, and operated this 1200-cwt. plant until 1939. It acquired the 1200-cwt. mill of McDaniel Milling Co. in 1941, and the 2000-cwt. mill of F. M. Martin Grain & Milling Co. in 1943. The first two of these mills have been enlarged year after year, and present sizes are: Toledo 26,000 cwt., Carthage 3300 cwt., Cheney 2300 cwt. Grand total 31,600 cwt.

National Milling Co. continued in existence until 1936, with Harold A. Anderson (b. 1894 Mo.) as president and manager. John H. Bailey (b. 1892 Colo.) served as manager of the milling division of National Biscuit Co. in 1943-57. He was succeeded by P. A. (Jim) Kier.

NOTE: *National Biscuit Co. refused to furnish data for this publication. The summary above has, therefore, been compiled from other sources, but is believed to be accurate.*

Sunshine Biscuits, Inc., the primary business of which is the production of crackers, operates four flour mills with aggregate capacity of 15,650 cwt. This puts the company in fifteenth place in size in the industry. Its grain elevators have space for 2,375,000 bushels. The mills are employed solely for making flour for the company's cracker plants, and millfeed is the only product sold. Company offices are in Long Island City, and the milling division is managed from Grafton, Ohio.

Loose-Wiles Biscuit Co., the name of which was changed in 1946 to Sunshine Biscuits, Inc., entered the milling business in 1928. Through a wholly-owned subsidiary, United Mills Corp., it first leased and then purchased the 1450-cwt. mill in Grafton from a company of the same name that had operated it from 1922. Howard E. Irvin (b. 1895 Ohio), who had been an official of the earlier company, became president of the Loose-Wiles subsidiary and manager of the Grafton mill.

Loose-Wiles acquired two more mills — the 2400-cwt. Moore-Lowry plant in Kansas City in 1933 and the 4200-cwt. mill of Wasco Warehouse Milling Co., The Dalles, Ore., in 1944. After the corporate name was changed in 1946, all subsidiaries were absorbed by the parent company, and Irwin became manager of the milling division of Sunshine Biscuits, Inc., continuing until 1963, when he was succeeded by Gordon M. Acker. The last mill purchase was in 1953, covering the 2400-cwt. mill in Loudonville from Standard Milling Co.

The Grafton mill was increased from time to time until it attained 3750 cwt. The Kansas City mill likewise grew to 4000 cwt. and the Loudonville plant to 3700 cwt.

Niagara Falls

Cataract City Milling Co.—An involuntary miller was Captain Joseph T. Jones (b. 1842 Pa., d. 1916), who became the owner of Cataract City Milling Co. in 1896. He had endorsed notes in a large amount for the previous proprietor just before the latter became insolvent. George J. Colpoys (b. 1868 N. Y., d. 1940) served as manager for the next 28 years, until the millsite was taken over by a power company. Captain Jones was one of the first to engage in the oil business after the discovery in his native state, and he added greatly to his fortune by developing Gulfport, Miss., and in railroading and paper manufacture.

The Cataract mill was established in 1870 and in later years had 2000 cwt. capacity.

Niagara Falls Milling Co.—Jacob F. Schoellkopf (b. 1819 Germany, d. 1899) was one of the foremost businessmen in Buffalo. He operated three tanneries, controlled three banks and was a pioneer power magnate. He had owned the Frontier and Buffalo mills for several years before he joined in 1875 with George B. Matthews (b. 1845 N. Y., d. 1942) in establishing a 2000-cwt. plant in Niagara Falls. It was the first flour mill to be turned by the power of the Niagara River.

Schoellkopf & Matthews was incorporated in 1899 as Niagara Falls Milling Co., which Matthews headed as president until 1914. Central Milling Co., owned by the same interests, was merged with Niagara Falls Milling Co. in 1900, the capacity then being 8000 cwt. Matthews was succeeded by his brother-in-law, William D. Olmsted (b. 1842 N. Y., d. 1924), and the latter's sons, George and John (b. 1882 N. Y., d. 1950) ran the business until 1928, when the mill was closed.

Pittsford

Pittsford Milling Co.—Two small mills in Rochester suburbs were acquired by Henry L. Perrigo (b. 1873, d. 1950)—

the mill in Pittsford about 1914 and the mill in Victor in 1921. He enlarged the first to 1200 cwt. and the latter to 1800 cwt., and ran them as Victor Flour Mills, Inc., until 1937. At that time the Victor mill was destroyed by fire. The Pittsford mill, which had been idle for several years, was then reopened and was operated until 1947. It was sold in that year to Interstate Grain Corp., but resold the following year to Berthold Rotholz and associates, who operated as Pittsford Milling Co. The mill was again sold in 1950 to Dutch interests, but was closed in 1951.

Rochester

J. G. Davis Co.—During the period of Rochester's greatest flour production, Joel G. Davis (b. 1813 N. Y., d. 1900) was a leader in the business there. He entered milling in 1855 by acquiring the Jefferson Mill which was built in 1835. After this mill was destroyed by fire in 1887, the founder and his son, H. Wheeler Davis (b. 1838 N. Y., d. 1914), purchased the Granite Mill, then the largest mill in Rochester and founded in 1825. Granite Mill was operated until 1924, barely missing the century mark.

J. G. Davis Co. was incorporated in 1899. H. W. Davis was president in 1899-1914; Martin F. Bristol (b. 1849 N. Y., d. 1925) in 1914-21; George G. Davis, son of H. W., in 1921-24.

Moseley & Motley Milling Co.—The last prominent mill in Rochester was that of Moseley & Motley Milling Co. It was established in 1862 by Jirah B. Moseley, whose father, Araunah, was an early Genesee miller. The enterprise was known as Flour City Mills and was incorporated in 1888. Moseley's partner was George H. Motley (b. 1834 England, d. 1881). The second George H. Motley (b. 1868 N. Y., d. 1927) was head of the company for 46 years. The latter's nephew, Wesley M. Angle, headed the company in 1927-36.

The 2000-cwt. mill went out of business in 1936.

NORTH CAROLINA

Flour milling in North Carolina has long been characterized by great numbers of small mills. The state had 975 such mills in 1900, and the 1958 report shows 81 mills—the largest number in any state. All but a few do business mainly or wholly in their respective communities.

Charlotte

Interstate Milling Co. is a prominent concern in the family flour trade of the Carolinas. Plant facilities consist of a flour mill of 1200 cwt. and feed mill of 400 tons.

The company was established in 1915 by Charles P. Moody and has been owned and managed from the beginning by his family. The original mill was 600 cwt. Moody was company president during his lifetime, and was succeeded in 1935 by his son, Stowe.

Durham

Austin-Heaton Co. is exclusively in the family flour business, chiefly in the Carolinas. It has been owned by Harris Milling Co. since 1961, but is operated as a separate entity. M. Arnold Briggs (b. 1887 N. C.), who has been called America's foremost small miller, is president, a post he has held since 1932.

General Julian S. Carr (b. 1845 N. C., d. 1924) founded the business. When he built the first mill in 1902 he took liberties with the spelling book and christened it Carrolina Roller Mills. The name was changed to Austin-Heaton Co. some years later, in harmony with the given names of one of the general's sons. A 1050-cwt. unit was added in 1917 to the original 400-cwt. mill, and the first plant was later dismantled.

General Carr, president in 1902-06, was succeeded by two sons—Julian S., Jr. (b. 1878 N. C., d. 1922) in 1906-11 and Austin H. (b. 1894 N. C., d. 1942) in 1911-17; and then by William M. Speed (b. 1879 N. C., d. 1932) in 1917-32.

Statesville

Statesville Flour Mills Co. has the largest flour mill in North Carolina, a 3000-cwt. plant with a pneumatic system installed in 1962. Its business is divided between family and bakery flour, chiefly in the Carolinas. The company was established in 1900 by Frank A. Sherrill (b. 1859 N. C., d. 1941), a merchant and cotton buyer who also had a small flour mill near Statesville, which is half way between Winston-Salem and Charlotte. The original mill was destroyed by fire in 1906, was rebuilt with 600 cwt. capacity and then gradually enlarged. Sherrill managed the business until the 1930's and was succeeded by his son, Karl B. (b. 1892 N. C., d. 1955). The latter was followed by the founder's son-in-law, J. Wesley Jones.

NORTH DAKOTA

North Dakota first became the premier state in wheat production in 1904 and it retained that place most of the time for the next quarter century and reached it occasionally thereafter. Flour mills first made their appearance in what is now the state in the 1870's, and by 1900 there were 97. The disadvantages of location largely prevented their development, and by 1958 the United States Census Bureau reported only three mills in the state. However, North Dakota milled 3,769,-000 cwt. of flour in 1961.

Grafton

Grafton Roller Mill Co.—Between Grand Forks and the Canadian border is Grafton, where William C. Leistekow built a mill in the early 1880's. This plant was purchased in 1906 by Henry B. Eggers (b. 1837 Germany, d. 1926), who also milled in St. Louis. It was enlarged to 1800 cwt. Henry B. Eggers, Jr. (b. 1876 Mo., d. 1951) became manager. The company failed in 1927 and the mill did not operate thereafter.

The Eggers family also had milling properties in Red Bud, Ill., and Hermann, Mo. at one time, and the Grafton segment built the mill in Lewistown, Mont., which grew into Montana Flour Mills Co.

Grand Forks

North Dakota Mill & Elevator is owned and operated by the State of North Dakota. It consists of a plant of 6500 cwt., two units of which mill spring wheat flour chiefly for the bakery trade in the central and eastern states and the third unit produces durum semolina for macaroni manufacturers throughout the nation. Family flour business is largely confined to North Dakota.

North Dakota Mill & Elevator was established soon after the Farmers' Nonpartisan League won control of the state government in 1917. The League was antagonistic to the milling industry, as well as to many other business interests, and it proceeded to enter the milling field via a small mill at Drake in 1919. This mill was operated about five years, and meanwhile a large new mill was opened in 1922 in Grand Forks. Heavy operating losses were sustained most years until 1940, and continuation of the mill became a prime political issue. However, opponents never quite succeeded in their objective of selling the plant, and the controversy has subsided considerably in late years.

Six of the first seven managers of the state mill held their posts less than two years each, the exception being Oliver L. Spencer (b. 1884 Ore., d. 1954), who held the reins in 1925-33. Successful operation of the mill was virtually impossible during the period when it was deeply embroiled in politics. Robert M. Stangler (b. 1889 N. D., d. 1955), who began a 16-year tenure in 1939, succeeded both in installing a business regime in the operation of the state mill and in getting it largely out of the political arena. Paul R. Fossen (b. 1906 N. D.), Stangler's associate, became manager in 1955.

Minot

Minot Flour Mill Co.—Minot Milling Co. was formed in 1900 to operate a 200-cwt. mill in the Northwestern North Dakota town of that name. The mill was purchased in 1906 by F. C. Laird and William Dunnell (b. 1870 Ont., d. 1940), who organized Minot Flour Co. The plant attained 800 cwt. capacity. Laird and Dunnell built a 400-cwt. mill in Glasgow, Mont., in 1916, which was operated as Glasgow Flour Mill Co. These mills and some elevator properties were consolidated in 1930 as Minot Flour Mill Co., and the Dunnells became sole owners soon afterward. William Dunnell was president, and was succeeded by his son, William H. (b. 1900 Minn.).

The Minot and Glasgow mills were purchased in 1951 by Russell-Miller Milling Co., but were not operated thereafter.

OHIO

Milling of flour in Ohio began in 1788 when one or more floating mills were established on the Miami River. Wheat was grown and grist mills were built in most of the pioneer settlements, and a brisk trade existed with southern flour markets even in early days. Wheat production increased rapidly and Ohio was the first wheat state for almost 20 years, beginning in 1839, and took first place occasionally as late as 1893. It has continued to be one of the chief soft wheat states to the present.

Ohio had 1396 mills in 1860, probably three-fourths of which made flour. In 1900 there were 883 mills in the state that ground wheat, and for many years Ohio Millers' State Association had a membership that ran into the hundreds. The larger soft wheat mills began to develop in the 1880's; they did a large export business at that time but later they were devoted chiefly to the soft wheat bakery business. From first World War days the number of Ohio mills declined rapidly and in 1958 there remained only 32. Flour production in Ohio in 1961 totalled 11,762,000 cwt., the state standing seventh.

Brookville

Loy's Mill is a modern 1000-cwt. plant with a pneumatic system and is owned and managed by a father and son who also are their own millers. The mill is near Brookville, a few miles northwest of Dayton, and its chief trade is with cracker makers. L. Warren Loy (b. 1864 Ohio, d. 1936) and his son, Emmett (b. 1893 Ohio), had a feed business, to which they added a small flour mill in 1930. Emmett and his son, Elmer, began building the present mill in 1950 and did nearly all the work themselves, while continuing to operate the original mill. The new mill went into production in 1958.

Cincinnati

Henry Nagel & Son have a pneumatic mill of 1250 cwt. that was built in 1961. Their trade is chiefly with pastry and cracker bakers. Four generations of Nagels have operated the business, which has continued for 106 years.

The first Henry Nagel (b. 1829 Germany, d. 1901) took over a small rye mill in 1857. He ran a succession of small mills in the next 25 years, and in 1883 built a 500-cwt. plant that ran for 78 years. The city then took the site and the present mill was erected on Spring Grove Avenue. Edward Nagel (b. 1861 Ohio, d. 1941) went into the business and became proprietor; and so in time did his son, Henry II (b. 1896 Ohio). Henry Jr. (b. 1922 Ohio) joined in 1945.

Cleveland

Fairchild Milling Co.—In 1910 a mill that had been operated for eight years by the Henkel interests was sold to Cleveland Milling Co., a concern headed by Elbert N. Fairchild, formerly a Pillsbury official. It had close connections with Cleveland Grain & Milling Co., well-known in the grain business.

Fairchild Milling Co. succeeded Cleveland Milling Co. in 1921 and continued until 1936, although Fairchild's connection with the company that bore his name and which he headed was not continuous. The property was finally foreclosed by a Cleveland bank.

The 3000-cwt. mill was acquired in 1936 by Montana Flour Mills Co., and was operated by that company for the next 18 years. In 1954 it was sold to International Milling Co. Present capacity is 4000 cwt.

Columbus

Gwinn Milling Co.—The Gwinns were millers in West Virginia from 1889, and after 1900 they also operated a small mill in Washington Court House, Ohio. In 1908 they established Gwinn Milling Co. in Columbus and built a 3000-cwt. mill. Othniel E. Gwinn (b. 1856 W. Va., d. 1929) was president the first 21 years, and during this period Benjamin W. Marr (b. 1864 W. Va., d. 1951) was general manager. Marr served in 1925-27 as chairman of Millers' National Federation.

Clarence E. Gwinn (b. 1897 W. Va.), son of the founder, was company president in 1929-34 and in 1945-51. The company was reorganized in 1934, following receivership, and J. Earl McLean (b. 1885 Ohio, d. 1955) was president in 1934-45. Donald H. Wilson was manager in 1945-49.

The mill operated irregularly for considerable periods in the decade that followed receivership. It suffered extensive fire damage in 1945 and 1947 and ceased to make flour. The company was liquidated in 1951.

Dover

Dover Milling Co. has a 1700-cwt. mill in Dover, 40 miles south of Akron, on a site occupied by mills for 120 years. It produces soft wheat bakery flour for eastern outlets. The company is owned by the Tanner family, which has been identified with flour milling in Ohio through three generations.

Dover City Mills was established in 1842 by Nathaniel Hayden and Elijah Welty on the Portsmouth-Cleveland Canal, the town then being known as Canal Dover. When the mill was purchased in 1858 by Alonzo H. and William H. Hardesty, it had 1000 cwt. capacity. The Hardestys built a second mill in Dover in 1882 and also had Capital Mills in Columbus, but these properties were closed before 1915. The Dover mill remained in Hardesty hands for 91 years, and was managed for 51 years (1892-1943) by Joseph C. Miller (b. 1868 Ohio, d. 1944). M. L. Underwood was manager in 1943-49.

Hardesty Milling Co., incorporated in 1903, was sold in 1949 to M. W. McConnell. Two years later the mill was ac-

quired by Clarence E. Gwinn and associates, and they organized
Dover Milling Co., Gwinn becoming president and James
Mayhall manager. Wilson P. Tanner (b. 1886 Ohio), long a
leader in the flour distributing trade, bought control in 1957,
and his son, Robert R. (b. 1920 N. Y.), has been president
and manager since 1958.

Fostoria

Mennel Milling Co. and its predecessors have been among
the leaders in northern soft wheat milling for three-quarters
of a century. The 7000-cwt. plant and 2,000,000 bushels of
grain storage are located in Fostoria, about 40 miles south of
Toledo. The company serves the bakery trade from the Middle
West to the Atlantic Coast.

The business was established in 1886 as Isaac Harter Co.,
changed in 1903 to Isaac Harter Milling Co., in 1912 to Harter Milling Co., and in 1917 to the present name. Michael D.
Harter (b. 1846 Ohio, d. 1896), one of the founders, became
a member of Congress (1891-95) and was author of the law
that defined shippers' rights under ocean bills-of-lading, a
measure that was a great boon to exporting millers. The Harters
largely owned the company but did not manage it.

Alphonse Mennel (b. 1849 France, d. 1926), a farm
machinery dealer, became manager in 1889 and president in
1896. Stock control of the company passed to the Mennels in
1917. The office was moved to Toledo in 1897 and remained
there for 62 years and then was returned to Fostoria.

In 1946 the company purchased Northwestern Elevator &
Mill Co. and its 900-cwt. mill in Mount Vernon, Ohio, and
operated this plant until 1954.

Company presidents: Alphonse Mennel in 1896-1924; his
son, Louis A. (b. 1878 Ohio, d. 1944) in 1924-36; another

son, Mark N. (b. 1882 Ohio) in 1936-45 and 1947-49; Louis A., Jr. (b. 1913 Ohio, d. 1955) in 1945-47; Henry D. Pahl (b. 1900 Iowa, d. 1962) in 1949-58; Donald M. Mennel (b. 1918 Ohio), son of Louis A., since 1958. Mark's son, Walter M. (b. 1917 Ohio) is vice president.

The first Louis A. Mennel was the actual manager of the business for many years. His brother Mark was one of the best-known members of the industry; he served on the board of Millers' National Federation for 33 years, not continuously, and in 1914-16 was Federation president—the youngest man to hold the office.

Grafton

United Mills Corp.—An old milling company in Grafton, a village southwest of Cleveland, failed in 1916, and the plant went to G. A. Bennett. The mill was lost by fire in 1919 and rebuilt with 1600 cwt. capacity. Bennett Milling Co. went into receivership two years later, and United Mills Corp. was formed by Louis C. Chase and Howard E. Irvin to take over the property. They ran the mill until 1928, when they sold it to Loose-Wiles Biscuit Co., and it became the nucleus of the milling enterprises of that concern.

Hamilton

Carr Milling Co.—Twenty-five miles north of Cincinnati John W. Carr established a mill and incorporated Carr Milling Co. His son, W. Burton Carr (b. 1849 Ohio, d. 1924) ran the business for many years. The company was acquired in 1929 by Frank E. Barker (d. 1937), who had been manager, and he became president. The 1000-cwt. mill was sold in 1937 to Blish Milling Co., but was closed by 1940.

Kent

Williams Bros. Co. is engaged in milling soft wheat flour exclusively. It operates a mill of 2000 cwt. in Kent, just east of Akron. The company has 300,000 bushels of grain storage. Its flour trade is chiefly in the northeastern states.

The business was established in 1880 by Charles A. Williams (b. 1859 Ohio, d. 1935) and his brother Scott. C. A. Williams became sole owner in 1900 when the company was incorporated, and he was president the remainder of his life. His son, Dudley A. (b. 1894 Ohio) succeeded to the office in 1935. James S. Green (b. 1880 Ohio) has been associated with Williams Bros. Co. since 1900, and has been secretary-treasurer for many years.

Loudonville

Loudonville Milling Co.—The first mill in Loudonville, halfway between Cleveland and Columbus, was built in 1835. It was purchased by A. A. Taylor in 1886 and incorporated into his Northwestern Elevator & Mill Co. It reached about 600 cwt. capacity.

Howard J. BeBout (b. 1876 Ohio, d. 1958), who had been Loudonville manager for Northwestern, purchased the Loudonville plant in 1912 and organized Loudonville Mill & Elevator Co. The mill was increased to 1200 cwt. After it was destroyed by fire in 1922 a new mill of 2400 cwt. was erected. The company was reorganized as Loudonville Milling Co., and BeBout was president and manager in 1912-47.

The mill was sold in 1947 to Standard Milling Co., and in 1953 to Sunshine Biscuits, Inc. Present capacity is 3700 cwt.

Mansfield

Hanley Milling Co.—Midway between Cleveland and Columbus is Mansfield, where Michael D. Harter built a mill in 1889. It was known as Hicks Brown Milling Co., and in 1899 it passed to Taylor-Tanner interests. Frank H. Tanner (b. 1858 Ohio, d. 1929) was president and manager in 1901-13, leaving to become full-time secretary of Ohio Millers' Association. He held this post for 16 years, during the great days of that organization.

The mill was idle when it was purchased in 1915 by Howard M. Witbeck, and it was known as Mansfield Milling Co. until 1921, when it was merged into Federal Milling Co. Louis C. Chase was manager in 1916-21.

The 1200-cwt. plant was acquired in 1927 by Thomas J. Hanley (b. 1859 Ireland, d. 1954), who had milled in Coshocton since 1891. Hanley Milling Co. was a family affair, and after about a decade the mill was run only sporadically. It was closed in 1946.

Marion

Marion Milling Co.—The first mill in Marion, 45 miles north of Columbus, goes back many years. Charles B. Jenkins was manager in 1896-1904 of Marion Milling & Grain Co. It was acquired in 1906 by John D. Owens, who organized Marion Mill & Feed Co. The plant was destroyed by fire in 1915, and after being rebuilt by Owens, it was known as Marion National Mill Co. It ceased to operate in 1928, and remained idle until 1935 when Kansas Milling Co. bought the property. It was enlarged to 1100 cwt. and was operated as Marion Milling Co. The mill was sold in 1962 to the Imbs' interests.

Massillon

Buckeye Cereal Co.—Massillon City Mills, in the town of that name 20 miles south of Akron, was owned by J. F. Pocock, a coal mine operator. Buckeye Cereal Co. was formed in 1910 and took over the 1000-cwt. mill. Pocock was president and E. M. Stults general manager. In the 1930's Stults became president and his son, Theodore M., manager. The mill was destroyed by fire in 1943.

Orrville

Orrville Milling Co.—The 1700-cwt. mill in Orrville, 20 miles southwest of Akron, was established in the early 1870's. E. P. Willaman (d. 1921) was president and manager for many years. Howard E. Irvin was manager in 1921-22, and the mill was then operated by Willaman's heirs for a year before it was dismantled.

Shelby

Moody & Thomas Milling Co.—A flour jobbing business was established in 1880 in Cleveland by Chandler R. Moody (b. 1857, d. 1933), and the firm operated a small mill in nearby Peninsula. After the mill was lost to fire in 1932, a new plant was built in Shelby, midway between Cleveland and Columbus. The jobbing business was closed in 1936, and the mill was later increased to 1250 cwt. The mill ceased to produce flour in 1962. Wallace H. Moody (b. 1892 Ohio), son of the founder, has headed the company since 1933.

Springfield

Ansted & Burk Co.—John W. Burk (b. 1850 Ont., d. 1917) was a prominent operative miller who rose to leadership in the industry and became the third president of Millers' National Federation, holding the office in 1906-08. Burk and his brother-in-law, E. W. Ansted, formed a partnership in 1897 and bought the Warder & Burnett Mill, which was built in 1846. They enlarged it to 1200 cwt., incorporated the company in 1903 and later increased the mill to 2400 cwt. Burk was president in 1903-17, followed by George W. Ansted, the co-founder's nephew, in 1917 - 33. Actual management for about 15 years was in the hands of Richard D. Patton (b. 1873 Ohio, d. 1926), son-in-law of Burk, followed by Luther B. Miller in 1926-35.

The mill was sold in 1933 to Ohio Farmers' Grain & Milling Co., but that cooperative association was in receivership in less than two years. William J. McDonald (b. 1895 Ohio, d. 1950) leased the mill in 1935 and later bought it, combining it with a blending plant and operating as Union National Mill. The mill was taken by fire in 1942, and then was rebuilt in a building owned by the city. The company had a somewhat checkered existence, and went out of business in 1950.

Toledo

National Milling Co.—Nordyke & Marmon Co. was a better builder of mills than it was an operator, and the mill that was built by the company in Toledo in 1892 was not a success until after David Anderson (b. 1867 Ireland, d. 1942) took over the management in 1909. Seven years later he bought control of the company, and he operated the 8000-cwt. mill until 1926. At that time the company was sold to National Biscuit Co.

National Milling Co. operated as a wholly-owned subsidiary until 1936, when it was merged into the parent company. Later the National Milling Co. name was discarded, and the Toledo and other mills have constituted the milling division of National Biscuit Co. Little if any flour has been sold, practically the entire output of the mills being used by National Biscuit Co. The Toledo mill has been enlarged by stages to 26,000 cwt. capacity, the third largest mill in the United States.

Anderson was president of National Milling Co. in 1909-26, his son, Harold A., succeeding to that post in 1926-36.

Northwestern Elevator & Mill Co.—The first important chain of mills in Ohio was that organized and managed by A. A. Taylor (d. 1886). Beginning in 1864 in Loudonville, he acquired plants in Massillon, Orrville, Mount Vernon and Toledo. The Massillon and Orrville mills were sold by 1880, but Loudonville was retained until 1912.

Northwestern Elevator & Mill Co. was formed in 1886, with Thomas Taylor (d. 1904), son of the founder, as president. Frank H. Tanner was general manager until 1901. In later years company affairs were concentrated in Mount Vernon and Toledo. These mills were enlarged to 900 and 2000 cwt. respectively.

Cyrus S. Coup (b. 1864 Ohio, d. 1948) was vice president and general manager in 1904-36 and president in 1936-42. His brother, William M. (b. 1868 Ohio, d. 1931) was associated in the management. The Toledo mill was sold in 1942 and used for grain storage, while the Mount Vernon mill went to Mennel Milling Co. four years later and operated until 1954 before it was closed.

Toledo Grain & Milling Co.—The 1000-cwt. mill of Toledo Grain & Milling Co. was built in 1889 by Daniel W. Camp (b. 1835 Pa., d. 1917). It was destroyed by fire in 1929. Jesse D. Hurlbut, son-in-law of Camp, managed the business for 33 years, beginning in 1896.

Troy

Allen & Wheeler Co.—Troy, 20 miles north of Dayton, had a flour mill in 1848. It was purchased in 1866 by Henry W. Allen (b. 1822 Mass., d. 1910) and T. B. Wheeler (b. 1835 Mass., d. 1918). After operating as a partnership almost

40 years, the business was incorporated in 1904. Allen was president to 1910, Wheeler to 1918, then Henry M. Allen (b. 1856 Ohio, d. 1927), son of the co-founder, in 1918-26 and his brother, Horace (b. 1860 Ohio, d. 1931) in 1926-31. Leonard A. Wheeler, son of the other co-founder, held the office in 1931-36. Henry M. Allen, who was a leader in the Ohio milling industry, was general manager for about 30 years.

The 1200-cwt. mill was sold in 1936 to R. S. Altman, a feed manufacturer, and was operated until 1944, when it was destroyed by fire.

OKLAHOMA

Opening of Cherokee lands to white settlers in 1889 was followed at once by the production of wheat and then by milling of flour. Guthrie Mill & Elevator Co., owned by A. A. Terlton and located in the territorial capital, was the first commercial mill in Oklahoma. The 400-cwt. plant was opened in 1890, and it was soon followed by mills in Tonkawa, Purcell, Tecumseh and El Reno. Flour milling became the first industry of Oklahoma and remained such until the development of the petroleum business. Oklahoma produced 9,345,000 cwt. of flour in 1961. There were 14 mills in the state in 1958.

It is probable that a grist mill on the shore of Lake Spavinaw, near Tulsa, built by a Mormon colony in 1856, was the first to be operated in Oklahoma by white men. The Indians doubtless had mills long before that, although the Indian mills ground corn rather than wheat.

Altus

Leger Mill Co.—Four Jackman brothers built a flour mill of 300 cwt. in Altus, near the Texas border in Southwestern Oklahoma, in 1903. It was increased to 1200 cwt. during the

1920's. The mill was operated until 1950, when it was converted to a feed plant. Company presidents were, successively, S. J., A. H., Charles M. and A. M. Jackman, the four brothers; and after 1947 David S., son of Charles M. Jackman.

Chickasha

Chickasha Milling Co.—After founding the mill in El Reno, Edwin D. Humphrey expanded his operations in 1899 to Chickasha, 50 miles southwest of Oklahoma City. This town was founded only seven years earlier, and the newness of the area is illustrated by three nearby Indian reservations not being opened for settlement until 1901. Humphrey acquired the Tait mill, which was built in 1894, and organized Chickasha Milling Co., which had a plant of 1000 cwt. that was later expanded to 1600 cwt.

Myron E. Humphrey (b. 1884 Kan.), son of the founder, began a 48-year milling career by going to Chickasha in 1904. The following year he became manager in an emergency, and continued in that post. He was elected company president in 1915. After 31 years, he moved to the board chairmanship in 1946, being succeeded as president by his son, Edwin N. (b. 1913 Okla.). Through most of this time he was recognized as the dean of the Oklahoma milling industry.

The mill and the elevator were sold in 1952 to Colorado Milling & Elevator Co., which closed the mill. Chickasha Milling Co. engaged subsequently in non-milling activities.

El Reno

Canadian Mill & Elevator Co.—First milling venture of Henry Lassen and Charles M. Jackman was a 300-cwt. plant in El Reno, 35 miles west of Oklahoma City, in 1894. It was named for the Canadian River on which it was located. They sold this mill in 1906 to Maney brothers. James W. Maney was president in 1906-30, Herman K. Schaefer in 1930-45, the latter's brother, Henry (b. 1862 Germany, d. 1951) in 1945-51. Operation was chiefly in the hands of general managers: Thomas F. Blake in 1906-09; H. K. Schaefer in 1909-14; Herman Dittmer (b. 1875 Germany, d. 1944) in 1914-21; John Maney in 1921-26; Walter H. Boon (b. 1886 Mo.) in 1926-42; Kermit P. Schaefer (b. 1909 Okla.), son of Henry, in 1942-51.

The Maneys enlarged the first mill to 1500 cwt. soon after purchase. When it was destroyed by fire in 1935, it was replaced by a new mill of 2000 cwt. The Schaefers obtained control in 1930. The company was sold in 1951 to Colorado Milling & Elevator Co., which enlarged the plant to 4300 cwt. It is operated as Oklahoma Flour Mills.

El Reno Mill & Elevator Co.—Edwin D. Humphrey (b. 1855 N. Y., d. 1915) was one of the pioneer millers of Oklahoma. His mill in El Reno was the second commercial flour mill in Oklahoma territory and the first to make export shipments from that area. He learned the milling trade in his home state before migrating to Abilene, Kan., where he was first a miller and then a banker. He re-entered the milling business by being the prime mover in establishing El Reno Mill & Elevator Co. and its 300-cwt. mill. That was in 1893, fourteen years before statehood, and very soon after white settlement was permitted there.

Humphrey managed the business until 1909, when he was succeeded by his son, Karl E. (b. 1885 Kan., d. 1955). The mill was expanded, and in 1916 a new 2000-cwt. mill was built. At the end of 1928 the company became a wholly-owned subsidiary of General Mills, Inc. It was merged into the parent company in 1937. The mill has continued to operate to the present, and its capacity is now 2700 cwt. Karl Humphrey was manager until after the sale, and thereafter he was a General Mills' official during the remainder of his business career.

El Reno Mill & Elevator Co. presidents: William E. Humphrey (b. 1853 N. Y., d. 1923), brother of the founder, in 1893-1907 and 1915-23; Edwin D. in 1907-15; Karl E. in 1923-37.

Enid

Enid Milling Co.—Railroad construction was the primary business of Maney Bros & Co., but as wheat production increased along the lines they built in Oklahoma they also engaged in milling flour. They bought Weatherford Milling Co., Thomas Milling Co., and Canadian Mill & Elevator Co., and when the Thomas plant burned in 1917 they acquired Enid Mill & Elevator Co. The latter had been built in 1896 by J. E. McCristy and Peter Trease in what became the wheat capital of the Sooner State. It was increased to 2000 cwt.

James W. Maney (b. 1862 Pa., d. 1945) was president of Enid Milling Co., which was managed jointly with the Canadian mill by Herman Dittmer in 1916-21 and John Maney (b. 1870 Iowa, d. 1926) in 1921-26. Later managers were John K. Landes in 1926-29 and Robert Maney (b. 1903 Okla.), son of James W., in 1929-30. The mill was closed in 1930.

Guthrie

Gresham Milling Co.—Oklahoma's pioneer mill, built in 1890 in Guthrie, 20 miles north of Oklahoma City, went through six ownerships and several periods of idleness before it was acquired in 1917 by Frank L. Gresham, a milling neophyte, who increased its capacity to 2400 cwt. The business flourished briefly, but it went into receivership in 1921 and carried with it a Guthrie bank.

Jefferson

Hacker Flour Mills—Just north of Enid is the village of Jefferson, site of a flour mill as early as 1906. Known for some years as Morrison Bros. Mill, C. G. being president and C. L. manager, the concern went bankrupt in 1921. The idle mill was purchased three years later by William T. Hacker (b. 1871 Kan., d. 1926), who launched W. T. Hacker Flour Mills.

Hacker's widow, Harriet E., took over the management for the next 14 years, followed by William T. Hacker, Jr. (b. 1911 Kan.). The mill was destroyed by fire in 1933 and was rebuilt with 1100 cwt. capacity. The company was incorporated in 1947 as Hacker Flour Mills. The mill was closed in 1948.

Kingfisher

Oklahoma Milling Co.—The Cherokee Outlet was opened to settlement in 1893, and that year a small flour mill was built in Kingfisher, 40 miles northwest of Oklahoma City, by William H. Kinney. It was managed for six years by S. K. Winemiller.

Oklahoma Milling Co. was formed by Jacob E. Ruth (b. 1848 Germany, d. 1935) in 1899, when he bought the Kinney mill. He was its manager until 1908 and its president until 1928, and was the founder of the Oklahoma Millers' Association. Ruth's son, Jona A. (b. 1876 Kan., d. 1931), was manager in 1908-26. Banks took over the property in 1926, and two years later the mill was sold to J. Perry Burrus and associates. The latter operated it for a short time as Bob White Flour Mills, Inc., then as Burrus Mill & Elevator Co. of Oklahoma, and it was merged into Burrus Mill & Elevator Co. The mill ceased to produce flour in 1949.

Oklahoma City

Acme Flour Mills Co.—George G. Sohlberg (b. 1861 Minn., d. 1947) and associates formed Acme Milling Co. in 1894 and built a mill of 400 cwt. in Oklahoma City. It was enlarged to 1600 cwt. in 1908 and 3600 cwt. in 1918, and the mill reached 4200 cwt. in 1952. Sohlberg became chief owner and president, and in the 1920's George G. Grogan, Jr. (b. 1881 Ga.) was general manager.

Acme Milling Co. was acquired in 1929 by the Moore-Lowry interests, which organized Acme Flour Mills Co. John H. Moore was president for five years, W. Alfred Chain holding the post in 1934-54. Jerry L. Yergler (b. 1894 Okla., d. 1946) was general manager in 1929-46, Charles C. Reynolds (b. 1898 Kan.) after 1946. Reynolds has also been president since 1954.

The flour mill was dismantled in 1958, but the company has remained in the grain storage business as Acme Grain Elevators, Inc.

Oklahoma City Mill & Elevator Co.—Established in the last year of the nineteenth century by Whit M. Grant and L. F. Kramer, Oklahoma City Mill & Elevator Co. had initial capacity of 500 cwt. The second mill of 2400 cwt. was built in 1905, and was increased in 1920 to 3900 cwt. Grant was president until 1909, and was succeeded by Fletcher B. Pope (b. 1880 Texas, d. 1941) of the Burrus group which acquired control at that time.

Frank Kell became chief owner and president in 1913, with T. Clyde Thatcher (b. 1872 Iowa, d. 1952) as general manager. Thatcher was Kell's right-hand man in his milling ventures, and became a leader in the milling industry of Oklahoma. The company was in the hands of Kell and Thatcher until 1928, when it was sold, along with several of the other Kell mills, to newly-formed General Mills, Inc.

Oklahoma City Mill & Elevator Co. was a wholly-owned subsidiary until 1937, and then it became part of the south-western division of the parent company. The mill discontinued flour production in 1953. James S. Hargett (b. 1886 Kan., d. 1962) was president of the southwestern division of General Mills, Inc. in 1935-51.

Perry

Perry Mill & Elevator Co.—For 25 years, beginning in 1894, a small mill was operated in Perry, 50 miles north of Oklahoma City, by David McKinstry and W. E. Caldwell. It was sold in 1919 to Frank Kell and associates, who organized Perry Mill & Elevator Co. and increased the mill to 1100 cwt. Harry C. Jackson was manager.

The Perry company was included in the 1928 sale of Kell properties to General Mills, Inc. The mill was closed in 1936.

Shawnee

Shawnee Milling Co. is the largest Oklahoma-owned mill-ing company. It has two mills—in Shawnee, 40 miles south-east, and in Okeene, 80 miles northwest, of Oklahoma City—with aggregate capacity of 8000 cwt. flour and 1400 cwt. corn meal, also a 350-ton feed plant and more than 3,000,000 bush-els of grain storage. It serves both the family and the bakery trade, mainly in the mid-South and Southwest.

Founder and for many years head of Shawnee Milling Co. was J. Lloyd Ford (b. 1876 Mich., d. 1958). He was a flour salesman in 1906 when he bought the 150-cwt. Shawnee Roll-er Mills, which had been established in 1897. The present name was adopted, the new enterprise grew, the mill was enlarged and six other small mills were acquired by Ford—five in Oklahoma and one in Kansas. The most important was in Okeene, purchased in 1917.

Fire destroyed the Shawnee plant in 1934, and it was replaced by a new 2500-cwt. mill. The Okeene mill was merged into the parent company at about that time, and the other branch mills were closed or sold. The Shawnee mill now has 5500 cwt. capacity, Okeene 2500 cwt.

Ford was president of Shawnee Milling Co. in 1906-46 and chairman his remaining years. The founder's son, Leslie A. (b. 1914 Okla.), has been president since 1946. Owen Wimberly (b. 1905 Ark.) is vice president and manager of the Okeene division.

Weatherford

Weatherford Milling Co.—Seventy miles west of Oklahoma City is Weatherford, where Henry Lassen built a small mill in 1899. It was sold in 1903 to James W. and John Maney. They enlarged the plant to 1400 cwt., and operated it until about 1922. The idle mill was destroyed by fire in 1926.

Yukon

Dobry Flour Mills Co.—After an association of a third of a century with the Kroutils in Yukon Mill & Grain Co., Antone F. Dobry (b. 1862 Austria, d. 1950) withdrew from the company in 1934. With his sons and son-in-law, he organized Dobry Flour Mills Co. and built a new 2000-cwt. mill across the street. T. A. Dobry, son of Antone F., was president and manager for about 10 years and then was succeeded by his brother-in-law, Frank Kostka. The mill was closed in 1953 and sold to the Oklahoma Farmers' Union, which converted it into a feed manufacturing plant.

Yukon Mill & Grain Co. is located 15 miles west of Oklahoma's capital, in a town that has become suburban in recent years. It is there that the second generation of Kroutils is running a business which comprises a 4000-cwt. flour mill, a 1000-cwt. corn mill and grain elevators of 2,000,000 bushels. They cater exclusively to the family trade from Oklahoma to the Carolinas, although in years gone by the company also had a sizable export business.

John F. Kroutil (b. 1875 Austria, d. 1954) and his brother, Frank L. (b. 1872 Austria, d. 1932), purchased Giesecke Bros. mill in 1900. They were joined later by their brothers, Thomas and Robert, and a brother-in-law, Antone F. Dobry. The mill was enlarged to 1500 cwt. in 1910 and Yukon Mill & Grain Co. was organized; the plant was destroyed by fire in 1921 and then rebuilt and enlarged further. The Dobry interest ended in 1934, when that family organized Dobry Flour Mills Co.

John F. Kroutil was president and manager for 54 years, Frank L. the plant operator. The former became heavily interested in other businesses, and by the middle 1930's the bulk of management duties fell upon Frank L.'s son, Raymond B. (b. 1900 Okla.). The latter became president in 1954, and Norman (b. 1910 Okla.), another son of Frank L., vice president.

OREGON

First flour mill in Oregon was established in 1843 in Oregon City. A milling industry of some consequence began to develop soon after the Civil War, largely at interior points, and its main outlet was to the Oriental trade. By the 1880's, Portland became the milling leader of the Pacific Northwest and continued to hold that position for half a century. Production of flour in Oregon was 6,273,000 cwt. in 1961, and there were 12 mills in the state three years earlier.

Pendleton

Collins Flour Mills—Henry W. Collins (b. 1884 Ore.), a leading figure in the Pacific Northwest grain trade for 50 years, built a 1500-cwt. flour mill in 1919 in Pendleton, two hundred miles east of Portland. The owner was president of Collins Flour Mills and R. M. (Doc) Crommellin (d. 1959) was manager in 1919-42. In 1937 the plant was leased to General Foods Corp., which in 1940 bought the property. The mill, now 2800 cwt., has continued in operation to the present.

Walters Flouring Mills — In 1893 Frederick Walters bought the Farmers' Custom Mill in Pendleton and turned it into an export mill. It became a 1000-cwt. plant and was operated by the Walters family until 1939. After being idle, the mill was purchased in 1943 by Kerr, Gifford & Co., and enlarged to 1400 cwt. It was destroyed by fire in 1945.

Western Milling Co.—Pendleton, capital of the eastern Oregon wheat country, had a mill known as Pendleton Roller Mills Co., built about 1900 by Dutch capital. It became idle in 1922, and three years later it was acquired by Isaac A. Welk (b. 1876 Russia, d. 1934) and Preston Shaffer Milling Co. They operated as Pendleton Flour Mills Co., and the mill was enlarged by steps to 1500 cwt. Welk was manager, being succeeded in 1931 by his son, Philip I.

Western Milling Co. became the name in 1929, when a lease was taken on the 800-cwt. plant of Lakeside Milling Co., Salt Lake City. This mill was shut down in 1933.

Western Milling Co. was merged into Preston Shaffer Milling Co. in 1938. The Pendleton mill was destroyed by fire in 1947, by which time it had been increased to 3400 cwt.

Portland

Astoria Flouring Mills Co.—Eastern Oregon interests, headed by Edgar W. Smith (b. 1888 Ore.), went to Astoria, at the mouth of the Columbia, and established a 600-cwt. mill in 1913. It was expanded to 1000 cwt. in 1916, and a second plant brought capacity up to 8000 cwt. in 1920. It became a great export mill, shipping 2,000,000 cwt. abroad in 1923— one-eighth of the nation's offshore flour business. Smith was president and manager in 1913-31. Office was in Portland.

Pillsbury Flour Mills Co. purchased control of Astoria Flouring Mills Co. in 1929 and became sole owner two years later. Name was changed to Pillsbury-Astoria Flour Mills Co., and somewhat later the business was incorporated into the Pillsbury enterprise. Pillsbury operated only the large plant in Astoria, and it was closed in 1961.

Centennial Mills, Inc. operates two mills of 6000 cwt. capacity each, in Portland and Spokane. It does a large export business, chiefly in the Pacific area, and its domestic business is mainly with the bakery trade in the West Coast states.

The business began in 1889, the year that Washington became a state. Founder was Moritz Thomsen (b. 1850 Denmark, d. 1932), who had been a sea captain. He built a 1000-cwt. mill in Spokane, and organized Centennial Mill Co. In 1898 he built a mill of similar size in Seattle and moved company offices there.

Centennial soon had a chain of mills operated by wholly-owned subsidiaries. Ritzville Flouring Mills was incorporated in 1901 by Thomsen and associates to operate a 1000-cwt. mill.

In 1905 they acquired Tacoma Grain Co., organized in 1901 by J. M. Ashton, and its 9000-cwt. mill. In 1912 they bought Wenatchee Milling Co., formed in 1902 by John T. Bibb; this mill had 1000 cwt. capacity. The Thomsen group also purchased mills in Sprague, Rearden and Portland. Total capacity of Centennial plants was about 25,000 cwt. by 1915.

The Seattle mill was dismantled in 1917, Sprague was closed in 1922 and Rearden in 1927, and the Portland mill converted to feed production in 1931. For a short time in the early 1920's the Hammond mill in Seattle was operated as Seattle Flour Mills Co. Ritzville ceased to produce flour in 1945 and the Tacoma mill was destroyed by fire in 1947. A new plant of 2800 cwt. replaced the old Spokane mill in 1940. The Milton-Freewater mill of Preston Shaffer was acquired in 1957 but was closed after a year. Crown Mills in Portland was purchased in 1948; its plant was enlarged and a pneumatic system was installed in 1961.

Centennial Mill Co. became Centennial Flouring Mills Co. in 1932, and the name was changed in 1953 to Centennial Mills, Inc. Crown Mills acquired the assets of Centennial Mills, Inc. in 1960, and then assumed the Centennial name. Centennial was thereupon merged with United Pacific Co., an investment trust. Offices had been moved to Portland in 1959.

Moritz Thomsen was president for 43 years. His son, Charles M., followed him in 1932-38, and Archibald W. Witherspoon (b. 1876 Mich., d. 1958) held the office in 1938-42. Louis P. Baumann (b. 1865 Mo., d. 1943) was general manager in 1932-38. Moritz Milburn (b. 1905 Wash.), grandson of the founder, was president and general manager in 1942-60, and since the latter date the office has been held by Dugald A. MacGregor (b. 1911 Calif.), whose father was once Crown manager. A Centennial man active in industry affairs was Howard W. Taylor (b. 1897 Wash.).

Crown Mills—Balfour, Guthrie & Co., Ltd., international shippers and commodity traders, established a flour mill of 1500 cwt. in Portland in 1911 and incorporated Crown Mills. The plant was enlarged to 4000 cwt. in 1918 and to 5000 cwt. in the 1940's.

The business was operated for 37 years by Balfour, Guthrie & Co., with a heavy emphasis on overseas shipments. Presidents were W. J. Burns (b. 1855 Scotland, d. 1947) in 1911-25; D. W. L. MacGregor (b. 1877 India, d. 1958) in 1925-47; George C. Fortune (b. 1903 Scotland) in 1947-48. Managers during this period were David A. Pattullo (b. 1867 Scotland, d. 1934) in 1911-31; Otto C. Johnson (b. 1877 Sweden, d. 1950) in 1931-39; and Andrew M. Chrystall (b. 1887 Scotland) in 1939-48.

Crown Mills was sold in 1948 to Centennial Mills, Inc., and the plant was subsequently enlarged to 6000 cwt., and a pneumatic system installed. In 1960 Crown Mills acquired the operating assets of Centennial Mills, Inc., and Crown's name was then changed to Centennial Mills, Inc. Crown managers during the Centennial regime were Chrystall until 1953 and Karl E. Bumgarner (b. 1906 Wash.) in 1953-59.

Centennial Mills, Inc., was merged into United Pacific Corp. in 1960.

Helix Milling Co. operates a flour mill of 1200 cwt. in Helix, near Pendleton, and is chiefly in the overseas trade. This company and Kerr Grain Corp. are controlled by Thomas Kerr, whose father, Peter (b. 1865 Scotland, d. 1926), came to Portland in 1895 as head of Kerr, Gifford & Co., an export-import firm. M. W. Hunt was manager of the firm's milling department until 1920, Joseph W. Ganong in 1920-33. Mills in Portland and The Dalles, with total capacity of 2400 cwt., were operated for many years. The mill in The Dalles was reopened in 1939 after being closed from 1931, but was destroyed by fire in 1943. The Portland mill was closed in 1939, at which time a small mill in Helix, idle from 1931, was leased and enlarged. The parent firm was liquidated later and was succeeded in part by the present companies.

Northern Flour Mills Co.—Strauss & Co. was chiefly a grain warehouse company, but it also owned Northern Flour Mills Co. The latter had plants in American Falls, Ida., Missoula, Mont., and Walla Walla and Vancouver, Wash., with total capacity of almost 5000 cwt. Isaac A. Welk, from whom the Ravalli mill in Missoula was purchased in 1918, was manager of the milling department.

The parent company became financially involved in 1924 and Northern Flour Mills Co. was liquidated. The Idaho mill was abandoned when the high dam was built and the site inundated; the Missoula plant was sold to Montana Flour Mills Co.; Vancouver was dismantled; and the Walla Walla mill was destroyed by fire in 1930.

Portland Flouring Mills Co.—Largest milling enterprise in the Pacific Northwest for many years was Portland Flouring Mills Co., which in first World War days had a 10,000-cwt. mill in Portland, along with more than 11,000 cwt. of capacity elsewhere in Washington and Oregon. Largest of the outside mills were in Tacoma, Spokane and Seattle; and there were plants also at nine country points.

Portland Flouring Mills Co. was established in 1884 by F. Wilcox and W. S. Lord, who took over bankrupt mills in

Portland, Oregon City and Salem. It became a large concern under the management of the co-founder's son, Theodore B. Wilcox (b. 1856 Mass., d. 1918). Wilcox was president for 30 years, and during much of that time the general manager was Joseph W. Ganong (b. 1863, d. 1936). The company did an immense business in the Orient for many years, and it reached its zenith around 1910. Max H. Hauser (b. 1873 Wash., d. 1946), a grain man, and Ganong purchased control in 1918, Hauser becoming president. Ganong left the company in 1920.

This large concern disintegrated within a few years. Most of the plants were old and inefficient, the company took tremendous losses in the post-war market decline and it was outmatched by other companies. Banking interests took the reins in 1921, and a year later they consolidated the company with Sperry Flour Co., which was in a similar situation. Within a few years, all but three of the former Portland plants had been closed, and only one now remains in operation—the mill in Tacoma.

Terminal Flour Mills Co. has a 6000-cwt. mill and 385,-000 bushels of elevator space in Portland. It is chiefly a Pacific Coast bakery and export business. The company is solely owned by the family of its founder, Mark P. Miller (b. 1868 Ind., d. 1940).

The Terminal mill was opened in 1923 and it then had 3000 cwt. capacity. Miller had been operating a mill in Idaho since 1902, and he continued to do so, also purchasing Spokane Flour Mills Co. in 1936. He was president and manager of them all. His successors: Harry H. H. Brown (b. 1901 Wash., d. 1942) in 1941-42; W. Harold (Hi) Younger in 1942-50; Karl E. Bumgarner in 1950-54; Mark P. Miller, Jr.

(b. 1924 Ore., d. 1956) in 1954-56; and Henry J. Schmitt (b. 1914 Wash.) since 1956.

Capacity of the Portland mill was increased in later years to the present total.

The Dalles

Wasco Warehouse Milling Co. — Local capital in The Dalles, 70 miles east of Portland, built a 1000-cwt. flour mill in 1902. It was enlarged, was destroyed by fire in 1912 and then rebuilt with 2400 cwt. capacity. It was increased to 3000 cwt. about 1930 and to 4400 cwt. in the 1940's.

E. O. McCoy (b. 1858 Wash., d. 1939) managed Wasco Warehouse Milling Co. in 1902-34, and was president in 1920-39. He was followed as manager by Melvin D. Beer (b. 1886 Ore., d. 1939) in 1934-39, and he by M. George Russi (b. 1878 Calif.) in 1939-44.

The mill was sold in 1944 to Loose-Wiles Biscuit Co., which subsequently became Sunshine Biscuits, Inc. It has since been operated as a captive mill by that company.

PENNSYLVANIA

Pennsylvania's first mill was built in 1643 at Tinicum, in the Swedish settlement near Chester, by Col. John Printz, governor of the colony. Soon after William Penn acquired the province in 1681, he established a mill in Philadelphia that was known as Penn's mill. Wheat growing and flour milling flourished in early Pennsylvania, and in 1750 Philadelphia became the leading milling center in the colonies. It retained first place until 1804, losing to Baltimore, but it continued to be a milling point of importance until after the first World War.

Great numbers of grist and custom mills operated in Pennsylvania, notably in the country east of the Allegheny Mountains. In that area there were few communities that did not have one or more mills. The census of 1870 enumerated 2985 mills in the state, which led all others by a wide margin; a large majority of them doubtless ground wheat. In 1900 there were 1580 flour mills, Pennsylvania again leading other states, but thereafter they declined until in 1958 only 50 remained in use.

Camp Hill

Spangler's Flour Mills, Inc. has two plants—a 2400-cwt. pneumatic flour mill built in 1956 at Camp Hill, in the environs of Harrisburg, and a mill of 1200 cwt. at Mount Joy, ten miles west of Lancaster. These mills chiefly produce soft wheat bakery flour. The company is controlled and headed by John M. Spangler (b. 1908 Pa.), who began in 1934 with a small mill at Camp Hill. It was later expanded to 1500 cwt. In 1956 it was purchased by the state of Pennsylvania to make flour for public institutions.

Highspire

Wheatena Corp., a breakfast cereal manufacturer, also has a flour mill of 1600 cwt. in Highspire, near Harrisburg. The primary product of the mill is used in the parent company's operations.

The Highspire mill is on a site that has been occupied by flour mills since 1775. The first mill was destroyed by fire in 1860. It was rebuilt with 150 cwt. capacity, and was purchased in 1915 by Henry J. Woolcott (b. 1859 England, d. 1934). The business was operated as Henry J. Woolcott & Son until 1920, when incorporation of Highspire Flour Mills, Inc., took place, with Woolcott as president. The mill was increased to 1000 cwt. in 1928, and at that time Highspire Flour Mills,

Inc., and Wheatena Co. were merged as Wheatena Corp., Wool-cott becoming board chairman. The mill reached its present capacity in 1962.

George B. Wendell (b. 1902 Mass.) has been president of Wheatena Corp. since 1953. Warren K. Harlacher (b. 1895 Pa.) was manager of the milling division in 1928-60, and was succeeded by his son, Eugene W. (b. 1921 Pa.).

North East

Blaine-Mackay-Lee Co.—On Lake Erie is the town of North East, where a flour mill operated for many years. It was owned until 1903 by Scoullar Milling Co., which sold to Blaine-Mackay-Lee Co. The original mill of 500 cwt. was destroyed by fire in 1917 and was replaced by a new plant of 1000 cwt. The mill ceased to produce flour in 1943, and the idle plant was sold in 1946 to the Orbes of New Jersey Flour Mills Co., and they organized North East Flour Mills, Inc. The mill was dismantled in 1949.

G. W. Blaine was president in 1903-36 and G. Blaine Mackay in 1936-43.

Philadelphia

Freihofer Flour Mills—It was the policy of William Frei-hofer Baking Co. to make its own flour to the extent possible, and to that end it had four mills—in Leesport, Pa., and Fred-erick, Md., acquired before 1916; the original Larabee mill in Stafford, Kan., purchased in 1921; and the Phoenix mill in Davenport, Iowa, bought in 1920 from Nelson B. Updike. The first three were owned by D. Wellington Dietrich (b. 1869 Pa., d. 1936), a company official and relative of the Freihof-ers. Phoenix was company property.

The experiment was evidently not very successful. The

Leesport and Stafford mills were idle before the middle 1920's, and the Frederick and Davenport mills were closed for considerable periods on several occasions. Frederick was not operated after 1939 except on lease to alcohol grits makers during the war years, and Davenport was finally dismantled in 1949.

The Phoenix plant was well known in Iowa milling history. It was first built in 1879, burned twice in two years, became Davenport Flour Mills Co. with an 1100-cwt. mill; the name was changed in 1896 to Phoenix Milling Co., the president of which was H. O. Seiffert in 1896-1919. At the end of that time it was sold to Updike, who operated the mill for about a year before selling to Freihofer.

Quaker City Flour Mills, Inc.—Isaiah Bell ran a flour mill around 1790 on Wissahickon Creek, in what is now Fairmont Park in Philadelphia, and his grandson established the famous firm of Samuel Bell & Sons, perhaps the foremost flour merchants of that time. James S. Bell left this firm in 1888 to become head of Washburn Crosby Co., and his brother, Samuel, Jr. (b. 1852 Pa., d. 1937), continued the business and also acquired a mill under the name of Quaker City Flour Mills, Inc. The mill was destroyed by fire in 1906 and was rebuilt with 2600 cwt. capacity. The mill discontinued operations in 1937. It was managed in later years by C. Herbert Bell (b. 1877 Pa., d. 1956), son of Samuel, Jr.

Shane Bros. & Wilson Co.—Like a meteor, Shane Bros. & Wilson Co. flared across the milling firmament and was gone almost as suddenly as it had appeared. The rise and fall of this company was one of the most sensational events in flour milling during the first World War period.

Fred O. Shane (b. 1864, d. 1929) and his brother, George

O. (b. 1867, d. 1928), along with W. J. Wilson, were flour merchants in Philadelphia. They developed a large and growing business and became the most extensive distributors in the nation.

The Shanes entered milling in 1912 through the purchase of famous old Millbourne Mills in Philadelphia, which was founded 18 years before the American Revolution. It was operated for almost a century, beginning in 1810, by three John Sellers in succession. The company, chartered in 1885, failed in 1907, and the plant was leased for five years to Russell-Miller Milling Co.

The second Shane mill, also acquired in 1912, was the celebrated Gardner Mills, Hastings, Minn., founded in 1863. Beginning in 1917 the Shanes expanded their holdings rapidly, acquiring the Llewellyn Christian mill in Shakopee, Minn., three Wisconsin rye mills—in Watertown, Portage and Milbourne; flour mills in Albert Lea, Minn., and Arlington, S. D.; and a corn mill in Circleville, Ohio. The original Larabee mill in Stafford, Kan. was leased and the Midland plant built in Kansas City. Total milling capacity was about 18,000 cwt.

Disaster came overnight. Wartime restrictions on usage of wheat were removed with little warning, and the value of the company's huge inventory of other cereals used as substitutes for wheat fell to a fraction of their cost. The Midland mill was sold almost before it began to run, the rye mills went on the block, the corn mill and Millbourne mill were closed, the Stafford lease was not renewed. Two of the Minnesota mills were owned by a subsidiary company managed by William Fulton; they continued in successful operation, but the troubles of the parent company caused them to be taken over by Philadelphia banks in 1921. When these mills were sold in 1924, they became the nucleus of King Midas Mill Co.

Shane Bros. & Wilson Co. went into receivership in 1923, but it was an anti-climax—the company had then been out of business for several years.

Treichlers

Mauser Mill Co. is in the Pennsylvania Dutch country north of Allentown, in a village that has been a flour mill site since 1794. The 1350-cwt. plant is devoted chiefly to the production of hard and soft wheat bakery flour for the eastern trade. The two principal officers have been associated in business for six decades—President Harry J. Lerch (b. 1875 Pa.) and Vice President Julius E. Lentz (b. 1881 Pa.), who have been employed by the company since 1901 and 1903, respectively.

Jacob B. Mauser (b. 1837 Pa., d. 1906) bought the Treichlers mill in 1886. Later he acquired three other mills in nearby towns. These plants each had about 200 cwt. capacity, and the Treichlers mill was expanded as the others were closed. The company was incorporated in 1902. Its presidents: J. B. Mauser in 1902-06; his son, J. Mark (b. 1873 Pa., d. 1924) in 1907-24; and Lerch, the founder's son-in-law, since 1924.

York

York Flour Mills, Inc. is located just outside York, which is between Harrisburg and Baltimore. The company operates a new pneumatic mill of 1500 cwt. and 500,000 bushels of elevator space. Its trade is with soft wheat bakers in the northeastern states.

The original plant, called the Codorus mill, was built in 1831 by George Small, who had several other mills in the vicinity, and it was run by the Small family until 1905. After ten years of idleness, the mill was taken over and rebuilt by Samuel W. Hershey. It then had 1100 cwt. capacity. It was sold in 1925 to York Mill & Elevator Co., and in 1928 to York Roller Mills Co. Joseph Weidemann (b. 1888 Pa., d. 1958) was manager for the next 30 years.

Philip M. Spalding (b. 1922 Mass.) became president and general manager in 1958, and the company name was changed to York Flour Mills, Inc., three years later.

SOUTH CAROLINA
Columbia

Allen Bros. Milling Co. has the largest flour mill in South Carolina. It has been owned and operated since 1926 by the Allen brothers, who came down from North Carolina and re-opened the idle Adluh mill. The company is exclusively engaged in the family trade, principally in the Carolinas and Georgia. The mill has 1000 cwt. capacity.

John B. Allen (b. 1896 N. C.) has been general manager of the company since 1933 and president since 1958. His milling career began in 1922 as an employee of his brother, Hampton B. (b. 1873 N. C., d. 1932) in the mill founded by the latter in their home town of Wadesboro. Four brothers, two largely inactive, joined in the partnership when the Columbia mill was purchased. Incorporation came in 1933. J. B. Allen and his family are now the sole owners. Ewart J. Edgerton (b. 1910 N. Y.), son-in-law of J. B. Allen, and John B. Allen, Jr. (b. 1928 S. C.) are associated in the management.

Spartanburg

Spartan Grain & Milling Co., primarily a feed manufacturer, also operates three small flour mills in South Carolina. These mills are in Spartanburg, Landrum and Newberry, and were acquired in 1920, 1930 and 1942 respectively, and have aggregate capacity of 1000 cwt. The company has feed plants of 460 tons. It is owned by the three Fretwell brothers.

The business was established in 1914 by Charles B. Fretwell (b. 1887 Md., d. 1961). It was a sole proprietorship until 1940, then a family partnership and in 1946 was incorporated. The founder was president in 1946-57, his son, Burlington A. (b. 1918 S.C.) since 1957.

SOUTH DAKOTA

The eastern third of South Dakota was once dotted with flour mills, and there were 120 in that area in 1900. By 1958 only two remained in operation and they were in the western part of the state. The first mills in what is now South Dakota were built soon after the Civil War.

Rapid City

Tri-State Milling Co. is located in the Black Hills metropolis of Rapid City. The company has a 2200-cwt. flour mill, two feed plants, a line of country elevators, a large seed business and a clay products plant. A 600-cwt. branch mill at Chadron, Neb., was destroyed by fire in 1962.

The business began inconspicuously in 1913, when Hans Quarnberg (b. 1855 Sweden, d. 1932) and his son, Carl A. (b. 1884 S. D.), bought a small flour mill at Belle Fourche. The father had been operating grist mills at various South Dakota points from 1880, the son was a bank cashier. The Belle Fourche mill was enlarged to 600 cwt., a small plant in Sturgis was added in 1919, and in 1929 the 600-cwt. plant of Rapid River Milling Co. was acquired. Company offices went to Rapid City in 1931. The older mills were closed after a new 1200-cwt. mill was built in Rapid City in 1938. It was subsequently enlarged.

Hans Quarnberg was company president in 1913-32; his son, Carl A., in 1932-57; another son, Paul R. (b. 1893 S. D.) in 1957-62; Edward F. Gronert (b. 1897 Minn.) since 1962.

Watertown

W. H. Stokes Milling Co.—From Janesville, Minn., where they had been associated with the Jennison interests, Stokes brothers went into Dakota territory in 1882 and built an 800-cwt. flour mill in Watertown, 40 miles west of the Minnesota border. It was called Watertown Roller Mills. After a decade, William H. Stokes (b. 1845 Wis., d. 1920) became sole proprietor. The mill was rebuilt in 1901 after destruction by fire, and it later reached 2400 cwt. The founder was president of the company until 1916, when he sold to his son-in-law, Frank E. Hawley (b. 1871 Conn., d. 1950) and William H. Stokes, Jr. (b. 1887 S.D.). General Mark Sheafe was president and Hawley manager. The mill was closed in 1928.

The small unit of the mill was reopened in 1933 and operated until 1951 as Watertown Milling Co. by A. Green. The plant was then sold to Tri-State Milling Co., and converted to a feed mill.

TENNESSEE

The earliest known grist mill in the Volunteer State was built in 1779 in Jonesboro, in the Great Smoky Mountain area. The first mill in Nashville was established in 1784. From these pioneer beginnings a great number of small mills developed, with a total of 719 in 1900. Nashville became a milling center of importance during the latter part of the nineteenth century, and remained such until about 1930. Meanwhile it became the leading center of flour blending. In 1958 Tennessee had 61 flour mills, the second largest number of any state.

Bristol

Sparger Mill Co.—George L. Carter, whose principal business was mining coal and railroading, bought an interest about 1900 in a flour mill built a few years earlier by the Sparger family, and subsequently he obtained control. The business was managed by Joshua W. Ring until 1922 and thereafter by J. Briggs McLemore. The 1000-cwt. mill was not operated after about 1930.

Chattanooga

Mountain City Mill Co.—The flour mill established in 1890 in Chattanooga by William F. Hutcheson (b. 1851 Tenn., d. 1933) reached 2400 cwt. capacity before the first World War, and it was one of the best-known mills in the South. Hutcheson headed the company through his lifetime and was succeeded by his son, Samuel C. (b. 1889 Tenn., d. 1952). The latter was manager in 1927-35, followed by Richard Bean (b. 1879 Ky., d. 1947) until 1939.

Ragland Bros., wholesale grocers, bought Mountain City Mill Co. in 1939, and Thomas Ragland (b. 1904 Tenn.) was president and manager until 1950. The mill has been leased since that time to Dixie Portland Flour Mills, and now has 9000 cwt. capacity.

Clarksville

Dunlop Milling Co.—Near the Kentucky line northwest of Nashville is Clarksville, where Joseph P. Dunlop (b. 1866 Tenn., d. 1937) built a small mill in 1892. Five years later he and John T. Rabbeth, who had been in the milling business in nearby Hopkinsville, replaced the first plant with one of 500 cwt. capacity. The latter was destroyed by fire in 1906 and Rabbeth withdrew from the concern. Dunlop Milling Co. was then organized and a mill of 2400 cwt. was erected.

Edward E. Laurent (b. 1884 Tenn., d. 1952), who had been associated with Dunlop from 1913, succeeded his father-in-law as head of the company. The plant was sold in 1930 to General Foods Corp., with Laurent remaining as local manager until 1942. Operation of the mill was discontinued in 1956.

Cleveland

Cleveland Milling Co. and its 1500-cwt. flour mill are in Cleveland, 30 miles east of Chattanooga. It is chiefly engaged in the family flour business in the Southeast.

The company was formed in 1901, and it has been controlled throughout its history by the Knox family. Hugh M. Knox (b. 1877 Tenn., d. 1956) was one of the organizers. He became manager in 1906 and president in 1927, and he retained these posts the remainder of his life. He was succeeded by his son, Thomas J. (b. 1907 Tenn.), who has been in the business more than 35 years.

Columbia

Columbia Mill & Elevator Co. is located in the phosphate mining country 50 miles south of Nashville. It was established in 1896 by W. Andrew Dale (b. 1870 Tenn., d. 1932). The mill was destroyed by fire in 1920 and rebuilt with 1000 cwt. capacity, later enlarged to 1250 cwt. Dale headed the business until 1932, and was succeeded in turn by R. L. McKinney, Norman Christley and Benton Savage, the latter being the present manager.

Franklin

Little Mill Co.—In Franklin, 20 miles south of Nashville, James B. Lillie built a flour mill in 1869. It was operated for 40 years by the founder and James B. Lillie, Jr., and it reached

1200 cwt. capacity. Lillie Mill Co. was acquired in 1909 by Charles H. Corn (b. 1859 Tenn., d. 1943) and his sons, Wilbur G. (b. 1886 Tenn.), and Ernest L. (b. 1888 Tenn., d. 1950) and operated by them until 1945. The mill was owned and operated in 1945-54 by Dudley E. Casey (b. 1902 Ky.), then was leased for two years to Dixie-Portland Flour Mills. The mill was destroyed by fire in 1957 soon after it was purchased and rehabilitated by Nebraska Consolidated Mills Co.

Jamestown

Jamestown Milling Co.—J. W. Evans was head of the group which incorporated Jamestown Milling Co. in 1927 and built a mill of 1000 cwt. in the Tennessee town of that name, in the Cumberland Mountains northwest of Knoxville. The mill operated about 10 years before the company was liquidated.

Johnson City

Red Band Co., Inc.—In extreme northeastern Tennessee is Johnson City, where George L. Carter and Clinchfield railroad interests built a 500-cwt. mill in 1909 and organized Modern Mill Co. The plant was increased to 1600 cwt. in 1913 and the company name changed to Model Mill Co. Joshua W. Ring was president and manager in 1909-22. He was succeeded by J. Briggs McLemore (b. 1875 Tenn., d. 1931), who had been secretary of Southeastern Millers' Association in the great days of that organization. Richard Bean was head in 1931-35.

Red Band, the name of the company's chief flour brand, became the corporate name in 1931, and two years later the property was purchased by General Mills, Inc. Red Band was merged into the parent company in 1937, but it is still used as a trade name. Present capacity of the mill is 2700 cwt.

Knoxville

J. Allen Smith & Co., Inc. has had great prestige in the soft wheat milling industry for the past 60 years or more. It is one of the large factors in the household flour business in six southeastern states, and in recent years it has also engaged in hard wheat flour production for the bakery trade. The mill has 5000 cwt. capacity of wheat flour and 1000 cwt. of corn meal. Elevator space is 400,000 bushels. Control of the company was acquired in 1963 by Colorado Milling & Elevator Co., and it is operated as a subsidiary.

Knoxville City Mills, established in 1883 by Jasper Lillie and J. A. Walker, was merged the following year with J. Allan Smith & Co., feed and seed brokers. In 1885 the first part of the present mill was built, and it was added to on several subsequent occasions.

Company presidents have been Jasper Lillie in 1883-85; J. Allen Smith (b. 1850 Ga., d. 1920) in 1885-1920; the latter's son, C. Powell Smith (b. 1881 Tenn., d. 1944) in 1920-39; Frank A. Tucker (b. 1902 Tenn.) in 1939-48; B. Leo Driscoll (b. 1891 Va.) in 1948-53; and James E. Skidmore (b. 1898 Ill.) since 1953.

From 1900 to 1940 much of the responsibility for management devolved upon company vice presidents. This post was held in 1900-15 by Hugh R. Goforth (b. 1868 Tenn., d. 1915) and in 1915-40 by Richard P. Johnson (b. 1869 Md., d. 1940). Johnson also became one of the national leaders of the milling industry.

Memphis

Dixie Portland Flour Mills, a wholly-owned subsidiary of Federal Compress & Warehouse Co., is twelfth in size in the milling industry. It operates two flour mills with aggregate capacity of 19,000 cwt., grain storage of 3,750,000 bushels and a flour-blending plant. It is a substantial factor in both bakery and family flour, chiefly in the South and Southeast.

This company is the outgrowth of a flour-blending business established in 1920 by Charles B. Stout (b. 1882 Ind.), whose milling career began in his father's small mill and included 12 years in Oregon. Dixie Portland Flour Co. became, in the course of time, the largest distributor of flour in the South, and at one stage it operated repacking plants in six cities from Norfolk to Mobile in addition to the original plant in Memphis. By 1940 the character of the business began to change, and what had been purely a family flour enterprise became also a large producer of bakery flour.

Stout was sole owner in 1920-59, selling to Federal Compress at the end of that period. His brother, John A. (b. 1892 Ind.), was president in 1959-60, and his son-in-law, Hubert C. Edwards (b. 1907 Tenn.), since 1960; both were long-time associates of the founder.

Dixie Portland mills are in Arkansas City, Kan., 10,000 cwt., and in Chattanooga, 9000 cwt. The former was purchased by Stout in 1940 from the Kell interests, and it then had 4000 cwt. Mountain City mill was leased in 1949 from Thomas Ragland; the 5000-cwt. plant was first enlarged and later a pneumatic system was installed.

The Dixie Portland complex in the past has included the following mills: Washington Flour Mill, Washington, Mo., successor to Regina Flour Mills Co., acquired 1926, closed 1932, capacity 1000 cwt.; Higginsville Flour Mill, Higginsville, Mo., successor to Higginsville Milling Co., acquired 1930, closed 1952, capacity 3000 cwt.; Longmont Farmers' Milling & Elevator Co., Denver, leased 1930 for two years; Majestic Flour Mill, Aurora, Mo., acquired 1932, destroyed by fire 1939, capacity 3000 cwt.; Dunlop Mills, Richmond, Va., acquired 1935, destroyed by fire 1949, capacity 3000 cwt.; and Eisenmayer Milling Co., Springfield, Mo., acquired 1939, closed 1942, capacity 1600 cwt.

Morristown

Pinnacle Mills—Morristown Flour Mills was founded in 1890 by Gaut & Merritt in the Tennessee town of that name, 40 miles northeast of Knoxville. They sold in 1897 to John S. Reed, who enlarged the mill to 1000 cwt. and in 1915 sold the company to Fain A. and J. O. Witt. In 1922 the business went to W. O. Howell, who rechristened it Pinnacle Mills and increased the capacity to 1400 cwt. A receivership occurred and the mill was dismantled in 1932.

Nashville

Colonial Milling Co.—The B unit of Liberty Mills was purchased in 1925 by Minos L. Fletcher, one of the principals in Ford Flour Co. Colonial Milling Co. was organized to operate the 4000-cwt. plant. Fletcher was president, his son and namesake general manager. The mill ran until 1949 and then was closed and dismantled.

Liberty Mills—Founded in 1890, Liberty Mills reached 8000 cwt. some years later and was the largest milling company in the South. Edmund M. Kelly (b. 1856, d. 1937), who had earlier been associated with Noel Mills, was one of the organizers and its first manager. He became president in 1900 and headed the company until receivership took place in 1924. Alternate periods of idleness and operation occurred during the ensuing eight years. One unit was sold in 1925 to Minos L. Fletcher and it became Colonial Milling Co. Liberty Mills was managed in 1926-27 by Gustave A. Breaux, then control passed to H. O. Blackwood (b. 1883, d. 1931) and he was president of Liberty Milling Co. The mill was closed in 1932, Charles J. Travis being the last manager.

Kelly served as president of Millers' National Federation in 1918-20.

Martha White Mills is one of the largest distributors of family flour in the Southeast although it arrived on the scene only in recent years. Directly or through affiliates it operates three flour mills, three corn mills, three feed mills and several other related enterprises. The flour mills are in Danville, Va., and Steeleville and Trenton, Ill., and have aggregate capacity of 3900 cwt. The company buys large amounts of flour.

Cohen E. Williams expanded a flour brokerage business in Nashville by acquiring Royal Flour Co. and its blending plant in 1941. He and his sons then bought a small mill in Lebanon, Tenn., and later the controlling interest in small mills in Jackson, Tenn., and Farmington, Mo. Their distribution grew rapidly. Royal Barry Carter Milling Co. was organized in 1946, and in 1952 it became Martha White Mills after the name of its principal brand. The small mills were replaced by purchase of Gilster Milling Co. in 1961 and Dan Valley Mills and Trenton Milling Co. in 1962.

The flour merchandising operations of this business complex have been directed from the start by Cohen T. Williams (b. 1906 Tenn.), who has been company president since 1946. His father, Cohen E. (b. 1884 Tenn.), is chairman. Joseph D. (b. 1916 Tenn.), also a son of Cohen E., is executive vice president. The Williams family owns the predominant share of the company and its affiliates.

Tullahoma

Middle Tennessee Milling Co.—Volunteer Milling Co.

was organized in 1890 by J. D. and F. A. Rath, bankers in Tullahoma, midway between Nashville and Chattanooga. The 1000-cwt. mill was purchased by Deems Riddle and then by E. W. Robertson & Sons and was renamed Middle Tennessee Milling Co. The business was operated for years by the Robertsons. The company became insolvent in 1935 and the mill was idle for five years. It was then reopened by a new company formed locally, but the business was not successful and the mill was closed permanently after a few years of intermittent operation.

TEXAS

Flour milling began almost simultaneously in two widely separated parts of Texas—on the plains north of Dallas and in the San Antonio region. There were flour mills in both these areas by 1845 and perhaps before that, but the probability is that the earlier mills may have ground corn rather than wheat. The industry developed as population increased, and in 1900 there were 117 flour mills in the state. Beginning early in the twentieth century, the Texas milling industry began to assume national importance, a condition that has continued to the present day. In 1961 Texas mills produced 16,348,000 cwt. of flour, the state ranking sixth. There were 34 mills operating in 1958.

The milling industry has provided the Lone Star State with two of its Governors—Ross S. Sterling in 1931-33 and W. Lee O'Daniel in 1939-42. The latter also served seven years in the United States Senate.

Amarillo

Great West Mill & Elevator Co.—Amarillo, the capital of the Texas Panhandle, became a mill city in 1920 when Frank Kell built the 1600-cwt. plant of Great West Mill & Elevator

Co. Walter A. Barlow was manager from the early 1920's until the middle 1930's. The mill was acquired in 1928 by General Mills, Inc., and was merged into the latter in 1937. The mill has remained in operation, and its present capacity is 2500 cwt.

Dallas

Burrus Mills, Inc. is the largest milling company in Texas and thirteenth in size in the nation. It operates flour mills in Dallas and Fort Worth with aggregate capacity of 16,000 cwt., a feed mill of 2400 tons, corn mill of 1200 cwt., a bag factory and more than 17,000,000 bushels of elevator space. The bulk of its flour business consists of exports and bakery flour to the South and Southeast, and a considerable family flour trade in Texas.

J. Perry Burrus (b. 1872 Mo., d. 1933) and associates became owners of seven milling companies—Collin County Mill & Elevator Co., bought in 1890 by William C. Burrus & Son; Burrus Mill & Elevator Co. in 1904; Morten Milling Co. in 1912; Gladney Milling Co. in 1913 (renamed Fant Milling Co.); Texas Star Flour Mills in 1924; Oklahoma Milling Co. (renamed Bob White Flour Mills, Inc.) in 1928; and Liberty Mills in 1929. They also bought Shreveport Milling Co. in 1904, but the mill was destroyed by fire in 1906, and they owned G. B. R. Smith Milling Co. in 1926-29. The Burrus interest varied from one-third in Texas Star to outright control in the others.

Tex-O-Kan Flour Mills Co. was formed in 1929 as a holding company for all the Burrus properties. The subsidiaries operated in a somewhat independent fashion except for general policies, but gradually their functions were taken over by the parent and after a decade the business was centralized. This has continued to the present. The company name was changed in 1951 to Burrus Mills, Inc.

The Collin County plant ceased to make flour in 1938; the Fant mill was sold the same year; the Burrus mill was replaced by a new plant in 1935; the Liberty and Bob White mills were closed in 1949; and Texas Star became inactive in 1956.

Burrus Mills, Inc. established a 4000-cwt. mill in Havana, Cuba, but after operating for eight years Burrus Molinos S. A. was expropriated in 1960 by the Castro regime. The company was also involved in the storage of wheat in tents in 1954-57, in which heavy losses were incurred.

The founder was president in 1929-33, and since 1933 the business has been headed by his son, Jack P. Burrus (b. 1902 Texas). Executive vice presidents: Charles H. Newman (b. 1891 Texas, d. 1953) in 1929-33; Fred Honea (b. 1888 Texas, d. 1963) in 1933-40; Henry H. Cate in 1940-45; Joseph C. Mitchell (b. 1897 Ala.) in 1946-56; Richard D. Zumwalt (b. 1912 Texas) since 1956.

Morten Milling Co.—New Century Milling Co., which was established in 1901, was acquired in 1910 by Edward W. Morten (b. 1861 Ind., d. 1929), J. Perry Burrus and William B. Newsom. The mill was rebuilt in a new location in 1912 and in 1917 it was enlarged to 6000 cwt. It was subsequently increased to 8000 cwt. Morten Milling Co. became part of the Tex-O-Kan system in 1929.

Morten managed the company until 1920, and was succeeded in 1920-33 by Fred Honea and in 1933-38 by Finis E. Cowan.

Denton

Morrison Milling Co. is principally owned by E. Walter Morrison (b. 1893 Texas), its founder and president, and it includes a flour mill of 1750 cwt., a corn mill and more than a million bushels of elevator space in the North Texas town of Denton. The flour produced there goes chiefly to southwestern destinations, but with a significant proportion also moving to Latin America.

The first mill on the Morrison site was built in 1886 by the Farmers' Alliance, an agrarian movement that flourished briefly in the latter part of the nineteenth century. Farmers' Alliance Milling Co. was reorganized about 1900 and became Alliance Milling Co. J. N. Rayzor (b. 1859, d. 1938) managed the business both before and after the reorganization. Alliance Milling Co. was reorganized in 1916, and after several ownerships and several managers it again became moribund. When the 800-cwt. plant was acquired by Morrison in 1936 it was almost idle.

Morrison Milling Co. was built up in a period when the milling tide was running strongly against small enterprises. The owner had 24 years' milling experience in Kansas, with the Red Star and Thomas Page organizations. His son, Edward W. (b. 1921 Kan.) is executive vice president.

Fort Worth

Bewley Mills—From a steamboating career on the Ohio River, Captain Murray P. Bewley (b. 1847 Ky., d. 1906) went to Fort Worth in 1877 and established a small mill in 1882 that later became Anchor Roller Mills. It reached 1200 cwt. in 20 years, operated by a partnership of the captain and his son, Edwin E. (b. 1881 Texas, d. 1946). Four years after incorporation in 1906, Bewley Mills and the slightly larger adjoining plant of Medlin Mills, founded in 1904, were consolidated physically and corporate-wise, in time reaching 3600 cwt. E. E. Bewley was president in 1906-36, although after 1925 he devoted most of his time to a large bank that he headed.

William P. Bomar (b. 1886 Tenn.) rose from warehouse foreman to sales manager to general manager in 1925, and from 1936 to 1955 was president of Bewley Mills. He was in the national limelight in both the flour and feed industries and was president of Millers' National Federation in 1946-48. Bomar and the Bewleys were the company's only stockholders for many years.

Bewley Mills was merged into Flour Mills of America, Inc., in 1955, and the following year the mill was closed.

Burrus Mill & Elevator Co.—Cameron Milling Co. had the largest flour mill in Texas (1200 cwt.) when it was rebuilt in 1887. The original mill was established in 1854. Plant capacity was 2400 cwt. in 1904 when the business was purchased by J. Perry Burrus and associates. The mill was replaced in 1935 by a new plant in a Fort Worth suburb, and its present capacity is 8000 cwt.

Burrus Mill & Elevator Co. control passed to Tex-O-Kan Flour Mills Co. in 1929. General managers were Euclid T. Fant to 1921, Kent Barber in 1921-26, W. Lee O'Daniel (b. 1890 Ohio) in 1926-35, J. Paul Smith in 1935-43.

Kimbell-Diamond Milling Co. operates three flour mills, with 4000 cwt. aggregate capacity. Its business is divided between bakery and family flour, nearly all in Texas. It is part of the great Kimbell business empire, the major segments of which consist of petroleum, wholesale groceries, cottonseed and its products, grain storage and various food plants.

The Kimbell entry into flour milling took place in 1898, when Benjamin B. Kimbell (b. 1856 Fla., d. 1922) bought the 400-cwt. Beatrice Mills in Whitewright, northeast of Dallas. His son, Kay (b. 1886 Texas), became manager while still a youth, the father being in the cattle and mercantile business. The mill was doubled in size; the Maurice Lasker mill in Wolfe City was acquired in 1917; the Whitewright mill was lost to fire in 1926; and during the 1930's a series of mill purchases took place—Diamond Milling Co., G. B. R. Smith Milling Co., and Chapman Milling Co., all in Sherman; Graham Mill & Elevator Co., Clifton Milling Co., Jacksboro Milling Co.; Seguin Milling & Power Co.; and Taylor Milling Co., Denton. At one time in this period the Kimbell interests operated eight flour mills with 12,500 cwt. capacity.

The Wolfe City and Chapman mills were destroyed by fire in 1931 and 1933, the Smith mill was sold to Commander-Larabee in 1932 and Diamond to Quaker Oats in 1941, and Jacksboro was closed in 1959 and Clifton in 1962. Whaley Mill & Elevator Co., which was purchased in 1943, was sold in 1947 to Fant Milling Co.

Kimbell headquarters was in Wolfe City until 1922, then after two years in Sherman it was moved to Fort Worth. Kimbell Milling Co. was incorporated in 1917, but in 1929 it became solely a grain company and K-B Milling Co. took over the mills. K-B Milling Co. and Diamond Milling Co. were merged in 1931 as Kimbell-Diamond Milling Co. Kay Kimbell has been president of this succession of companies throughout. Milling managers: J. Paul Smith in 1931-35; Henry H. Cate in 1935-36; Charles H. Newman in 1938-40; C. Binkley Smith (b. 1895 Texas), son of G. B. R. Smith, from 1940 to the present.

Universal Mills—Gaylord J. Stone (b. 1888 Va., d. 1952) came from a milling tradition, his father having operated a mill in the Virginia mountain country. After Stone became established as a feed manufacturer in Texas, he added a flour mill. He was first located in Waxahachie, but his feed plant was lost to fire in 1921. With associates, he then built a feed mill in Fort Worth under the name of Universal Mills, and in 1929 a flour mill of 1600 cwt. was erected. It was increased to 3600 cwt. in 1932. Stone was president and manager.

The flour mill was closed in 1952, but the company cantinued in the formula feed business for several years after that.

Gainesville

Whaley Mill & Elevator Co.—The mill built by J. M. Whaley in 1854 in Gainesville, near the Oklahoma border north of Fort Worth, was wrecked by an explosion 25 years later. In 1889 a new mill was built on the site by J. A. O. Whaley and his nephew, James C. Whaley (b. 1860 Texas, d. 1937). It was replaced in 1918 by another new mill, of 1200 cwt. capacity, called Whaley Mill & Elevator Co., largely owned by James C. Whaley and A. F. Jones and managed by Whaley. The latter's affairs became involved and his interest passed to a Dallas bank. The manager for some years was Harry Rosenstein.

In 1939 Fred Honea, who had ended a 33-year association with the Burrus concerns, became manager and part owner of Whaley Mill & Elevator Co. In 1943 the business was sold to Kay Kimbell, who operated it under the Whaley name until 1947 and then sold the mill to Fant Milling Co. It was later enlarged to 2000 cwt., and the mill has continued to operate. Honea was associated with Fant in 1944-61.

Galveston

Texas Star Flour Mills—The original plant that was later known as Texas Star Flour Mills was built in 1876 by John Reymershoffer. It was sold in 1904 to Maurice Lasker, and after 1914 was operated by his son, Edward, who was company president. At that time the mill had 3200 cwt. capacity, but was later enlarged to 6800. In 1924 the Laskers sold one-third interest each to J. Perry Burrus and Frank Kell, and Burrus became president. James E. Haviland (b. 1887, d. 1956) and Charles H. Newman were managers in this period.

When Tex-O-Kan Flour Mills Co. was formed in 1929, Burrus acquired the Kell interest in Texas Star and it was controlled but not wholly owned by Tex-O-Kan. Haviland was manger in 1929-35, Paul H. Bimmerman in 1935-45.

The mill became inactive in 1956.

Greenville

Greenville Milling Co.—Albert F. Richter (b. 1866 N. Y., d. 1934) managed the 1200-cwt. plant of Greenville Milling Co., in the town of that name 45 miles northeast of Dallas, through almost all of its 34-year existence. J. B. Clayton was the first president, Frank J. Phillips succeeded him, and after 1924 Richter was president as well as manager. The plant was sold to International Milling Co. in 1934, and was increased by stages to 4600 cwt. It has continued in operation.

Houston

Arrow Mills, Inc.—Ross S. Sterling (b. 1875 Texas, d. 1949), an oil man who became Governor of Texas in 1931-33, established the Houston mill in 1920 and organized Houston Mill & Elevator Co., of which he was president and Frank J. Becker (b. 1860 Iowa, d. 1930) was general manager. The mill had 3000 cwt. capacity.

American Maid Flour Mills became the company name in 1923, and Benjamin E. Caldwell was manager for the next eight years, followed by T. E. McCarty. Sterling's business empire collapsed in 1931.

Houston Milling Co. was formed in 1936 by French interests when they purchased the plant. Henry H. Cate was president for the next four years, during which the mill was increased to 6600 cwt. Marcel Heyman (b. 1897 Germany, d. 1941) succeeded Cate and was followed in 1941-45 by Erich B. Reiner (b. 1898 Germany). The mill was sold in 1945 to Continental Grain Co., which organized Arrow Mills, Inc., as a subsidiary. Finger Lakes & Upper Hudson Flour Mills, also owned by Continental, was merged into Arrow Mills, Inc. Finis E. Cowan (b. 1896 Calif., d. 1958) became president in 1945. Flour milling ceased in Houston in 1952.

Houston Milling Co. remained in the grain business, the name being changed first to Lathrop Grain Co., then to Interstate Grain Corp. Offices were moved to Kansas City in 1945.

McKinney

Collin County Mill & Elevator Co.—William C. Burrus was a Confederate officer, teacher and grist miller. After running a small mill near McKinney, 30 miles north of Dallas, he and his son, J. Perry, bought the Farmers' Alliance mill in that town in 1890 and organized Collin County Mill & Elevator Co. They rebuilt the plant with 1500 cwt. capacity and later raised it to 2000 cwt.

Collin County Mill & Elevator Co. was the start of the great Burrus chain, and it became a Tex-O-Kan subsidiary in 1929. The mill was operated until 1938. It was managed successively by Euclid T. Fant, Harry C. Jackson and Gibson Caldwell (b. 1886 Texas).

New Braunfels

H. Dittlinger Roller Mills Co.—Prince Carl led 700 German emigrants to the Comal River country in 1845, with the help of three Connecticut Yankees named Torrey. Three years later, John F. Torrey, whose line of Indian trading posts became famous, built a 200-cwt. flour mill in the New Braunfels settlement, about 25 miles northeast of San Antonio. This mill was destroyed by fire in 1860; its successor was partially wrecked by a tornado; and the mill was carried away by a flood in 1872.

Peter Faust & Co. built a 400-cwt. mill in 1887 on the site of the earlier mills. Hippolyt Dittlinger (b. 1859 Mo., d. 1946), one of the original partners, became sole owner in 1901. Mill capacity was increased to 1600 cwt. in 1914, to 2200 cwt. in 1950 and to 3700 cwt. (2600 flour, 1100 corn meal) in 1962. The feed mill has reached 500-ton size. The 1200-cwt. mill of Landa Industries was purchased in 1930 and converted into the feed plant.

H. Dittlinger Roller Mills Co. was incorporated in 1909. Its presidents: Dittlinger in 1909-30; H. F. Menglen (b. 1886 Ohio) in 1930-33; Alfred Liebscher (b. 1895 Germany) in 1930-55. Liebscher, son-in-law of Dittlinger, joined the company in 1918.

The business was sold in 1955 to Flour Mills of America, Inc., and the flour and feed plants remain in operation.

Landa Industries—The Dittlinger feed mill stands on a site that was occupied by flour mills for 87 years. The first was built in 1848 by William R. Merriwether, a Tennesseean. He sold in 1860 to Joseph Landa. Landa's son, Harry, took over in 1875, enlarged the mill to 1200 cwt., and ran the business until 1926. The Landa properties, which also included a cottonseed oil mill, were then sold to J. E. Jarrett and associates.

The enterprise went into bankruptcy in 1930, and the flour mill was sold to H. Dittlinger Roller Mills Co. The mill was operated until 1935 and then converted to the production of feed.

Paris

Paris Milling Co.—Bassano Roller Mills was established in 1856 in Paris, a hundred miles northeast of Dallas, by the Bassano brothers from England. It became Paris Milling Co. in 1873, and the company was incorporated in 1909. The mill was consumed in the great Paris fire of 1916, and in its place there appeared a new 1000-cwt. mill, along with 450,000 bushels of elevator space. Milling of flour was terminated in 1952, and thereafter the company engaged principally in the formula feed business.

James C. Whaley, who also had large interests in land, cattle, oil and lumberyards, controlled Paris Milling Co. for many years and was its president in 1920-37. Carl M. McWherter (b. 1882 Tenn., d. 1956), son-in-law of Whaley, was general manager in 1913-45 and president in 1937-56, and was followed in both these posts by Carl M., Jr. (b. 1916 Texas).

Plainview

Harvest Queen Milling & Elevator Co.—At the base of the Texas Panhandle is Plainview, where Jones Bros. built a small mill in 1906. It was purchased in 1910 by Chris Hinn and his son, Albert G. (b. 1881 Wis., d. 1940). They formed Harvest Queen Milling & Elevator Co., Albert G. becoming president. The first mill was destroyed by fire in 1926, and a new plant of 1200 cwt. was then built. The company became insolvent in 1931, and Horatio G. Stinnett, Jr. (b. 1887 Texas, d. 1950), the receiver, who had been a miller in Sherman, became president after reorganization. The mill was increased to 2400 cwt. in 1946. The company has remained in the grain business, but the mill was closed in 1951.

San Antonio

Liberty Mills — Gustav Giesecke (b. 1865 Texas, d. 1935) established Liberty Mills, 500 cwt. capacity, in 1894, and he managed the business for 36 years. A new plant of 2000 cwt. was erected in 1916. The company became a subsidiary of Tex-O-Kan Flour Mills Co. in 1929. Martin C. Giesecke (b. 1892 Texas), son of the founder, was manager in 1930-38, Joseph C. Mitchell after 1938.

Liberty Mills was dismantled in 1949.

Pioneer Flour Mills has been owned and operated for more than 112 years by the members of one family—the second oldest milling enterprise in the nation. It has a flour mill of 3850 cwt., corn mill of 1250 cwt., a mix plant and grain elevator of 450,000 bushels. It principally serves the South Texas trade, both family and bakery, and in that area it has several fifth generation customers.

This business was founded by Carl Hilmer Guenther (b. 1825 Germany, d. 1902), who built a little mill near Fredericksburg, Texas, in 1851. It was equipped with buhr stones that were hauled 300 miles from Galveston by ox team. In 1859 Guenther moved to the site on the San Antonio River that is occupied today by the family-owned mill.

The original mill was replaced in 1900, and the new mill was enlarged in 1914 and 1924. The partnership of C. H. Guenther & Son gave way in 1898 to a corporation, Pioneer Flour Mills, of which Guenther's son, Erhard R. (b. 1868 Texas, d. 1945), was president for 43 years. The destiny of the business was controlled between father and son for 94 years.

Arthur Storms (b. 1873 Texas, d. 1945), cousin of Erhard Guenther, was associated with him in the management for 47 years, and they passed away the same week. Adolph G. Beckmann (b. 1888 Texas, d. 1954), who joined the company in 1907 and who was a nephew of Erhard Guenther, was president in 1945-54, followed in 1954-57 by a cousin, Ernst Schuchard (b. 1893 Texas), and then by Beckmann's son, Alfred G. (b. 1917 Texas), to the present.

Seguin

Seguin Milling & Power Co.—Eugene Nolte, banker and political leader, established a flour mill of 1200 cwt. in Seguin, 35 miles east of San Antonio, early in this century. He owned the mill until 1937, when it was sold to Kay Kimbell. It was later enlarged to 1600 cwt., and it has continued in operation. Joseph Gibbs was manager for many years, both in the Nolte and Kimbell eras.

Sherman

Chapman Milling Co.—The Farmers' Alliance mill that was established in 1887 in Sherman became the property ten years later of Richard A. Chapman (b. 1829, d. 1928). He formed Chapman Milling Co. and later enlarged the mill to 1200 cwt. The business was managed in later years by his sons, George (d. 1926) and Richard A., Jr. The mill became idle in 1927 and was purchased in 1931 by Kay Kimbell and converted into an oatmeal plant. It was destroyed by fire in 1933.

Diamond Mill Co.—The Stinnetts were pioneer millers, and in 1887 Horatio G. (b. 1862 Texas, d. 1934) of the clan joined Major Rucker in the ownership of Magnolia Mills in Sherman. The 250-cwt. mill had been built a decade earlier by

Rucker. Stinnett became president of Diamond Mill Co. when it was incorporated in 1892. The business continued under that name for 40 years, Horatio G., Jr. becoming manager in 1917; capacity of the mill was increased to 2000 cwt.

Kay Kimbell acquired a half-interest in Diamond Mill Co. in 1924 and became sole owner eight years later. The mill was increased to 4000 cwt., and operated as Kimbell-Diamond Milling Co. The plant was sold in 1941 to Quaker Oats Co., which rebuilt it for the production of breakfast cereals.

Fant Milling Co. has two flour mills in North Texas aggregating 5500 cwt., a million-and-one-third bushels of grain storage and two refrigerated dough plants. It does a large family flour business in Texas and adjacent states and distributes frozen products across half the nation.

This business originated in 1904, when W. O. Brackett (b. 1871, d. 1957) and W. R. Brents added a small mill to their grain elevator. Nine years later Sherman Mill & Grain Co. was acquired by J. Perry Burrus and associates, who organized Gladney Milling Co., with Samuel Gladney (b. 1880 Texas, d. 1935) as head. A new mill of 1500 cwt. was built in 1920. Financial involvements of Gladney brought on a reorganization, from which Fant Milling Co. emerged. It was headed by Euclid T. Fant (b. 1872 Miss., d. 1937), long in the Burrus organization. The company was merged in 1929 with Tex-O-Kan Flour Mills Co., and it was a subsidiary of the latter for nine years.

James A. Fant (b. 1898 Texas) and Ferdinand Moore purchased the company in 1938 and formed a new Fant Milling Co. The mill was enlarged until it reached 3500 cwt.; the Whaley mill in Gainesville was acquired in 1947 and increased to 2000 cwt.; the flour mix business was entered in

1949; and in 1954 there was established Gladiola Biscuit Co., a subsidiary that has refrigerated products plants in Greensboro, N. C., and Dallas.

James A. Fant succeeded his father as president of the first Fant company in 1931-38, and he has headed the new company since 1938 except for two years when it was operated as a partnership.

G. B. R. Smith Milling Co.—Eagle Mills, built in 1866, was acquired in 1909 by George B. R. Smith (b. 1848 Texas, d. 1924), a rancher and grain dealer who also had operated a flour mill in Celina, Texas. The company bearing his name was formed at that time, and the mill was subsequently enlarged to 1000 cwt. Smith's son, J. Paul (b. 1891 Texas), was president in 1924-33.

Company control changed three times in six years—to the Burrus group in 1926, to the Kimbell interests in 1929 and to Commander-Larabee in 1932. The mill was enlarged to 4000 cwt. during this period. Harry L. Stover (d. 1951) was manager in 1933-37 and Ellis D. English in 1937-41.

The mill was sold in 1941 to Quaker Oats Co., and has since been operated by that company.

Vernon

Kell Mill & Elevator Co.—In 1892 a small mill was built by Joseph Kell in Vernon, 50 miles northwest of Wichita Falls. Kell's cousin, Frank, purchased an interest in 1910 and he later came into control of the company. The mill was rebuilt in 1920 and it then had 1400 cwt. capacity. It became a General Mills property in 1928, and the mill was operated until 1937. George R. Wilson was manager in 1923-37.

Waco

Waco Mill & Elevator Co.—Second flour mill to pass into the hands of Frank Kell was Waco Mill & Elevator Co., in 1905, in the Texas city of that name. T. Preston Duncan was president and manager in 1908-21 of the 1600-cwt. company. Harry L. Stover was manager during the 1920's. The Waco mill was acquired by General Mills, Inc. in 1928, and four years later it was dismantled.

Wichita Falls

Wichita Mill & Elevator Co.—Frank Kell (b. 1859 Texas, d. 1941) was a fabulous tycoon even in Texas. He was master of a business empire that embraced railroads, oil wells, cotton gins, ranches, cattle, banks, hotels, cement plants, glass works and many other enterprises but flour milling was apparently his favorite line of business. In the 1920's Kell owned the controlling interest in eight milling companies, with aggregate capacity of about 25,000 cwt.

Mrs. Kell's grandfather, Joel M. Stinnette (b. 1805 Va., d. 1876) established grist mills at several points in North Texas between 1847 and 1860. Kell's first connection with the industry began in 1886 as wheat buyer for Texas Star Flour Mills., in which he owned a substantial interest many years later.

Wichita Valley Milling Co. and its 800-cwt. plant were purchased by Kell in 1898. It was renamed Wichita Mill & Elevator Co., and the mill was enlarged several times, being rebuilt in 1917 with 5000 cwt. capacity. T. Preston Duncan (b. 1871 Texas, d. 1948) managed the company in 1921-29.

Waco Mill & Elevator Co. became a Kell property in 1905, followed by Kell Mill & Elevator Co. in 1910, Oklahoma City Milling & Elevator Co. in 1913, Perry Mill & Elevator Co. in

1919, Great West Mill & Elevator Co. in 1920, Plant Flour Mills Co. in 1926 and Kansas Mill & Elevator Co. in 1927. At various times Kell owned an interest in several other mills.

A few months after General Mills, Inc. was formed in 1928, Kell sold his six Texas and Oklahoma companies to that concern. The latter refused, however, to take the St. Louis and Arkansas City plants, and they proved to be the unhappiest milling ventures of Kell's career. The St. Louis mill went out of business in 1931, and the Kansas company went through receivership before it reached stability and success.

Wichita Mill & Elevator Co. operated under that name until 1937, when it was merged into the parent company. Present plant capacity in Wichita Falls is 6200 cwt.

UTAH

Brigham Young and Isaac Chase built the first flour mill in Utah. It was known as the old Mormon Mill, and it stood within the present limits of Salt Lake City. It dated from 1852, and the mill operated to some extent until after the beginning of the twentieth century. In 1900 there were 77 flour mills in Utah, 13 of them remaining in 1958.

Ogden was a grain market of some consequence by the 1870's, and a milling industry gradually developed there. The Ogden mills became important by about 1915, and the capacity was increased considerably in later years. Utah mills turned out 5,784,000 cwt. of flour in 1961.

Two Governors of Utah were millers—Charles R. Mabey (b. 1877 Utah, d. 1935) in 1921-25 and Henry H. Blood (b. 1872 Utah, d. 1942) in 1933-41. Mabey was president of Bountiful Milling Co., Bountiful, and Blood was manager of Kaysville-Layton Milling Co., Kaysville.

Ogden

Hylton Flour Mills—Five flour mills were acquired in 1951 by W. G. Holley, a lumberman, and he formed Holley Milling Co., with headquarters in Ogden. Two of the mills were in Ogden, the others in Salt Lake City, Laramie, Wyo., and Elko, Nev. Their total capacity was 2800 cwt.

Holley Milling Co. was sold in 1922 to J. J. Hylton, who had a small mill in Nevada. He organized Hylton Flour Mills. The other mills were closed or sold within the next few years, leaving only the 1000-cwt. Phoenix mill in Ogden. It had been built in 1883 by D. H. Peery, succeeding the Weber mill of 1866 that was destroyed by fire in 1882. The Phoenix mill was taken over in 1888 by Ogden Milling & Elevator Co.

Hylton Flour Mills was managed until 1931 by W. W. Percival. It was operated under a receivership for several years and was closed in 1935.

VIRGINIA

The Old Dominion has many distinctions in flour milling. America's first grist mill was located in Jamestown Colony, operating at least as early as 1621. The Father of Our Country was one of the foremost millers of his time, his Mount Vernon mill enjoying an extensive trade in the West Indies as well as at home. Richmond was the site of the nation's largest mills for more than 60 years, and the city was one of the principal milling centers.

In 1958 Virginia had 48 flour mills, all but a very few being local in nature.

Danville

Dan Valley Mills has a 1400-cwt. flour mill in Danville, 80 miles southeast of Roanoke, and is exclusively in the family flour business in the Virginia-Carolina area. Control of the company was acquired in 1962 by the Cohen Williams interests, and it is operated as a part of the Martha White enterprises.

The mill was built in 1894 by James I. Pritchett (b. 1857 Va., d. 1932). It was increased in 1904 to 800 cwt., and attained its present size in 1949. Pritchett was president in 1894-1932, James I. Pritchett, Jr. (b. 1883 Va.) in 1932-57, and James A. Smith (b. 1894 N. C.), who had been general manager from 1944, was president in 1957-62. Present manager is E. B. Dowdy (b. 1928 Va.).

Lynchburg

Piedmont Mills, Inc. is on the banks of the James River, at a point where flour has been milled for 150 years. The present business consists largely of soft wheat bakery flour, produced in a 2200-cwt. pneumatic mill. The company has 500,-000 bushels of grain storage.

The first mill was built at the end of the War of 1812, and a visitor noted in 1830 that the mills of Lynchburg annually exported more than 50,000 cwt. of flour. The mill was owned by the Langhornes before 1840. Successive owners were John L. Langhorne, William L. Morris in 1860, Charles L. Langhorne in 1867, Stephen C. Hurt & Sons in 1880 and William Hurt in 1898.

Piedmont Mills, Inc., was organized and acquired the property in 1905. The mill was rebuilt and then enlarged to 1200 cwt. It was enlarged to its present size in 1962. James I. Pritchett was president in 1905-32, James I. Pritchett, Jr. in 1932-57, and James E. Key (b. 1897 Va.) since 1957. Managers have been N. D. Eller in 1905-16, W. Blakey Walker (b. 1890 Va., d. 1947) in 1916-44, Key since 1944.

Richmond

Dunlop Mills—Richmond milling history ended when fire consumed famous old Dunlop Mills in 1949. It was one of three great flour mills that made the Virginia capital one of the chief milling points for more than 75 years during the nineteenth century.

Dunlop Mills was built in 1852 on the site of an earlier mill that was operated by Dunlop, Moncure & Co. from the early 1800's. The business was incorporated in 1888 as Dunlop & McCance Milling Co., and was purchased in 1891 by Warner Moore (b. 1840 Mo., d. 1936) and Thomas L. Moore (b. 1860 Md., d. 1929). They formed Warner Moore & Co., and operated as Dunlop Mills with Thomas L. Moore as the active head until 1927. It was then managed by Edwin C. Fockler (b. 1891 Md.). The mill had 2400 cwt. capacity. The business continued until 1932, when it was liquidated. The mill was sold to Dixie-Portland interests in 1935 and operated until the 1949 fire.

Warner Moore & Co. acquired historic Gallego Mills in 1903. It was established in 1798 by Joseph Gallego, and when rebuilt in 1833 on the site that it was to occupy for 102 years it was the largest flour mill in the nation. Gallego Mills was owned for many years by John A. Chevallie. The mill was destroyed by fire in 1848 and rebuilt in 1860 with 2000 cwt., destroyed again in 1865 and in 1904 and rebuilt as a 2500-cwt. plant. It was dismantled in 1935.

The third great Richmond mill was Haxall Mills, built in 1809 by Philip and William Haxall and operated in later years by William G. Crenshaw and then by Richard B. Haxall. It was lost to fire in 1872 and rebuilt but became inoperative before 1900.

Roanoke

Lindsey, Robinson & Co.—Howery-Taylor Milling Co. had a small plant in Roanoke that was established after 1900 to replace an earlier mill that was destroyed by fire. C. Grattan Lindsey (b. 1879 Va., d. 1942) and J. Ellis Robinson, flour jobbers, acquired the mill in 1921 and operated as Lindsey, Robinson & Co. The mill was enlarged twice, reaching 2000 cwt. in 1946. Lindsey was president, being succeeded by his son and namesake, who became a large operator in the formula feed business. The company went into receivership in 1960.

Roanoke City Mills, Inc. has a flour mill of 3600 cwt., corn mill of 1000 cwt., feed plant of 1200 tons and 400,000 bushels of grain elevator capacity. It has been owned and managed throughout its existence by members of the Ring family. The company mills both hard and soft wheat and serves both the family and the bakery trade in the area from South Carolina to New York.

The flour mill was built in 1918 with 1500 cwt. capacity, and has been enlarged from time to time. The company entered the formula feed business in 1928, and the present plant facilities were completed in 1948.

This Roanoke enterprise was founded by Joshua Wright Ring (b. 1873 Va.), who first engaged in the milling business in 1892 at Pulaski, Va. His milling experience covers more than 70 years. He was president of the company for 34 years and has been its board chairman since 1952. He was president and manager of the Carter-owned mills in Bristol and Johnson City, Tenn., for a long period ending in 1922. His brother, M. Fleming Ring (b. 1876 Va., d. 1951), was his associate for many years.

The founder's son, J. Kirk Ring (b. 1895 Va.), who joined

the company the year it was formed, has been president since 1952. M. Fleming Ring, Jr. (b. 1922 Va.) is vice president and in charge of feed operations.

Shenandoah

Shenandoah Milling Co.—In the famous valley of the Shenandoah is a town of that name where Avis Roudabush operated a small mill for some years. It was enlarged to 1200 cwt. in the late 1920's and called Shenandoah Milling Co. Roudabush closed this mill about 1935 and subsequently built a plant of 2400 cwt. in Norfolk, which was known both as Shenandoah Milling Co. and as Seaboard Milling Co. It ran some what spasmodically and ceased to operate in 1940. He then returned to Shenandoah and reopened the mill for about a year.

Staunton

White Star Mills has an 1800-cwt. flour mill in Staunton, in Virginia's Shenandoah Valley. It is chiefly engaged in the family flour business in Virginia and the Carolinas. The mill was erected in 1892 with 1000 cwt. capacity and was increased in 1946.

White Star Mills was established by Michael Kivlighan (b. 1863 Va., d. 1942) and associates, and it has been operated as a series of partnerships. The present owners are J. Harold Kivlighan (b. 1902 Va.), son of a founder, and Mrs. Katherine R. Lahens, granddaughter of another founder.

Michael Kivlighan managed White Star Mills for 50 years. His son has been manager the past 20 years.

WASHINGTON

Washington is foremost in flour production among the Pacific and Mountain states, its 1961 total being 9,960,000 cwt., although only eight mills operated within its borders.

Hudson's Bay Co. established the first mill in Washington, at its Vancouver trading post in 1828. The first merchant mill was built in 1865 at Waitsburg, near Walla Walla, and although flour was exported soon thereafter the industry was not very important until about 1890. Spokane was the first milling center of the state, but was surpassed by Tacoma and both of them finally fell behind Seattle.

Cheney

F. M. Martin Grain & Milling Co.—A mill that also produced a governor was established in 1907 in Cheney, a few miles southwest of Spokane, by Frank M. Martin (b. 1860 Ohio, d. 1925), who had been farming in that vicinity. The mill was destroyed by fire in 1913 and was rebuilt with 1600 cwt. capacity. The founder's son, Clarence D. (b. 1887 Wash., d. 1955) followed his father as president. He was Governor of Washington in 1933-41. Elizabeth Goerling managed the business after 1933.

The mill was sold in 1943 to National Biscuit Co., and was subsequently enlarged to 2300 cwt.

Pasco

Pasco Grain & Milling Co.—Charles B. Shoemaker and associates built a 1600-cwt. mill in 1917 in Pasco, where the Snake River flows into the Columbia, and organized Pasco Flour Mills Co. This company failed in 1921, and the plant was purchased by M. W. Hunt and associates and Pasco Grain & Milling Co. was formed, with Hunt as president and George Gregory as manager. The plant was increased to 2000 cwt. W. Harold (Hi) Younger became manager in 1924, Charles A. Peplow in 1927. The mill was sold in 1927 to Royal Milling Co., and dismantled soon afterward.

Seattle

Fisher Flouring Mills Co. is the largest single-plant company in the industry, and is one of the principal exporters of flour and supplier of the Pacific Coast bakery trade. The company has a flour mill of 15,000 cwt., feed plant of 1000 tons, grain storage for 2,750,000 bushels, and through wholly or partially owned subsidiaries it has extensive real estate holdings and it controls two television stations and one radio station. The company is the largest domestic producer of bulgur and it has an established line of specialty flours and a breakfast cereal.

The Fisher mill on Harbor Island, across the bay from downtown Seattle, was opened in 1911, and additions to the original mill were made in 1917, 1924 and 1947. Pneumatic conveying was installed in 1960 in part of the plant.

Central figure in company history is Oliver D. Fisher (b. 1875 Mo.), general manager from plant construction to 1942, president in 1922-48 and board chairman since 1948. He was one of the stalwarts of the industry for a generation, was president of Millers' National Federation in 1937-38, and a director of that organization for 29 years—a record for continuous service. He also has large interests in insurance, lumber and banking, and for many years was a member of 27 corporation boards.

Oliver Williams Fisher (b. 1842 Ohio, d. 1922) was apprenticed at 12 years to a grist miller, and for a quarter of a century he milled flour in Kentucky, Ohio, Ontario and Missouri. He then engaged in the lumber business. In 1903 he and his sons bought Gallatin Valley Milling Co., Belgrade, Mont., and this small mill was operated for 50 years by the Fishers.

Fisher Fouring Mills Co. was launched by the Fishers and their business associates. O. W. Fisher was president in 1911-

22, and his five sons held executive positions—Will P. (b. 1869 Ky., d. 1938), Burr (b. 1872 Mo., d. 1924), Oliver D., Daniel R. (b. 1878 Mo.) and Wallace (b. 1891 Mo.).

Fisher Flouring Mills Co. acquired a Seattle radio station in 1926 and started a television station in that city in 1952. It has a majority interest in a new television station in Portland. The company began developing the bulgur process in 1955 in cooperation with the United States Department of Agriculture and has been in commercial production since 1958.

John L. Locke (b. 1896 Ohio) was general manager in 1942-60 and has been president since 1948. He has been one of the national milling leaders of the past 20 years and was president of Millers' National Federation in 1948-50. Kenneth R. Fisher (b. 1906 Wash.), son of Will P., became general manager in 1960. National prominence has also been attained by W. Stanley Allen (b. 1880 England, d. 1954), J. Stanwood Davis (b. 1890 Mass.) and William L. Haley (b. 1889 Tenn.), vice presidents with service records ranging from 43 to 50 years.

Charles H. Lilly Co.—Charles H. Lilly, who had principally been in the hay business, had a small mill in Seattle in 1909 and then built a 1000-cwt. mill on Harbor Island in 1911. This was operated by Lilly and later was managed for many years by C. F. Larsen. The company went out of business in 1938, and the building was acquired by Fisher Flouring Mills Co. and converted into a bulgur plant in 1955.

Seattle Flour Mills Co.—Hammond Milling Co. was established in 1902 in Seattle by the principals in Hammond Timber Co. and Missoula Mercantile Co. The original 1500-cwt. plant was increased to 4000 cwt. in 1905. Ownership passed to Portland Flouring Mills Co. about ten years later, and when that concern bogged down financially the Seattle mill was leased for a brief period to the Dutch syndicate that had other mills in the Northwest, and then in 1920 to Centennial Mill Co. It was operated for two years or so as Seattle Flour Mills Co., and then was closed.

Spokane

Spokane Flour Mills Co. operates a mill of 2800 cwt. and 200,000 bushels of elevator space. It is managed in conjunction with Terminal Flour Mills Co., their owners being the same. President and manager since 1956 is Henry J. Schmitt.

Inland Empire Milling Co., which had been established by Dutch interests along with mills in Seattle and Pendleton, was purchased in 1903 by Lodewyk C. Lens (b. 1867 Holland, d. 1942) and associates and renamed Spokane Flour Mills Co. It was engaged primarily in overseas trade and was operated by the Lens group until 1936. The mill had 1500 cwt. capacity.

Spokane Flour Mills Co. was purchased in 1936 by Mark P. Miller, and has since been part of the Miller chain. Mill capacity was increased in postwar years.

Walla Walla

Preston Shaffer Milling Co.—Washington's first merchant mill was built in 1865 in Waitsburg, in the southeastern corner of the state; and fittingly, it was called Washington mill. It operated more than 90 years and was the genesis of the Preston Shaffer chain.

Washington Mill was purchased in 1866 by William G. Preston (b. 1833 N. Y., d. 1916) and P. A., his brother. In 1886 the Prestons and Frank Parton incorporated Preston Parton Milling Co., and the name was changed to Preston Shaffer Milling Co. in 1911 after William B. Shaffer (b. 1861 Ill., d. 1925) became dominant in the company.

The company's second mill, built in 1904, was at Athena, just over the Oregon border. Peacock Mill Co., established in 1888 in Milton-Freewater, also in the same Oregon area, became a subsidiary in 1917 and the mill was rebuilt ten years later. The company became joint owner in 1925 with Isaac A. Welk of Pendleton Flour Mills Co., renamed Western Milling Co. in 1929, with mills in Pendleton and Salt Lake City. Preston Shaffer absorbed the subsidiaries in 1938, and the following year the main office was moved from Waitsburg to Walla Walla.

Prior to the formation of Western Milling Co., the Preston Shaffer mills had about 2600 cwt. capacity. The total reached 7200 cwt. a few years after consolidation. The Pendleton mill was destroyed by fire in 1947, and the other mills were increased to 5500 cwt.

Edgar H. Leonard (b. 1873 Wash., d. 1954), who came to Preston Shaffer from Portland Flouring Mills Co. in 1915, was the company leader for a third of a century and was a national figure in the industry. He served as president in 1925-54. The Welks were his close associates throughout that time. Philip I. Welk (b. 1904 Kan.), son of I. A., was general manager after 1939 and president after 1954. Earlier presidents were W. G. Preston in 1886-1911 and W. B. Shaffer in 1911-25.

The company was liquidated in 1957, after the Milton-Freewater mill was sold to Centennial Mills, Inc., and the two smaller mills were closed.

Wilbur

Columbia River Milling Co.—Flour milling began in Wilbur, 65 miles west of Spokane, in 1889. Alexander Alexander (b. 1862 Ont., d. 1951) came in as head miller in 1892 and was manager before 1900. Later he was chief owner and president of Columbia River Milling Co., and the original mill was enlarged to 1000 cwt. A mill of equal size in nearby Hartline was acquired in 1910 and operated until 1925. The Wilbur mill remained in production until 1946, when it was destroyed by fire.

WEST VIRGINIA

Most illustrious figure among the millers of West Virginia was Thomas J. Jackson, the immortal Stonewall of Civil War fame. As a young man he worked in and operated a flour mill near Clarksburg, but after his graduation from West Point he became an instructor at Virginia Military Institute and never returned to milling.

With few exceptions, West Virginia mills have been small in size and localized in nature. There were 428 mills in the state in 1900, but only a few remain.

Bluefield

Bluefield Milling Co.—The mountain town of Bluefield had a flour mill of 1000 cwt. that was built in 1893. The original firm of Gooch, McCue & Wright was changed in 1901 to McCue & Wright Milling Co., and in 1918 to Wright Milling Co. Bluefield Milling Co., formed in 1923, took over the business at that time. The mill was closed in 1940. J. Lewis Alexander was the last manager.

Charleston

Charleston Milling Co.—Largest mill in West Virginia was in its capital city, the 1200-cwt. plant of Charleston Milling

& Produce Co., built in 1914. It was enlarged in 1942 to 1600 cwt., and the company name was changed to Charleston Milling Co. Harvey G. Davis (b. 1886 Va., d. 1954) was president and manager for many years. The mill was closed about 1953.

Huntington

Gwinn Bros. & Co.—The Gwinns, who had a small mill in the West Virginia village of Glenwood, built an 800-cwt. plant in 1899 in Huntington, operating as Gwinn Bros. & Co. Two of the brothers went on to Ohio to manage mills that were owned by the group, but they retained their Huntington company shares. W. W. Gwinn headed the business until 1915, being succeeded by D. Byrd Gwinn (b. 1875 W. Va., d. 1941) as president and manager, and he in turn was succeeded in 1941 by his son, James A. (b. 1913 W. Va., d. 1961). The mill reached 1100 cwt. in later years, with a corn mill of equal size. It was destroyed by fire in 1958 and was rebuilt, but the mill was closed and the company liquidated in 1962.

WISCONSIN

Prairie du Chien, on the Mississippi, was the site of the first flour mill in the Northwest, built in 1818 by John Shaw. During the quarter-century that Wisconsin was an important wheat state, ending about 1875, a large number of flour mills were established. Milwaukee was the chief supplier of mill equipment and it played a large part in promoting the roller mill. Milwaukee, Superior and LaCrosse were milling centers of importance for many years, and Gen. C. C. Washburn was Governor of Wisconsin in 1870-72. Wisconsin was long the principal rye milling state. In 1900 there were 424 flour mills in the state, but only 12 remained in 1958.

Appleton

Willy & Co.—Appleton, a hundred miles northwest of Milwaukee, was the site of a mill built in 1855 by S. R. Willy (b. 1830 England, d. 1914) and operated by him for 59 years. His brother, T. A. (b. 1845 England, d. 1916) was associated in the enterprise for 50 years beginning in 1866. Plant capacity grew to 1000 cwt. wheat and 250 cwt. rye.

The Willy heirs ran the mill until 1921, then sold to Henry E. MacEachron and associates who had a milling property in Wausau. This group operated initially as Willy Co., and then as Appleton Cereal Mills, but it was not successful and the mill was closed in 1924.

DePere

John P. Dousman Milling Co.—Following a fire in 1892 that destroyed Arndt Bros. & Dousman flour mill in DePere, a town adjacent to Green Bay, the junior partner bought out the Arndts and then organized John P. Dousman Milling Co. This concern had a mill that reached 1000 cwt. capacity of wheat and rye flour. Dousman (b. 1846 Wis., d. 1927) was president and manager until 1922, when his interests were sold to Lee M. Powell, who had been associated with Milwaukee mills. His Powell Milling Co., which took over the Dousman property, became insolvent within a year, and the mill reverted to the Dousman family. It was operated somewhat spasmodically for a few years and was closed by 1930.

Green Bay

John H. Ebeling Milling Co.—Green Bay was the site of a wheat and rye mill of 1000 cwt., that was operated for many years by John H. Ebeling as sole proprietor and then by a company that bore his name. The mill ceased to operate about 1935.

Janesville

Frank H. Blodgett, Inc.—Wisconsin achieved statehood in 1848, and in that same year Beloit City Mills was established in the town laid out in 1836 by Caleb Blodgett. This launched a mill that was operated for 113 years by the members of the family. The business ended in 1961, when the site was required for municipal purposes.

John Hackett (b. 1808 Vt., d. 1886), son-in-law of Blodgett, ran Beloit City Mills until 1867, part of that time in partnership with his brother-in-law, Selvey K. Blodgett (b. 1812 N. Y., d. 1881). Blodgett then became sole owner, and in time was succeeded by his son, William (b. 1835 Ind., d. 1901). The mill was lost to fire in 1898, and the company moved 15 miles to Janesville and purchased and remodeled Hodson's mill, which dated back into the 1870's.

Blodgett Milling Co. was incorporated in 1891, and the name was changed to Blodgett-Holmes Co. in 1917 and to Frank H. Blodgett, Inc. in 1924. Company presidents: William Blodgett in 1891-1901; his son, Frank H. (b. 1866 Wis., d. 1949) in 1901-37; the latter's son, Frank C. P. (b. 1896 Wis., d. 1947) in 1937-47; and Kenneth B. Jeffris (b. 1891 Wis., d. 1962), son-in-law of Frank H. Blodgett, in 1947-61.

For more than a century the Blodgetts were rye and buckwheat millers, wheat having been milled only in the early years. Mill capacity was 1500 cwt. buckwheat and 1190 cwt. rye flour.

LaCrosse

Listman Mills Co.—Wisconsin's largest flour mill was in LaCrosse. Listman Mills Co. reached 13,200 cwt. in 1907, and was then one of the largest in the nation.

The mill was built in 1879 by E. V. White, and the following year, it became the property of William Listman (b.

1831 Germany, d. 1919). The plant was destroyed by fire in 1889 and rebuilt with 1400 cwt. capacity. Listman left La-Crosse in 1893 for Superior, and the milling company was managed by George M. Heath (b. 1860, d. 1929) in 1894-1912, and by Albert L. Goetzmann (b. 1869 Iowa, d. 1941) in 1912-20. Goetzmann had been secretary of Millers' National Federation in 1905-12 and he became president of the organization in 1920-22, serving on a full-time basis most of that period.

Listman Mills Co. was purchased in 1918 by Kansas Flour Mills Corp., and operated thereafter for about two years before it was closed by a strike and not reopened. The plant was destroyed by fire in 1935.

Menomonie

Wisconsin Milling Co.—In the heyday of lumbering on the Red Cedar River, Knapp-Stout Co. built a flour mill in 1857 in Menomonie, 60 miles east of the Twin Cities. Fifty years later it was enlarged to 1300 cwt. capacity, and Wisconsin Milling Co. was formed. E. Oliver Wright (b. 1870 Mo., d. 1947) became president and manager in 1911, and continued to run the business until the mill was closed in 1945.

Milwaukee

John B. A. Kern's Sons, Inc.—Eagle Mills, built in the 1870's and having 4000 cwt. capacity in later years, was operated by John B. A. Kern and then by his sons. John F. Kern (b. 1862 Wis., d. 1926) became president in 1892. The plant was sold about 1915 and the company had no mill for several years. It then reactivated Reliance mill, which Charles Mane-gold had closed in 1910, but it was operated only a couple of years.

Ladish Milling Co.—American Malting Co.'s Bay View plant was converted in 1919 into a flour mill of 1900 cwt., with Ladish-Stratton Milling Co. as the owner and H. W. Ladish, the maltster, as president. Harold M. Stratton (b. 1878 Wis., d. 1962), a noted figure in the grain trade, soon withdrew, and the name became Ladish Milling Co. Lee M. Powell (d. 1928) was manager. The venture ended in bankruptcy in 1922.

Bernhard Stern & Sons, Inc.—At the beginning of the twentieth century Milwaukee had seven flour mills and was a strong contender for second place in the industry. Perhaps the best known of the Milwaukee mills, although not the largest, was Atlas Mills. The plant was built in 1878 by Bernhard Stern (b. 1832 Germany, d. 1909), and it attained 3200 cwt. capacity of wheat and rye flour. The business was operated for many years as a partnership headed by Stern, and then as Bernhard Stern & Sons, Inc. The founder headed the company for many years, and was followed both as manager and as president by his son, Walter (b. 1871 Wis., d. 1942). The latter was also a noted civic leader.

The Stern mill survived all its Milwaukee rivals, and it was the only flour mill in the city after 1923. The Stern company was liquidated in 1926, and a few months later the mill building was destroyed by fire.

New Richmond

Doughboy Industries, Inc. is engaged in several sizable business lines, one of which is operation of a durum mill of 1200 cwt. The company also has formula feed capacity of 1600 tons.

New Richmond, 30 miles northeast of St. Paul, had a grist mill in 1856. It was replaced in 1889 by New Richmond Roller Mills Co., the president of which for 44 years was Orville W. Mosher (b. 1853 Wis., d. 1933). After the mill was destroyed by fire in 1916, it was replaced by a plant of 1000 cwt. John V. McNally (b. 1865 Wis., d. 1921) was manager for many years. Mosher was succeeded as president by his son, Frank B.

The company was acquired in 1936 by Edward J. Cashman (b. 1904 Minn.), who expanded its activities considerably and changed the name in 1946 to Doughboy Industries, Inc. In 1949 the mill began making durum flour and in 1956 it was converted to semolina production. Ray Wentsel (b. 1909 Minn.) became vice president and milling division manager in 1946.

Watertown

Globe Milling Co. is the largest exclusive rye miller in the nation. It operates a 1000-cwt. plant in Watertown, 40 miles northwest of Milwaukee. The market for its products is largely in northern and eastern metropolitan centers.

Watertown's first mill dates from 1842, only six years after the first settlers arrived in the community. It was known as Globe Mills after 1845. Globe Milling Co. was formed in 1874 by Christian May, through a consolidation of two Watertown mills. It had 2000 cwt. capacity. One of the mills was lost through fire in 1891 and was not replaced. The Mays left milling in 1898 to found a great flour company in Pittsburgh and they sold Globe to William D. Sproesser, a banker, and Henry Mulberger, who became manager. Some years later Mulberger also became a banker and was succeeded by George E. Manschot.

Shane Bros. & Wilson bought the Sproesser-Mulberger milling business in 1918, also acquiring the idle Columbia mill in Portage from York Bros, and enlarging it to 1000 cwt. At about that time Globe ceased to mill wheat and became a rye mill only. Kenneth L. Burns (b. 1877 Iowa, d. 1948) became manager in 1919. When the Shane empire broke up in 1921, the Globe and Columbia plants were taken over by a reorganized Globe Milling Co. with the aid of outside capital. The Columbia mill was sold in 1924 and was destroyed by fire soon afterward.

Burns was president and manager in 1921-48, and since that period these posts have been held by his long-time associate, Sidney C. Northrop (b. 1895 Minn.).

Wausau

Cereal Mills Co.—Wausau, in North Central Wisconsin, was the site of Cereal Mills Co., established in 1878. In later years it attained 1600 cwt. capacity. Fred W. Gennrich was the last head of the company. The plant was taken by fire in 1929.

Northern Milling Co.—Henry E. MacEachron (b. 1852, d. 1937), who spent 55 years in the milling business, built a 1000-cwt. mill in Wausau in 1915. It was run by his Northern Milling Co. until 1937, although after 1930 operation was only spasmodic. The mill was converted in 1938 to durum production by Martin Luther and Frank Voiello, but became idle within a year and was not reopened.

WYOMING
Sheridan

Sheridan Flouring Mills, Inc. is the largest milling company in Wyoming. It operates a flour mill of 2500 cwt., grain storage of 750,000 bushels and several small related lines. Flour business is mainly with bakery customers scattered over many states and with the household trade in Wyoming and Montana. Sheridan is close to the Montana border, about midway in the state.

The flour mill was built in 1900 and rebuilt after destruction by fire in 1919. It then had capacity of 800 cwt. Denio Milling Co. was organized in 1904; it was headed by J. W. Denio (b. 1847 N. Y., d. 1928) and his son, Ralph (b. 1879, d. 1927). The company was in financial trouble in the middle 1920's and was twice reorganized within a few months.

Sheridan Flouring Mills, Inc., was formed in 1927, largely by businessmen in the town. Wilbur D. Kistler was general manager in 1927-28, succeeded by W. Kenneth Cole (b. 1893 Colo., d. 1956) in 1928-56 and he by Jesse K. Beeson (b. 1895 Wis.), who has continued in the post.

Index

435

438

Corson, Harley T., 151
Coup, Cyrus S. and Wm. M., 367
Cowan, Finis E., 346, 401, 407
Cowgill Flour Mills, Inc., 304
Cowgill, Henry S., 226, 304
Cowgill, Lloyd, 304, 308
Coyne, Thos. R., 186
Craft, Henry G., 324
Crescent Milling Co., 262
Crete Mills, 335
Crete, Neb., 335
Crocker, Wm. G., 294
Crommellin, R. M., 377
Crookston Milling Co., 260
Crookston, Minn., 260
Crosby, Franklin M., 294
Crosby, John, 292-294
Crosby, John, Jr., 293
Cross, Earl F., 176
Crown Mills, 379, 380
Cunningham, Thos. O., 306

—D—

Daisy Roller Mill Co., 242, 260, 261, 280
Dale, W. Andrew, 393
Dallas, Texas, 14, 82, 182, 283, 289, 399-401
Dalton, Ga., 178
Dannals, Chas. N., 178
Daniels, Thos. L. and John H., 266
Dan Valley Mills, 398, 416, 417
Danville, Va., 398, 416, 417
Davenport, Iowa, 276, 277, 327, 340, 385, 386
Davis Co., J. G., 353
Davis, Donald D., 274
Davis, Harvey G., 427
Davis, Horace, 173, 174
Davis, H. Wheeler, 353
Davis, Jefferson, 207
Davis, J. Lewis, 206
Davis, J. Stanwood, 423
Dayton, Ohio, 37
DCA Food Industries, Inc., 248, 254, 348
Dean, Murry M. and Sons, 192
Decatur, Ala., 338
Dedrick, Benj. W., 156
Deere, John, 36
Delaware, 28, 29
Denio Milling Co., 434
Denton, Texas, 402, 404

Denton, Wm. M., 178
Denver, Colo., 174-177, 339
De Pere, Wis., 428
Depression and milling, 83, 84
Des Moines, Iowa, 61, 207, 208, 273, 274
Detroit, Mich., 37, 101, 249, 251, 252, 277
Diamond Mill Co., 404, 411, 412
Dickinson, Chas. E., 347
Dickinson, Robt. S., 339
Diefenbach, John F., 298
Dietrich, D. Wellington, 385
Dietz, Carl F., 82
Dillon, Matthew F., 156
Dillon, Stanley A., 279, 290
District of Columbia, 177, 178
Dittlinger, Hippolyt, 408
Dittlinger Roller Mills Co., H., 309, 408, 409
Dittmer, Herman, 370, 371
Dixie Portland Flour Mills, 107, 177, 213, 244, 303, 306, 327, 330, 392, 394-397, 418
Dobry, Antone F. and T. A., 375
Dobry Flour Mills Co., 375
Donovan, Daniel S., 182
Dorchester, Mass., 27
Doughboy Industries, Inc., 431, 432
Dousman Milling Co., John P., 428
Dover Milling Co., 360
Dover, Ohio, 360
Dowagiac, Mich., 252
Dowagiac Milling Co., 252
Dowdy, E. B., 417
Dower, John L., 175, 176
Doyle, Chas., W. C. and King, 255
Dress, Wm. B., 198
Driscoll, B. Leo, 395
Duerr, Wm. R., 313
Dulle, Joseph H. and H. J., Jr., 308
Dulle Milling Co., G. H., 241, 307, 308
Duluth, Minn., 260-262
Duluth-Superior Milling Co., 69, 260, 261, 321, 345
Duluth Universal Milling Co., 261, 262, 271
Duncan, T. Preston, 414
Dundas, Minn., 44
Dunlop Milling Co., 198, 392, 393
Dunlop Mills, 349, 397, 418
Dunnell, Wm. and W. H., 357
Dunwoody, John F. and W. B., 308

445

453

DATE DUE
